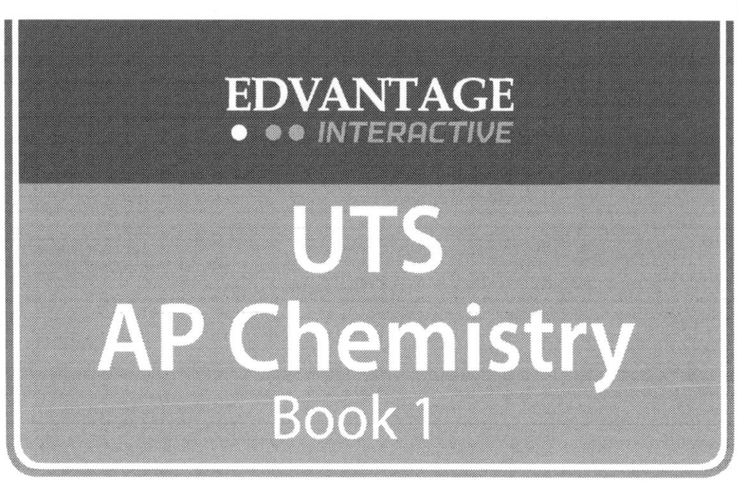

Development Team

Authors

Cheri Smith
Yale Secondary
School District 34 Abbotsford

Gary Davidson
School District 22 Vernon

Megan Ryan
Walnut Grove Secondary
School District 35 Langley

Chris Toth
St. Thomas More Collegiate
Burnaby, British Columbia

Program Consultant
Lionel Sandner
Edvantage Interactive

Customization by
Jennifer Pitt-Lainsbury
UTS, Toronto

COPIES OF THIS BOOK MAY BE OBTAINED BY CONTACTING:

Edvantage Interactive

E-MAIL:
info@edvantageinteractive.com

TOLL-FREE FAX:
866.275.0564

TOLL-FREE CALL:
866.422.7310

EDVANTAGE
INTERACTIVE

UTS AP Chemistry – Book 1

ISBN 978-1-77249-415-0
University of Toronto Schools – 2017 Version

Care has been taken to trace ownership of copyright material contained in this text. The publishers will gladly accept any information that will enable them to rectify any reference or credit in subsequent printings.
Vice-President of Marketing: *Don Franklin*
Director of Publishing: *Yvonne Van Ruskenveld*
Design and Production: *Donna Lindenberg*
Proofreading: *Eva van Emden*
Editorial Assistance: *Rhys Sandner*
Index: *Noeline Bridge*
Photos: *p. 33, K. Jung; p. 34, Bureau international des poids et mesures (BIPM)*

The AP Big Ideas at the beginning of each chapter are quoted from AP Chemistry: Course and Exam Description, revised edition, effective Fall 2013, published by the College Board, New York, NY. Advanced Placement, AP and College Board are registered trademarks of the College Board.

QR Code — What Is This?

The image to the right is called a QR code. It's similar to bar codes on various products and contains information that can be useful to you. Each QR code in this book provides you with online support to help you learn the course material. For example, find a question with a QR code beside it. If you scan that code, you'll see the answer to the question explained in a video created by an author of this book.

You can scan a QR code using an Internet-enabled mobile device. The program to scan QR codes is free and available at your phone's app store. Scanning the QR code above will give you a short overview of how to use the codes in the book to help you study.

Note: We recommend that you scan QR codes only when your phone is connected to a WiFi network. Depending on your mobile data plan, charges may apply if you access the information over the cellular network. If you are not sure how to do this, please contact your phone provider or us at info@edvantageinteractive.com

Contents

Book 1

Book 2

Book 3

Book 4

1 Oxidation-Reduction and Its Applications

Big Ideas

- Oxidation and reduction are paired chemical reactions in which electrons are transferred from one substance to another in a predictable way.
- The control and applications of oxidation and reduction reactions have significant implications for industry, health and safety, and the environment.

Overall Expectations

By the end of this course, students will

- F1. analyse technologies and processes relating to electrochemistry, and their implications for society, health and safety, and the environment;
- F2. investigate oxidation-reduction reactions using a galvanic cell, and analyse electrochemical reactions in qualitative and quantitative terms;
- F3. demonstrate an understanding of the principles of oxidation-reduction reactions and the many practical applications of electrochemistry.

Learning Goals	**Success Criteria**
Relating Science to Technology, Society and the Environment	*Relating Science to Technology, Society and the Environment*
□ Understand and explain how electrochemical cells work as alternative sources of energy (rechargeable batteries in computers, automobiles)	□ I can identify and explain several examples of currently used electrochemical energy sources □ I can evaluate the viability of electrochemical energy sources as alternatives to other energy sources in terms of economic, environmental, societal benefits □ I understand and can articulate both the limitations and the possibilities of recent developments in electrochemical cells □ I can corroborate my ideas based on recent research
□ analyse health and safety issues involving electrochemistry	□ I understand and can explain how electrochemistry redox reactions explain the corrosions of metals and the consequent effects on human life and health □ I can identify the types of waste produced in electroplating processes and how these wastes affect living systems □ I can assess whether medical and dental applications produce electrochemical reactions and whether these reactions cause potential health concerns
Developing Skills of Investigation and Communication	*Developing Skills of Investigation and Communication*
□ depict, articulate and understand electrochemical terms and processes	□ I can properly write and describe: half-reactions, balanced redox reactions, oxidation numbers, oxidizing agents and reducing agents □ I can properly draw and label electrochemical cells
□ conduct an inquiry to analyse an oxidation-reduction reaction in qualitative terms	□ I can determine if a reaction is a redox reaction □ I can conduct a redox reaction and explain all of my observation from the reaction based on my understanding of the process of reduction and oxidation of the reactants

☐ write balanced chemical equations for oxidation-reduction reactions	☐ I can use the half-reaction method to balance redox reactions and support my answers by using oxidation numbers
☐ build a galvanic cell and measure its cell potential	☐ I can build a variety of galvanic cells and determine the E°cell with a voltmeter and compare the observed result with the theoretical E°cell
☐ analyse the processes in galvanic cells	☐ I can set up and draw an electrochemical cell and correctly identify the cathode, the anode, the half-reactions, the electrolytes, the direction of electron flow in the wire and ion flow in the cells and the salt bridge based on observations and understanding ☐ I understand how chemical energy is converted into electrical energy in galvanic
☐ predict the spontaneity of redox reactions	☐ I can use a table of Standard Reduction Potentials (SRP) to determine the spontaneous redox reaction achieved by combining any two reactions on the table
☐ Analyze electrolytic cells in non-aqueous environments (AP)	☐ I understand the special conditions needed to conduct an electrolytic reaction in a non-aqueous environment (AP)
☐ Build and analyze an electrolytic cell for aqueous systems (AP)	☐ I can set up and describe the reactions occurring in the aqueous half-reactions in an electrolytic cell (AP) ☐ I can determine when the water half-reactions occur and when they do not (AP)
☐ Analyse the processes in an electrolytic cell (AP)	☐ I understand the conversion of electrical and chemical energy in electrolytic cells (AP) ☐ I understand why electrolytic process are important even though they are non-spontaneous (AP) ☐ I can describe several applications of electrolytic cells (AP)
Understanding Basic Concepts	*Understanding Basic Concepts*
☐ Explain redox reactions	☐ I can identify what elements are gaining electrons and which ones are losing electrons based on an analysis of oxidation numbers
☐ Identify the components of a galvanic cell	☐ I can properly identify the cathode, the anode, the salt bridge, the electrolytes, the half reactions, the load and the direction of electron flow ☐ I can explain how each component functions in a galvanic cell and why there are two reactions to consider
☐ Identify the components of an electrolytic cell (AP)	☐ I can properly identify the cathode, the anode, the electrolytes, the half reactions, the power source and the direction of electron flow ☐ I can explain how each component functions in an electrolytic cells and why there are four reactions to consider
☐ Describe the potential of galvanic cells	☐ I can determine the overall cell potential of galvanic cells by using the SRP table
☐ Describe energy requirements of electrolytic cells (AP)	☐ I can determine the potential difference required to drive the non-spontaneous reaction in an electrolytic cell (AP)
☐ Explain how the hydrogen half-cell is used as a standard reference electrode	☐ Understand that SRPs are relative to a standard ☐ Understand the concept of potential difference
☐ Explain some applications of electrochemistry in common industrial processes	☐ Explain how metals are refined through electrolysis ☐ Explain how hydrogen is produced through electrolysis
☐ Explain the corrosion of metals in terms of an electrochemical process	☐ Identify the chemical reactions involved in the corrosion of certain metals ☐ Determine which metals corrode most easily and which metals experience little corrosion ☐ Describe ways to inhibit metal corrosion

In the AP curriculum, these topics relate to AP Big Idea 3: Changes in matter involve the rearrangement and/or reorganization of atoms and/or the transfer of electrons.

1.1 Oxidation-Reduction

Warm Up

1. Complete the following table of compounds of multivalent metals.

Name	Formula	Metal Ion Charge
	$FeCl_3$	
	$Fe(CH_3COO)_2$	
	$Mn(BrO_3)_2$	
	MnO_2	
	$KMnO_4$	

2. How did you determine the ion charge of the metal in each case?

____

____

Electrochemistry

In Grade 11 Chemistry , you learned about the importance of chemistry to our everyday lives. We use conversions of chemical energy to other energy forms to do work for us, such as heating our homes and moving our vehicles. The heat or enthalpy stored in chemical bonds is being used at this very moment to sustain every living cell in your body.

There is another form of chemical conversion that is critical to life. This is the conversion of chemical to electrical energy. This conversion and the reverse change of electrical to chemical energy make up the study of **electrochemistry.**

Electrochemistry is the study of the interchange of chemical and electrical energy.

All electrochemical reactions have one thing in common. They involve the transfer of electrons from one reacting species to another. Most of the major types of chemical reactions you learned about in previous years involve electron transfer.

Synthesis and decomposition reactions involving species in elemental form always involve electron transfer. Single displacement and combustion reactions also fall into this category.

Reactions that involve electron transfer are commonly called **oxidation-reduction reactions.** Such reactions are often referred to as **redox reactions** for short.

Double displacement reactions are the major group of reactions that do not involve electron transfer. Synthesis and decomposition reactions involving oxides are a smaller group. Reactions that *do not* involve electron transfer are referred to as **metathesis reactions.**

Oxidation Numbers: A System for Tracking Electrons

The easiest way to determine whether electrons have been transferred between elements during a chemical reaction is to keep track of each atom's **oxidation number** (also referred to as the **oxidation state**).

> The **oxidation number** is the real or apparent charge of an atom or ion when all bonds in the species containing the atom or ion are considered to be ionic.

You probably referred to the oxidation number as the *combining capacity*. Multivalent metals such as iron, for example, may combine with chlorine to form $FeCl_2$ or $FeCl_3$, depending on the oxidation number of the iron ion involved. The compound containing iron with an oxidation number of +2 has the formula $FeCl_2$ and is called iron(II) chloride. This distinguishes it from $FeCl_3$ or iron(III) chloride, which contains iron with an oxidation number of +3. Notice that the charge is indicated before the number in an oxidation number.

Oxidation numbers (states) may be assigned to any atom in any aggregation, whether the atom exists in an element, a monatomic ion, or as part of a polyatomic ion or compound. The aggregation is simply the arrangement of atoms the element is in. As we're assuming all species are ionic in order to assign oxidation numbers, we should remember that the more electronegative elements gain electrons, so all electrons in an ionic bond should be assumed to belong to the more electronegative element. The easiest way to assign oxidation numbers to atoms is to follow the simple set of rules given in Table 1.1.1.

Table 1.1.1 *Rules for Assigning Oxidation numbers*

Rule	Statement about Oxidation Number	Examples
1.	Atoms in elemental form = 0	Na, O_2, P_4, As, Zn
2.	Monatomic ions = the ion's charge	K^+, Ca^{2+}, Fe^{2+}, Fe^{3+}, Cl^-
3.	Oxygen = 2– except in peroxides (O_2^{2-}) = – and OF_2 = 2+	Na_2O_2, OF_2
4.	Hydrogen = + except in **metal** hydrides = –	CaH_2, LiH
5.	Oxidation numbers in compounds must sum to zero.	CuCl, $CuCl_2$ contain copper(I) and copper(II)
6.	Oxidation numbers in polyatomic ions must sum to the ion charge.	ClO_4^-, ClO_3^- contain chlorine = 7+ and 5+
7.	Always assign the more electronegative element a negative oxidation number.	PF_5 contains F = – and thus P = 5+
8.	In a compound or ion containing more than two elements, the element written furthest to the right takes its most common oxidation number.	SCN^- contains N = 3– (most common), S = 2– (negative value), thus C = 4+.

If the species contains oxygen and/or hydrogen, it is usually a good idea to assign their oxidation numbers first. For a species containing multiple types of atoms, assign the more electronegative element first. If the more electronegative element can have more than one oxidation number, use its most common oxidation number.

It is important to note that we always calculate the oxidation number of *one* atom of a particular element. While they are useful in the *calculation* of oxidation numbers, the subscripts that may be assigned to a particular atom have *no effect* on the oxidation number of that atom.

Practice Problems 1.1.1 — Assigning Oxidation Numbers

Assign the oxidation number of each atom in the following species:

1. H_2O
2. Cs_2O_2
3. CO_3^{2-}
4. $Na_2Cr_2O_7$
5. BaH_2
6. NH_4^+
7. S_8
8. $Al_2(SO_4)_3$

Oxidation and Reduction

When an atom gains electrons during a reaction, its oxidation number becomes less positive or more negative. This is logical as the electrons being gained are negative particles. A substance whose oxidation number becomes smaller is being reduced.

A *decrease in oxidation number* is called **reduction**.

On the other hand, when an atom loses electrons during a reaction, its oxidation number becomes more positive. This is because the number of protons (positive charges) does not change, but there are fewer electrons. Consequently, the atom now has more positive protons than negative electrons and hence the net charge is greater. The substance whose oxidation number increases is being oxidized.

An *increase in oxidation number* is called **oxidation**.

In the equation shown below, the oxidation number of the iron increases by two, while the oxidation number of the Cu^{2+} ion decreases by two. Hence, iron metal is oxidized and copper(II) ion is reduced.

oxidation

$$Fe(s) + Cu^{2+}(aq) \rightarrow Fe^{2+}(aq) + Cu(s)$$

reduction

It is important to realize that reduction and oxidation always occur together in a reaction. If one atom has its oxidation number increase due to a loss of electrons, another substance must have its oxidation number decrease due to a gain of electrons. This is why reactions that involve electron transfer are called oxidation-reduction reactions or redox reactions for short. These reactions are always *coupled* and the oxidation number changes are entirely due to the transfer of electrons.

Remember that we always state the oxidation number for just *one* atom of a particular element, *no matter what subscript or coefficient* may be associated with the atom. Figure 1.1.1 shows a handy mnemonic device to help you remember what happens to electrons during the redox process.

A *gain of electrons* is **REDUCTION**, while a *loss of electrons* is **OXIDATION**.

LEO goes GER

lose electrons = oxidation gain electrons = reduction

Figure 1.1.1 *Leo can help you remember the redox process.*

Quick Check

Study the following reaction:

$2\ Al + Fe_2O_3 \rightarrow Al_2O_3 + 2\ Fe$

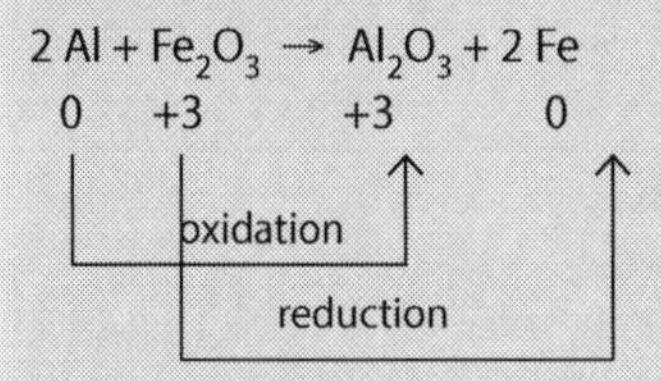

1. (a) Are electrons gained or lost by each iron(III) ion? ___________________

   How many? ______________

   (b) Are electrons are gained or lost by each Al atom? ___________________

   How many? ______________

2. How many electrons were transferred in total during the reaction? ______________

3. What happened to the oxide ion, O^{2-}, during the reaction?

   ____

Agents Cause Electron Transfer

Examination of the Quick Check above indicates that the number of electrons lost by the species being oxidized must always equal the number of electrons gained by the species being reduced.

So far we have examined electron transfer in terms of the species that lost or gained the electrons. Another approach is to view the event from the perspective of the species that cause the electron loss or gain. In this sense, the species that gets oxidized causes another species to gain electrons and be reduced. For this reason, the species that gets oxidized is called a reducing agent. A similar argument describes the chemical that takes electrons from another species and is consequently reduced, as an oxidizing agent (Figure 1.1.2).

A substance that is *reduced* acts as an **oxidizing agent**, while a substance that is *oxidized* acts as a **reducing agent**.

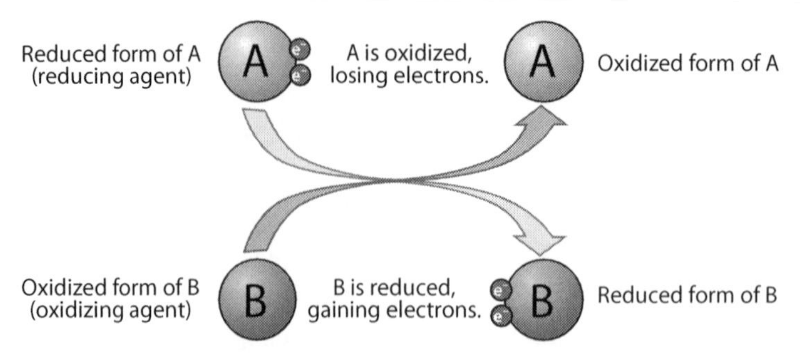

Figure 1.1.2 *Species being oxidized and reduced act as reducing and oxidizing agents.*

Solving Problems with Redox Reactions

In the sample problem below, the second example may not appear to fit any of the traditional five categories of classification from our past chemistry studies. (It is the combustion of ammonia.) Often redox reactions do not fit our classic categories. You will encounter many more of these in the rest of this chapter.

Sample Problem 1.1.1 — Recognizing Oxidizing and Reducing Agents

Indicate the oxidizing and reducing agent in each of the following reactions:

(a) $Mg(s) + 2\ HCl(aq) \rightarrow MgCl_2(aq) + H_2(g)$ (b) $4\ NH_3(g) + 7\ O_2(g) \rightarrow 4\ NO_2(g) + 6\ H_2O(l)$

What to Think About	How to Do It
(a) $Mg(s) + 2\ HCl(aq) \rightarrow MgCl_2(aq) + H_2(g$ 1. Assign oxidation numbers to all atoms in the equation. (You may wish to write these values above each atom to help keep track.) 2. Indicate the increase in oxidation number as an oxidation and the decrease in oxidation number as a reduction. 3. The species that was oxidized is the reducing agent. The one that was reduced is the oxidizing agent. This is a classic single displacement reaction.	Mg: 0 → +2 H: +1 → 0 Cl: 1 → −1 Magnesium atom was oxidized. Hydrogen ion was reduced. Reducing agent: magnesium atom (Mg) Oxidizing agent: hydrogen ion (H^+) Notice that the Mg atom lost two electrons, while each H^+ ion gained one.
(b) $4\ NH_3(g) + 7\ O_2(g) \rightarrow 4\ NO_2(g) + 6\ H_2O(l)$ 1. Assign oxidation numbers to all elements in the equation. Notice that even though hydrogen is written second in the formula for ammonia, ammonia is not a *metal* hydride so hydrogen is assigned its usual oxidation number of +1. 2. Indicate the increase in oxidation number as an oxidation and the decrease in oxidation number as a reduction. 3. The species that was oxidized is the reducing agent. The one that was reduced is the oxidizing agent.	H: +1 → +1 O: 0 → −2 (in both products) N: −3 → +4 Oxygen gas was reduced. N in ammonia was oxidized. Oxidizing agent: oxygen gas (O_2) Reducing agent: ammonia (NH_3) NOTE: When the atom that is oxidized or reduced belongs to a covalent compound, we indicate the *entire species* as the agent.

Practice Problems 1.1.2 — Recognizing Oxidizing and Reducing Agents

Determine the oxidizing and reducing agent in each of the following reactions. Write the appropriate formula for each agent. Begin by clearly indicating the oxidation numbers of all elements in each equation. Question 1 is done as an example. Hint: Always show the agent as it would appear in a *net ionic equation.* (See H^+ in Sample Problem 1.1.1 above, as HCl is a strong acid.)

1. $\overset{0}{C}(s) + 2\ \overset{0}{H_2}(g) \rightarrow \overset{-4+1}{CH_4}(g)$ O.A. = C(*s*) R.A. = $H_2(g)$

2. $3\ Sr(s) + 2\ FeBr_3(aq) \rightarrow 2\ Fe(s) + 3\ SrBr_2(aq)$

3. $5\ CO(g) + Cl_2O_5(s) \rightarrow 5\ CO_2(g) + Cl_2(g)$

4. $4\ PH_3(g) \rightarrow P_4(g) + 6\ H_2(g)$

5. $Ba(s) + 2\ H_2O(l) \rightarrow Ba(OH)_2(s) + H_2(g)$

1.1 Review Questions

1. Elements that get oxidized (act as reducing agents) form (a)__________________ ions when they react. This means reducing agents are generally (b)__________________. Reducing agents may also be (c)_______________ charged ions. The most active reducing agents likely belong to the (d)__________________ family on the periodic table. The most active oxidizing agents must belong to the (e)____________________ family.

2. Give the oxidation number for the underlined element in each of the following species:

   (a) $\underline{Ca}I_2$ (b) $\underline{O}F_2$ (c) $\underline{C}_6H_{12}O_6$ (d) $Rb_2\underline{O}_2$ (e) $\underline{S}_2O_3^{2-}$ (f) $Be\underline{H}_2$ (g) $\underline{Br}O^-$ (h) $\underline{Cl}_2$

3. (a) What is an oxidizing agent?

   (b) What is a reducing agent?

   (c) How would you expect electronegativity to be related to the strength of each?

4. For each of the following reactions, indicate the species being oxidized and reduced and show the oxidation numbers above their symbols.

   (a) $2\ KBrO_3(s) \rightarrow 2\ KBr(s) + 3\ O_2(g)$ Oxidized: Reduced:

   (b) $Sr(s) + 2\ CuNO_3(aq) \rightarrow Sr(NO_3)_2(aq) + 2\ Cu(s)$ Oxidized: Reduced:

   (c) $2\ F_2(g) + O_2(g) \rightarrow 2\ OF_2(g)$ Oxidized: Reduced:

   (d) $NH_4NO_3(s) \rightarrow N_2O(g) + 2\ H_2O(l)$ Oxidized: Reduced:

5. Determine the oxidizing and reducing agent in each of the following reactions. Then indicate the number of electrons transferred by one atom of the reducing agent.

(a) $2\ Sn(s) + O_2(g) \rightarrow 2\ SnO(s)$ OA: RA: No. e^-:

(b) $2\ V(s) + 5\ I_2(g) \rightarrow 2\ VI_5(s)$ OA: RA: No. e^-:

(c) $Sr(s) + 2\ HCl(aq) \rightarrow SrCl_2(aq) + H_2(g)$ OA: RA: No. e^-:

(d) $C_3H_8(g) + 5\ O_2(g) \rightarrow 3\ CO_2(g) + 4\ H_2O(g)$ OA: RA: No. e^-:

6. The pictures indicate the same reacting system following a 12 h period.

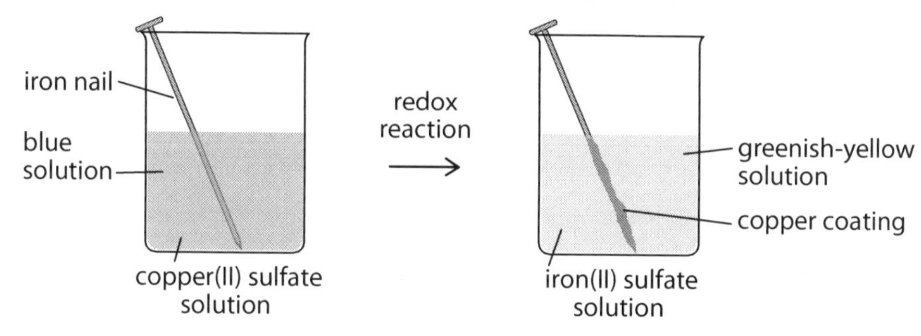

(a) Write a balanced redox equation (in net ionic form) to show what has occurred in the beaker over time.

(b) Which substance is the oxidizing agent? The reducing agent?

(c) How many electrons were transferred in the equation?

7. Give the oxidation number of the underlined element in each species:

(a) $\underline{P}^{3-}$ (b) $(NH_4)_2\underline{Zr}(SO_4)_3$ (c) $Na_2\underline{C}_2O_4$ (d) $\underline{N}_2H_5Cl$ (e) $\underline{Mn}O_4^{2-}$

8.

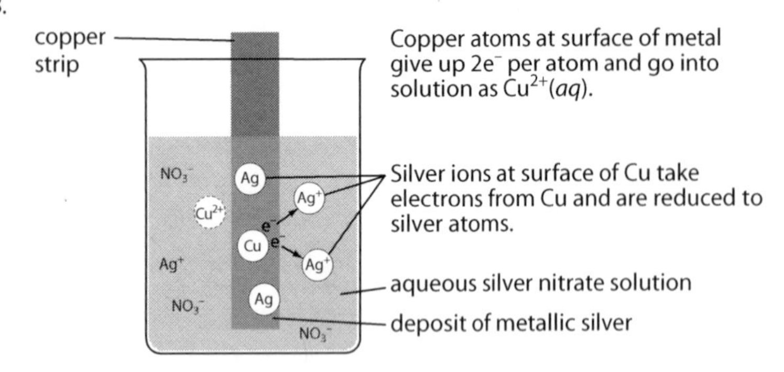

(a) Write a balanced net ionic equation to represent the redox reaction occurring in the beaker.

(b) Which substance is getting oxidized? Reduced?

(c) Which substance is the reducing agent? The oxidizing agent?

(d) How many electrons are transferred in each reaction?

9. What family on the periodic table would likely contain:

(a) The strongest reducing agents?

(b) The strongest oxidizing agents?

10. (a) Which of the following substances could be formed by the oxidation of ClO^-: ClO_4^-, Cl_2, ClO_2^-, Cl^-, ClO_3^-?

(b) The reduction of ClO^-?

1.2 Balancing Oxidation-Reduction Equations

Warm Up

Examine the following equation: $Zn(s) + Cu^+(aq) \rightarrow Zn^{2+}(aq) + Cu(s)$

1. Which species acts as a reducing agent and consequently is oxidized? ______________

2. Which species acts as an oxidizing agent and consequently is reduced? ______________

3. How many electrons are lost by each atom of the reducing agent as it is oxidized? ______________

4. A Cu^+ ion accepts only one electron to become a neutral Cu atom. How many Cu^+ ions does it take to accept two electrons?
____

5. Add coefficients to the equation so that the number of electrons donated by the reducing agent equals the number of electrons received by the oxidizing agent.

6. Does the net charge of the reactants now equal the net charge of the products? ______________

The Conservation of Mass *and* Charge

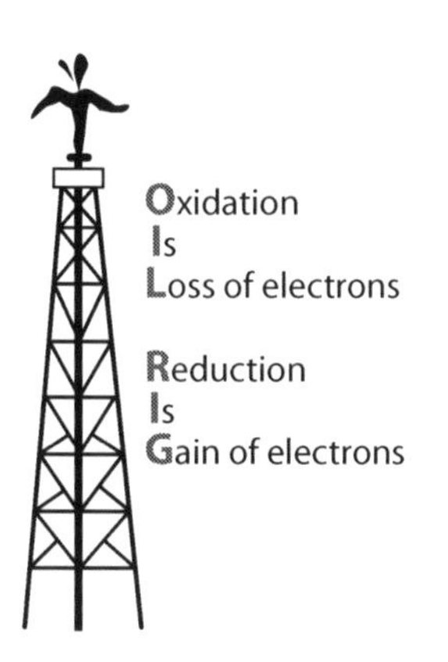

Figure 1.2.1 *Remember the OIL RIG.*

For the past several years, you've been applying Antoine Lavoisier's Law of Conservation of Mass to every chemical reaction you've encountered. This law states that the mass of the products equals the mass of the reactants in any chemical reaction. This is because no atoms are gained or lost during a chemical reaction. In junior science, you learned to place coefficients in front of various chemical species to make sure that the total number of atoms of each type on the reactant side would equal the total number of atoms of the same type on the product side of the equation.

In Chemistry 11, you learned to write net ionic equations for a variety of reaction types. In these equations, it was necessary to balance the charge as well as the number of each type of each atom. In oxidation-reduction reactions, charge is balanced by making certain that the number of electrons lost equals the number gained. This is sometimes done by simple inspection. An example is the reduction of copper(I) ion by zinc metal in the Warm Up question above. Examination reveals that two Cu^+ ions are reduced for every Zn atom oxidized, so the balanced equation is:

$$Zn(s) + 2\,Cu^+(aq) \rightarrow Zn^{2+}(aq) + 2\,Cu(s)$$

There are many oxidation-reduction reactions that are considerably more complex than this simple example. For these more complicated cases, we require a system to help us determine the number of electrons lost and gained so we can balance not only the number of atoms of each type, but also the number of electrons transferred.

Half-Reactions

It is possible to separate the reduction and oxidation portions of a redox reaction and to represent them as two separate **half-reactions**. For example, the sample reaction from the Warm Up may be broken into the following half-reactions:

$$Zn \rightarrow Zn^{2+} + 2e^- \text{ (oxidation) } \textit{and } Cu^+ + e^- \rightarrow Cu \text{ (reduction)}$$

Notice that the half-reactions include the number of electrons lost, in the case of oxidation, or gained, in the case of reduction.

A **half-reaction** is an equation representing either an oxidation or a reduction, including the number of electrons lost or gained.

Balancing questions usually specify whether the reaction is occurring under acidic or basic conditions. Sometimes this will be readily apparent from the chemical reactants. If this isn't obvious or isn't stated, the conditions are likely acidic. It is possible, however, that it is occurring under neutral conditions. This means that when you balance it, you find that any H^+ or OH^- ions will cancel out and not appear in the final reaction statement.

Balancing Half-Reactions

Balancing a half-reaction requires the application of the following steps:

OTHER atoms — Balance atoms other than H and O.

All atoms *except* oxygen and hydrogen should be balanced first. This is not always necessary, so people tend to forget to balance the "other" atoms. Do *not* forget this step and watch the way coefficients affect charges.

OXYGEN atoms — Balance oxygen atoms by adding H_2O.

Redox reactions occur in aqueous solution. Consequently, you may add as many water molecules as required to balance the number of oxygen atoms.

HYDROGEN atoms — Balance hydrogen atoms by adding H^+ ions.

As most reactions occur in an acidic environment, you may add as many hydrogen ions, H^+, as are needed.

CHARGE — Balance the charge by adding electrons.

Always add the electrons to the *more positive* (or less negative) side. Add the number of electrons needed to ensure that the charge is the *same* on both sides of the equation. This is a good time to *check* that the total number of atoms of each type is in fact the same on both sides, so the equation is indeed balanced in terms of mass and charge.

Sample Problem 1.2.1(a) — Balancing Half-Reactions in Acidic Conditions

Balance the following half-reaction occurring under acidic conditions: $ClO_4^- \rightarrow Cl_2$
Does this represent an oxidation or a reduction?

What to Think About	How to Do It
1. Balance atoms *other than* O and H. This requires a coefficient 2 in front of the perchlorate ion, ClO_4^-. Because the "other" atoms are often already balanced, students frequently do not need to balance them and as a result they tend to forget to apply the first step. *Always* check the "other" atoms first.	$2\ ClO_4^- \rightarrow Cl_2$
2. Balance *oxygen atoms* by adding *H_2O molecules*. As there are now 8 oxygen atoms on the reactant side, add 8 water molecules to the products.	$2\ ClO_4^- \rightarrow Cl_2 + 8\ H_2O$
3. Balance *hydrogen atoms* by adding *H^+ ions*. As there are now 16 hydrogen atoms on the product side, add 16 H^+ ions on the reactant side.	$16\ H^+ + 2\ ClO_4^- \rightarrow Cl_2 + 8\ H_2O$
4. Balance the charge by adding the e^- to the *more positive side*. As the total charge on the reactant side is +14 and there is no charge on the product side, add 14 electrons on the reactant side.	$14\ e^- + 16\ H^+ + 2\ ClO_4^- \rightarrow Cl_2 + 8\ H_2O$ An **oxidation number check** is helpful to perform on half-reactions. Note that the number of electrons gained matches the oxidation number change. $\overset{+7}{2\ ClO_4^-} \rightarrow \overset{0}{Cl_2}$ [Gain of $7e^-$ (x2) = $14e^-$ gained.] ✓
Electrons are gained (they are "reactants").	This is a **reduction**.

While all redox reactions occur in aqueous solution, some occur in basic, rather than acidic conditions. When balancing a reaction that is occurring under basic conditions, chemists simply add a step to our sequence to convert from an acidic to a basic environment. When a redox reaction is to be balanced in base, *the hydrogen ions must be neutralized*. This is accomplished by adding hydroxide ions, OH^-, to cancel any H^+ ions. If hydroxide ions are added to one side of the equation, the same number must be added to the other side.

Thus, complete the first four steps and then…

BASE — Add OH^- ions to both sides to neutralize all H^+ Ions.

The number of OH^- ions added to neutralize the H^+ must be balanced by adding the same number of OH^- ions to the other side of the reaction. Free H^+ and OH^- ions on the same side of the equation should be combined to form the corresponding number of H_2O molecules. This step may result in water molecules showing up on both sides of the equation. Be sure to cancel so that H_2O appears on one side of the equation only.

It is critically important to pay close attention to all charges during the balancing process. Dropping the charge from an ion or inadvertently changing a charge will lead to a wrong answer every time!

Sample Problem 1.2.1(b) — Balancing Half-Reactions in Basic Conditions

Balance the following half-reaction: $I_2 \rightarrow IO_4^-$ in base.
Does this represent an oxidation or a reduction?

What to Think About	How to Do It
1. Balance atoms *other than* O and H. A coefficient 2 is needed in front of IO_4^-.	$I_2 \rightarrow 2\,IO_4^-$
2. Balance *oxygen atoms* by adding *H_2O molecules.* As there are 8 oxygen atoms on the product side, add 8 H_2O molecules as reactants.	$8\,H_2O + I_2 \rightarrow 2\,IO_4^-$
3. Balance *hydrogen atoms* by adding *H^+ions* to the product side. As there are now 16 hydrogen atoms on the reactant side, add 16 H^+ to the product side.	$8\,H_2O + I_2 \rightarrow 2\,IO_4^- + 16\,H^+$
4. Add the e^- to the *more positive side*. As the total charge on the product side is +14 and there is no charge on the reactant side, add 14 electrons on the product side.	$8\,H_2O + I_2 \rightarrow 2\,IO_4^- + 16\,H^+ + 14e^-$
5. The objective for balancing a reaction in base is to *neutralize the H^+ions*. As there are 16 H^+ ions on the product side, add 16 OH^- ions to both sides. Each combination of H^+ with OH^- forms an H_2O molecule. Water molecules present on both sides of the equation algebraically cancel. *NEVER leave H_2O molecules on both sides.*	~~$8\,H_2O$~~ $+ I_2 \rightarrow 2\,IO_4^- + 16$ ~~H^+~~ $+ 14e^-$ $16\,OH^-$ $\quad\quad\quad\quad$ $16\,OH^-$ $16\,OH^- + I_2 \rightarrow 2\,IO_4^- + 8\,H_2O + 14\,e^-$
Electrons are produced-hence they are lost.	Oxidation number check: $\overset{0}{I_2} \rightarrow 2\,\overset{+7}{I}O_4^-$ $\quad$ [Loss of $7e^-$ (x2) = $14e^-$ lost] ✓ This process is an **oxidation**.

Practice Problems 1.2.1 — Balancing Half-Reactions in Acidic and Basic Conditions

Balance the following half-reactions. Assume the reactions occur in acid unless specified otherwise. In each case, indicate whether the half-reaction is an oxidation or a reduction.

1. $Sm \rightarrow Sm^{3+}$
2. $NO_3^- \rightarrow NH_4^+$
3. $IO_4^- \rightarrow IO_3^-$ (basic)
4. $S_2O_3^{2-} \rightarrow SO_4^{2-}$
5. $BrO_3^- \rightarrow Br_2$ (basic)

Redox Reactions

The equation for an oxidation-reduction reaction is a combination of two of the half-reactions we have just finished balancing (an oxidation and a reduction). When a reducing agent is oxidized, the electrons are not actually *lost* in the usual sense of the word. In fact, chemists know exactly where those electrons go. They are, of course, gained by an oxidizing agent that will become reduced. The goal of balancing a redox reaction is to ensure the number of electrons lost by a reducing agent (as it becomes oxidized) exactly equals the number of electrons gained by the oxidizing agent (as it becomes reduced).

Oxidation-reduction (redox) reactions are characterized by a balanced loss and gain of electrons.

There are two common methods for balancing redox reactions. We will begin by focusing on the method that involves balancing two half-reactions. This method is appropriately called the *half-reaction method*. It consists of the following steps:

SEPARATE the redox equation into its half-reactions.

In most cases, it is easy to identify the two half-reactions by noting species in the reactants that contain atoms in common with species in the products.

BALANCE each half-reaction.

Give yourself plenty of room and don't forget to compare the change in oxidation numbers with the electron gain or loss.

MULTIPLY each half-reaction by an integer to balance the transfer of electrons.

Take the time and space to rewrite each reaction and take care as you transcribe the formulas and coefficients to avoid errors.

ADD the half-reactions together.

Algebraically cancel those species that appear on both sides of the equation. Again: be care*ful* — not care*less*! No common species should remain on both sides of the equation.

If the equation is basic, ADD OH^- to *both sides* to neutralize the H^+ ions *only after* recombining the equations.

Balancing redox equations can seem tedious at times, as there are many steps involved. Errors made early will lead to a series of mistakes but even one late error will result in the wrong answer. Taking care in transcribing steps and checking each process as you go will lead to consistent success.

Sample Problem 1.2.2 — Balancing Redox Reactions: Acidic

Balance the following redox reaction: $IO_3^- + HSO_3^- \rightarrow SO_4^{2-} + I_2$

What to Think About	How to Do It
1. Separate the redox equation Into its two half-reactions. Look for common atoms to assist you. IO_3^- and I_2 both contain iodine. HSO_3^- and SO_4^{2-} both contain sulfur.	$IO_3^- \rightarrow I_2$ $HSO_3^- \rightarrow SO_4^{2-}$
2. Balance each half-reaction. Note: There must be an electron *gain* on one side and *loss* on the other. If not, you have made an error!	$10e^- + 12\,H^+ + 2\,IO_3^- \rightarrow I_2 + 6\,H_2O$ $H_2O + HSO_3^- \rightarrow SO_4^{2-} + 3\,H^+ + 2e^-$ Don't forget to do a quick check of oxidation numbers at this point. $\overset{+5}{2\,IO_3^-} \rightarrow \overset{0}{I_2}$ $\overset{+4}{HSO_3^-} \rightarrow \overset{+6}{SO_4^{2-}}$ $(-5 \times 2 = 10e^-$ gain$)$ $(+2 = 2e^-$ lost$)$ ✓
3. Balance the electron loss and gain. Look for the *lowest common multiple*. Multiply the second half-reaction by 5 and rewrite both equations.	$1(10e^- + 12\,H^+ + 2\,IO_3^- \rightarrow I_2 + 6\,H_2O)$ $5(H_2O + HSO_3^- \rightarrow SO_4^{2-} + 3\,H^+ + 2e^-)$
4. Add the balanced half-reactions together, cancelling where appropriate.	$\cancel{10e^-} + 12\,H^+ + 2\,IO_3^- \rightarrow I_2 + 6\,H_2O$ $5\,H_2O + 5\,HSO_3^- \rightarrow 5\,SO_4^{2-} + 15\,H^+ + \cancel{10e^-}$ $5\,HSO_3^- + 2\,IO_3^- \rightarrow 5\,SO_4^{2-} + 3\,H^+ + I_2 + H_2O$

Once you have balanced a full redox reaction, it is worth taking the time to do a full balancing check. You may have performed similar checks when balancing standard equations at some point in your chemistry past. A table is a helpful tool:

Species	Reactants	Products
Hydrogen	5	5
Sulfur	5	5
Oxygen	21	21
Iodine	2	2
Charge	–7	–7

✓

Be sure to take care in how you assign charges, do not drop or change ion charges during transcription. More than one student has done a wonderful job of correctly balancing an equation that wasn't assigned to them because they changed one of the species.

Practice Problems 1.2.2 — Balancing Redox Reactions in Acid

Balance each of the following equations in acidic solution. Perform a check for each.

1. $H_3AsO_4 + Zn \rightarrow AsH_3 + Zn^{2+}$

2. $C_2H_5OH + NO_3^- \rightarrow CH_3COOH + N_2O_4$

Disproportionation Reactions

Some redox reactions can be rather difficult to break into half-reactions. One of the most troublesome almost appears, at first glance, to be a half-reaction. Take the reaction,

$$Sn^{2+} \rightarrow Sn^{4+} + Sn$$

The tin(II) ion is both oxidized (to form the tin(IV) ion) and reduced (to form tin metal). A reaction such as this is called a disproportionation reaction.

A **disproportionation** reaction is a redox reaction in which the same species is both oxidized and reduced.

Occasionally, multiple reactants form only one product. A chemical change of this sort is called a **comproportionation** reaction. This may be the reverse of a disproportionation in which one species is reduced to form a product and a different species is oxidized to give the same product.

Sample Problem 1.2.3 — Balancing Disproportionation Reactions: Basic

Balance the following in base: $IAsO_4 \rightarrow AsO_4^{3-} + I_2 + IO_3^-$

What to Think About

1. Separate the half-reactions. Both half-reactions must contain the same reactant, so this is a disproportionation reaction. Arsenic must be a product in both half-reactions. Hence the remaining two iodine-containing species must be split between the two half-reactions.

2. Balance each half-reaction and check the oxidation numbers with the electron loss and gain.

3. Multiply the second half-reaction by 3.

4. Sum the two halves with appropriate cancelling.

5. To balance in base, add 18 OH^- ions to each side; then cancel 9 H_2O's.

   A final check is always a good idea.

How to Do It

$IAsO_4 \rightarrow AsO_4^{3-} + I_2$

$IAsO_4 \rightarrow AsO_4^{3-} + IO_3^-$

$6e^- + 2\,IAsO_4 \rightarrow 2\,AsO_4^{3-} + I_2$

$3\,H_2O + IAsO_4 \rightarrow AsO_4^{3-} + IO_3^- + 6\,H^+ + 2e^-$

$\overset{+3}{2\,IAsO_4} \rightarrow AsO_4^{3-} + \overset{0}{I_2}$ (-3 x 2 = gain 6e$^-$)

$\overset{+3}{IAsO_4} \rightarrow AsO_4^{3-} + \overset{+5}{IO_3^-}$ (+2 = loss of 2e$^-$) ✓

$6e^- + 2\,IAsO_4 \rightarrow 2\,AsO_4^{3-} + I_2$

$9\,H_2O + 3\,IAsO_4 \rightarrow 3\,AsO_4^{3-} + 3\,IO_3^- + 18\,H^+ + 6e^-$

$9\,H_2O + 5\,IAsO_4 \rightarrow 5\,AsO_4^{3-} + 3\,IO_3^- + I_2 + 18\,H^+$

(+ 18 OH^-) (+ 18 OH^-)

$18\,OH^- + 5\,IAsO_4 \rightarrow 5\,AsO_4^{3-} + 3\,IO_3^- + I_2 + 9\,H_2O$

Species	Products	Reactants
Hydrogen	18	18
Arsenic	5	5
Oxygen	38	38
Iodine	5	5
Charge	–18	–18

Practice Problems 1.2.3 — Balancing Disproportionation Reactions

Balance the following reactions in a basic environment. Perform a check for each.

1. $HXeO_4^- \rightarrow XeO_6^{4-} + Xe + O_2$

2. $BrO_3^- + Br^- \rightarrow Br_2$ (a comproportionation)

3. $CH_3COO^- \rightarrow CH_4 + CO_2$

An acronym you may find helpful in remembering how to balance redox reactions is OOHe as described below
OOHe — **O**ther atoms, **O**xygen (with H_2O), **H**ydrogen (with H^+), **e**lectrons

1.2 Review Questions

1. Electrons can be used to cancel positive charges or to increase negative charge. Complete the following table by indicating how many electrons must be added to the reactants or the products to balance the electrical charge.

	Reactants	Products	Add
e.g.	2+	3+	$1e^-$ to the products
(a)	3+	2–	
(b)	1–	3–	
(c)	2–	4+	
(d)	1+	5+	

Examine your answers. Are you following the suggestion to *always add electrons to the more positive side?*

2. Balance the electrical charge of each of the following half-reactions by adding the appropriate number of electrons to either the reactants or products. Indicate whether the half-reaction is an *oxidation* or a *reduction*.

(a) $2\ NO_3^- + 2\ H_2O \rightarrow N_2O_4 + 4\ OH^-$

(b) $2\ Cr^{3+} + 7\ H_2O \rightarrow Cr_2O_7^{2-} + 14\ H^+$

(c) $ClO_4^- + 4\ H_2O \rightarrow Cl^- + 8\ OH^-$

(d) $S_2O_5^{2-} + 3\ H_2O \rightarrow 2\ SO_4^{2-} + 6\ H^+$

3. Balance the following half-reactions under acidic conditions. Indicate whether each is an *oxidation* or a *reduction*.
   (a) $ClO_4^- \rightarrow Cl_2$

   (b) $FeO \rightarrow Fe_2O_3$

   (c) $N_2O_4 \rightarrow NO_3^-$

4. Balance the following half-reactions under basic conditions. Indicate whether each is an *oxidation* or a *reduction*.
   (a) $CrO_4^{2-} \rightarrow Cr(OH)_2$

   (b) $S_2O_3^{2-} \rightarrow S_4O_6^{2-}$

   (c) $IO_3^- + Cl^- \rightarrow ICl_2^-$

5. Balance the following reactions using the half-reaction method. Assume acidic conditions unless stated otherwise.

(a) $Sn^{2+} + MnO_4^- \rightarrow Sn^{4+} + MnO_2$ (basic)

(b) $V^{2+} + H_2SO_3 \rightarrow V^{3+} + S_2O_3^{2-}$

(c) $IO_3^- + I^- \rightarrow I_2$ (basic)

(d) $ClO_3^- + N_2H_4 \rightarrow NO + Cl^-$

(e) $NO_3^- + Zn \rightarrow Zn^{2+} + NO$ (basic)

(f) $ClO_3^- \rightarrow ClO_4^- + Cl^- + Cl_2$
Use the ΔON values to help you determine how to break this into two half-reactions.

(g) $SnS_3O_3 + MnO_4^- \rightarrow MnO_2 + SO_4^{2-} + Sn^{4+}$ (basic)

(h) $Mg_3(AsO_4)_2 + SiO_2 + C \rightarrow As_4 + MgSiO_3 + CO$

6. **Extension:** Use the half-reaction method to balance the following reactions occurring in aqueous solution:

(a) $K_2Cr_2O_7 + CH_3CH_2OH + HCl \rightarrow CH_3COOH + KCl + CrCl_3 + H_2O$

You must first convert the equation into net ionic form, balance the net ionic equation, and then convert it back into the original formula equation. This is the reaction performed in the prototype BAT (Breath Alcohol Testing) mobiles.

(b) C.W. Scheele prepared chlorine gas in 1774 using the following reaction:

$NaCl + H_2SO_4 + MnO_2 \rightarrow Na_2SO_4 + MnCl_2 + H_2O + Cl_2$

Balancing Redox Equations: Practice

1. Balance each of the following equations that occur in ACIDIC aqueous solution.

   a) $H_2C_2O_4 + IO_3^- \rightarrow CO_2 + I^-$
   b) $NO + Cr_2O_7^{2-} \rightarrow NO_3^- + Cr^{3+}$
   c) $Cl_2 + S_2O_8^{2-} \rightarrow ClO_3^- + SO_4^{2-}$
   d) $Cu + NO_3^- \rightarrow Cu^{2+} + NO_2$
   e) $H_2O_2 + Cr_2O_7^{2-} \rightarrow O_2 + Cr^{3+}$
   f) $MnO_4^- + SO_2 \rightarrow Mn^{2+} + SO_4^{2-}$

2. Balance each of the following equations that occur in BASIC aqueous solution.

   a) $Cr(OH)_3 + IO_3^- \rightarrow CrO_4^{2-} + I^-$
   b) $Ag_2O + CH_2O \rightarrow Ag + CHO_2^-$
   c) $MnO_4^- + N_2H_4 \rightarrow MnO_2 + N_2$
   d) $S_2O_3^{2-} + OCl^- \rightarrow SO_4^{2-} + Cl^-$
   e) $MnO_4^- + I^- \rightarrow MnO_4^{2-} + IO_4^-$

3. In some redox reactions a given element is both oxidized *and* reduced in what is called a *disproportionation* reaction. Balance the following equations that represent disproportionation reactions using the method of your choice. Hint: An ion or compound containing an atom that undergoes both oxidation and reduction may be written twice in order to more easily account for the disproportionation.

   a) $H_2O_2 \rightarrow H_2O + O_2$
   b) $HNO_2 \rightarrow HNO_3 + NO + H_2O$
   c) $Cl_2 + OH^- \rightarrow ClO_4^- + Cl^- + H_2O$
   d) $P_4 + H_2O \rightarrow H_2PO_4^- + PH_3 + H^+$
   e) $CO(NH_2)_2 + HNO_2 \rightarrow CO_2 + N_2$

4. Balance the following redox equations that take place in aqueous solution.

   a) $NO + As \rightarrow N_2O + HAsO_2$ (acidic)
   b) $ClO_3^- + MnO_2 \rightarrow Cl^- + MnO_4^-$ (basic)
   c) $ClO_4^- + Br^- \rightarrow Cl^- + BrO_3^-$ (acidic)
   d) $H_2O_2 + Cr_2O_7^{2-} \rightarrow O_2 + Cr^{3+}$ (acidic)
   e) $TeO_3^{2-} + N_2O_4 \rightarrow Te + NO_3^-$ (basic)
   f) $ReO_4^- + IO^- \rightarrow IO_3^- + Re$ (basic)
   g) $NaHAsO_3 + KBrO_3 + HCl \rightarrow NaCl + KBr + H_3AsO_4$
   h) $Al + MnO_4^- \rightarrow MnO_2 + Al(OH)_4^-$ (basic)

1.3 Using the Standard Reduction Potential (SRP) Table to Predict Redox Reactions

Warm Up

1. Compare Table A7 Standard Reduction Potentials of Half-Cells with Table A6 Relative Strengths of Brønsted-Lowry Acids and Bases at the back of the book. List four similarities between the tables.

   (a) ______________________________ (c) ______________________________

   (b) ______________________________ (d) ______________________________

2. The half-reactions in the SRP table are written as ____________________.

   This means the reactant species are all ______________________ agents.

3. Find the strongest reducing agents on the SRP table. What family do these reducing agents belong to?

   ____

4. What element is the strongest oxidizing agent? __________ What family does this element belong to?

   ____

Using the Standard Reduction Potential (SRP) Table

Chemists use the standard reduction potential (SRP) table to predict whether a chemical species will spontaneously give electrons to or take electrons from another species. The oxidizing agents, which are the species that take electrons, are on the left side of the SRP table. The reducing agents, which are the species that give electrons, are on the right side of the SRP table.

> Chemical species in the left column of the SRP table will only take electrons spontaneously from species *below them* in the right column.

In chemical terms, oxidizing agents only spontaneously oxidize the reducing agents below them in the SRP table. For example, Br_2 spontaneously oxidizes Ag but not Cl^- (Figure 1.3.1).

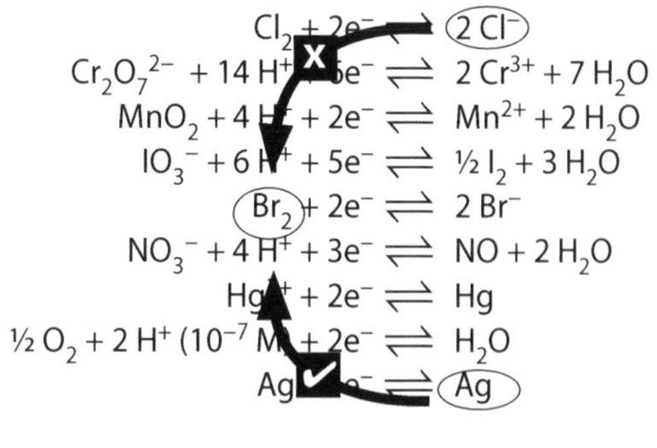

$$Cl_2 + 2e^- \rightleftharpoons 2\,Cl^-$$
$$Cr_2O_7^{2-} + 14\,H^+ + 6e^- \rightleftharpoons 2\,Cr^{3+} + 7\,H_2O$$
$$MnO_2 + 4\,H^+ + 2e^- \rightleftharpoons Mn^{2+} + 2\,H_2O$$
$$IO_3^- + 6\,H^+ + 5e^- \rightleftharpoons \tfrac{1}{2}\,I_2 + 3\,H_2O$$
$$Br_2 + 2e^- \rightleftharpoons 2\,Br^-$$
$$NO_3^- + 4\,H^+ + 3e^- \rightleftharpoons NO + 2\,H_2O$$
$$Hg^{2+} + 2e^- \rightleftharpoons Hg$$
$$\tfrac{1}{2}\,O_2 + 2\,H^+ (10^{-7}\,M) + 2e^- \rightleftharpoons H_2O$$
$$Ag^+ + e^- \rightleftharpoons Ag$$

Figure 1.3.1 *You can tell that Br_2 spontaneously oxidizes Ag because Ag is below Br_2 in the SRP table.*

Of course, the event can also be described from the reducing agent's point of view.

Chemical species in the right column only give electrons spontaneously to chemicals *above them* in the left column.

In chemical terms, reducing agents only spontaneously reduce the oxidizing agents above them in the SRP table. For example, Ag reduces Br_2 but Cl^- doesn't. Thus, spontaneous redox reactions occur with the oxidation half-reaction below the reduction half-reaction on the SRP table. Electrons are passed in a clockwise direction. Remember that the oxidizing agent (Br_2) gets reduced and the reducing agent (Ag) gets oxidized.

reduction ½ reaction →

$$Br_2 + 2e^- \rightleftharpoons 2\,Br^-$$
$$NO_3^- + 4\,H^+ + 3e^- \rightleftharpoons NO + 2\,H_2O$$
$$Hg^{2+} + 2e^- \rightleftharpoons Hg$$
$$\tfrac{1}{2}\,O_2 + 2\,H^+ (10^{-7}\,M) + 2e^- \rightleftharpoons H_2O$$
$$Ag^+ + e^- \rightleftharpoons Ag$$

← oxidation ½ reaction

$$2\,Ag \rightarrow 2\,Ag^+ + \cancel{2e^-}$$
$$Br_2 + \cancel{2e^-} \rightarrow 2\,Br^-$$
$$2\,Ag + Br_2 \rightarrow 2\,Ag^+ + 2\,Br^-$$

Sample Problem 1.3.1 — Determining Whether a Spontaneous Redox Reaction Will Occur

For each of the following, state whether a reaction will spontaneously occur. If so, write the balanced equation for the reaction.

(a) $Fe^{3+} + Cl^-$ (b) $Ca + Zn^{2+}$ (c) $I^- + Al$

What to Think About	How to Do It
(a) $Fe^{3+} + Cl^-$ 1. Identify the oxidizing agent and the reducing agent. 2. Oxidizing agents only take electrons spontaneously from reducing agents below them in the SRP table.	Fe^{3+} is an oxidizing agent. Cl^- is a reducing agent. Cl^- is not below Fe^{3+} in the SRP table so Fe^{3+} will not oxidize it. No reaction.
(b) $Ca + Zn^{2+}$ 1. Identify the oxidizing agent and the reducing agent. 2. Oxidizing agents can only take electrons spontaneously from reducing agents below them in the SRP table. 3. Write the two half-reactions, balance the transfer of electrons if necessary and then add the half-reactions together.	Ca is a reducing agent. Zn^{2+} is an oxidizing agent. Ca is below Zn^{2+} in the SRP table so Zn^{2+} will oxidize it. $Ca \rightarrow Ca^{2+} + \cancel{2e^-}$ $Zn^{2+} + \cancel{2e^-} \rightarrow Zn$ $Zn^{2+} + Ca \rightarrow Ca^{2+} + Zn$
(c) $I^- + Al$ 1. Identify the oxidizing agent and the reducing agent.	I^- and Al are both reducing agents so no reaction occurs.

Practice Problems 1.3.1 — Determining Whether a Spontaneous Redox Reaction Will Occur

For each of the following, state whether a spontaneous reaction will occur and if so, write the balanced equation for the reaction.

1. $I^- + Br_2$
2. $F_2 + Al^{3+}$
3. $Ag^+ + Sn$
4. $I_2 + Cl^-$

Single Displacement Reactions

Recall that both metals and non-metals are more stable as ions because as ions they have complete valence shells. Non-metals have high electron affinities, needing only one, two, or three electrons to complete their valence shells. Non-metals, as strong oxidizing agents, are found at the top left side of the SRP table, where they are shown being reduced to form anions (negatively charged ions). Non-metals can also be oxidized to form non-metallic oxides and oxyanions. For example, chlorine can be oxidized to chlorine dioxide (ClO_2), the hypochlorite ion (ClO^-), the chlorite ion (ClO_2^-), the chlorate ion (ClO_3^-), or the perchlorate ion (ClO_4^-). Metals, on the other hand, can only be oxidized. A metal empties its valence shell and the complete shell beneath it becomes its new valence shell. Most metals, as strong reducing agents, are found at the bottom, right side of the SRP table, where they are shown being oxidized to form cations (positively charged ions).

Recall that one chemical species passes or loses one or more electrons to another species in redox reactions. In the synthesis of ionic compounds, metals give electrons to non-metals and both form ions that are more stable than their neutral atoms. In the SRP table, this is reflected by most of the non-metals being above most of the metals. Single displacement reactions are also a type of redox reaction. In single displacement reactions, a non-metal oxidizes a different non-metal's anion, or a metal reduces a different metal's cation. Think of a non-metal displacement reaction as an electron tug-of-war between two non-metals for the "extra" electron(s) that one of them already possesses. A metal displacement reaction can be viewed as a metal atom trying to force its valence electron(s) onto a different metal's stable ion. In both cases, we use the SRP table to determine which chemical species wins.

Sample Problem 1.3.2 — Determining the Outcome of a Single Displacement Reaction

Will chlorine and sodium bromide spontaneously react to produce bromine and sodium chloride? If so, write the balanced net ionic equation for the reaction.

What to Think About	How to Do It
1. Write the balanced formula equation.	$Cl_2 + 2\ NaBr \rightarrow Br_2 + 2\ NaCl$
2. Write the complete ionic equation.	$Cl_2 + 2\ Na^+ + 2\ Br^- \rightarrow Br_2 + 2\ Na^+ + 2\ Cl^-$
3. Write the net ionic equation.	$Cl_2 + 2\ Br^- \rightarrow Br_2 + 2\ Cl^-$
4. Identify the oxidizing agent and the reducing agent.	Cl_2 is an oxidizing agent. Br^- is a reducing agent.
5. Oxidizing agents only spontaneously take electrons from reducing agents below them in the SRP table.	Br^- is below Cl_2 in the SRP table so Cl_2 can oxidize it as shown in part 3 above.

The chlorine atoms won the electron tug-of-war with the bromide ions in the sample problem above. The chlorine atoms that were sharing a pair of valence electrons to complete their valence shells now each have an electron of their own and the bromine atoms are forced to share valence electrons (Br_2). The sodium ions were spectator ions because they were unchanged by the reaction. We began with chlorine dissolved in a solution of sodium bromide and finished with bromine dissolved in a solution of sodium chloride.

Practice Problems 1.3.2 — Determining the Outcome of a Single Displacement Reaction

For each of the following, determine whether a reaction will occur and if so, write the balanced net ionic equation for the reaction.

1. $I_2 + CaF_2$

2. $Al + CuSO_4$

3. $Cl_2 + NaCl$

4. $Sn + Al(NO_2)_3$

The Strength of Oxidizing and Reducing Agents

Have you noticed that oxidizing and reducing agents closely parallel Brønsted-Lowry acids and bases? Brønsted-Lowry acids and bases pass protons back and forth. Oxidizing and reducing agents pass electrons back and forth. An acid and its conjugate base are the same chemical species with and without the proton. A reducing agent and its complementary oxidizing agent are the same chemical species with and without the electron. In the Warm Up exercise you identified similarities between the SRP table (Table A7) and the table of acid strengths (Table A5).

Recall that the weaker an acid, the stronger its conjugate base because the less an acid's tendency to give its proton away, the greater its conjugate base's tendency to take it back. Although the term *conjugate* is not used by chemists to describe the reduced and oxidized forms of a chemical species, the same inverse relationship exists between their strengths.

The stronger a reducing agent (A^-) is, the weaker its complementary oxidizing agent (A) is.

In other words, if a chemical species has a strong tendency to give an electron away then it will have a weak tendency to take it back.

Oxidizing Agents		Reducing Agents
STRONG ↑	$F_2 + 2e^- \rightarrow 2\,F^-$	WEAK ↓
	$2\,H^+ + 2e^- \rightarrow H_2$	
WEAK	$Li^+ + e^- \rightarrow Li$	STRONG

Just as there are amphiprotic species that can act as both proton donors and acceptors, there are also some chemical species that can act as both reducing agents and oxidizing agents. Multivalent transition metals have ions such as Cu^+, Sn^{2+}, and Fe^{2+} that can be further oxidized or reduced back to the metal. H_2O_2 can also be an oxidizing agent or a reducing agent. Can you find it in both columns of the SRP table?

The halogens are a little difficult to spot in the SRP table. An element's oxidizing strength corresponds with its electronegativity. Its ability to oxidize various chemical species corresponds with how strongly it attracts the shared pair of electrons in a covalent bond. Electronegativity increases as you move up a group in the periodic table and thus the relative positions of the halogens in the SRP table are the same as they are in the periodic table (Table 1.3.1). Fluorine can therefore oxidize any of the other halide ions. Chlorine can oxidize any halide ion other than fluoride, etc.

Table 1.3.1 *The Position of the Halogens in the SRP Table*

Oxidizing agent		Reducing agent
$F_2 + 2e^-$	⇌	$2\,F^-$
$S_2O_8^{2-} + 2e^-$	⇌	$2\,SO_4^{2-}$
$H_2O_2 + 2\,H^+ + 2e^-$	⇌	$2\,H_2O$
$MnO_4^- + 8\,H^+ + 5e^-$	⇌	$Mn^{2+} + 4\,H_2O$
$Au^{3+} + 3e^-$	⇌	Au
$BrO_3^- + 6\,H^+ + 5e^-$	⇌	$\frac{1}{2}\,Br_2 + 3\,H_2O$
$ClO_4^- + 8\,H^+ + 8e^-$	⇌	$Cl^- + 4\,H_2O$
$Cl_2 + 2e^-$	⇌	$2\,Cl$-
$Cr_2O_7^{2-} + 14\,H^+ + 6e^-$	⇌	$2\,Cr^{3+} + 7\,H_2O$
$\frac{1}{2}\,O_2 + 2\,H^+ + 2e^-$	⇌	H_2O
$MnO_2 + 4\,H^+ + 2e^-$	⇌	$Mn^{2+} + 2\,H_2O$
$IO_3^- + 6\,H^+ + 5e^-$	⇌	$\frac{1}{2}\,I_2 + 3\,H_2O$
$Br_2 + 2e^-$	⇌	$2Br^-$
$AuCl_4^- + 3e^-$	⇌	$Au + 4\,Cl^-$
$NO_3^- + 4\,H^+ + 3e^-$	⇌	$NO + 2\,H_2O$
$Hg^{2+} + 2e^-$	⇌	Hg
$\frac{1}{2}\,O_2 + 2\,H^+\,(10^{-7}\,M) + 2e^-$	⇌	H_2O
$2\,NO_3^- + 4\,H^+ + 2e^-$	⇌	$N_2O_4 + 2\,H_2O$
$Ag^+ + e^-$	⇌	Ag
$\frac{1}{2}\,Hg_2^{2+} + e^-$	⇌	Hg
$Fe^{3+} + e^-$	⇌	Fe^{2+}
$O_2 + 2\,H^+ + 2e^-$	⇌	H_2O_2
$I_2 + 2e^-$	⇌	$2\,I^-$

Some redox terminology is counter-intuitive. For instance, the strength of an oxidizing agent is called its **reduction potential** (E°). *Reduction potential* means *potential to be reduced*, not *potential to reduce*. Oxidizing agents get reduced and therefore have a reduction potential. Reduction and oxidation potentials are measured in volts. This will be explained in section 1.4. $F_2(g)$ is the strongest oxidizing agent shown in the SRP table, with a reduction potential of 2.87 V. Note that the *-ates* ions (e.g., bromate, permanganate, chlorate, dichromate) are strong oxidizing agents.

Likewise, **oxidation potentials** measure the strength of reducing agents since reducing agents become oxidized when they give up electrons. When the reduction half-reactions are read backwards, from right to left, they are oxidation half-reactions. Oxidation potentials of reducing agents are simply the opposite of the reduction potentials of their complementary oxidizing agents. For example, Al^{3+} has a reduction potential of −1.66 V while Al has an oxidation potential of +1.66 V. Li(*s*) is the strongest reducing agent shown in the SRP table we are using, with an oxidation potential of 3.04 V.

To change your standard reduction potential (SRP) table into a standard oxidation potential (SOP) table, you would turn it around 180° so it reads upside down and backwards, and you would reverse the E° signs (+ to – and – to +).

Quick Check

1. Which is the stronger reducing agent, Co or Sr? ____________
2. Which is the stronger oxidizing agent, Fe^{3+} or Al^{3+}? ____________
3. Which has the greater oxidation potential, Br^- or I^-? ____________
4. Which has the greater reduction potential, Cr^{3+} or Sn^{2+}? ____________
5. A and B are hypothetical elements. A^{2+} is a stronger oxidizing agent than B. Which has the greater oxidation potential, A or B^-? ____________
6. What is the reduction potential of Ag^+? ____________
7. What is the oxidation potential of Ca? ____________

Determining the Predominant Redox Reaction

In chemical mixtures, there are sometimes more than two chemical species available to react. We use the SRP table to predict which species will react.

The predominant redox reaction between the chemicals in a mixture will be between the strongest available oxidizing agent and the strongest available reducing agent.

Sample Problem 1.3.3 — Determining the Predominant Redox Reaction

Write the predominant redox reaction that will occur in a mixture of Cl_2, Ag^+, Sn^{2+}, and I^-.

What to Think About	How to Do It
1. Identify the oxidizing agent(s) and the reducing agent(s).	Cl_2, Ag^+, and Sn^{2+} are oxidizing agents. Sn^{2+} and I^- are reducing agents.
2. Use the SRP table to determine which species is the strongest oxidizing agent and which species is the strongest reducing agent.	(see table below) Cl_2 is a stronger oxidizing agent than Ag^+ or Sn^{2+}. Sn^{2+} is a stronger reducing agent than I^-.
3. The strongest oxidizing agent will oxidize the strongest reducing agent.	Cl_2 will oxidize Sn^{2+}.
4. Write the two half-reactions and balance the transfer of electrons if necessary. Then add the half-reactions together.	$Sn^{2+} \rightarrow Sn^{4+} + 2e^-$ $Cl_2 + 2e^- \rightarrow 2\ Cl^-$ $Cl_2 + Sn^{2+} \rightarrow Sn^{4+} + 2\ Cl^-$

Increasing Strength (oxidizing agents, upward) / Increasing Strength (reducing agents, downward)

Oxidizing Agents		Reducing Agents
$ClO_4^- + 8\ H^+ + 8e^-$	$\rightleftharpoons$	$Cl^- + 4\ H_2O$
$Cl_2 + 2e^-$	$\rightleftharpoons$	$2\ Cl^-$
$Cr_2O_7^{2-} + 14\ H^+ + 6e^-$	$\rightleftharpoons$	$2\ Cr^{3+} + 7\ H_2O$
$Br_2 + 2e^-$	$\rightleftharpoons$	$2\ Br^-$
$NO_3^- + 4\ H^+ + 3e^-$	$\rightleftharpoons$	$NO + 2\ H_2O$
$Hg^{2+} + 2e^-$	$\rightleftharpoons$	Hg
$\frac{1}{2}\ O_2(g) + 2\ H^+ (10^{-7}\ M) + 2e^-$	$\rightleftharpoons$	H_2O
$I_2 + 2e^-$	$\rightleftharpoons$	$2\ I^-$
$Ag^+ + e^-$	$\rightleftharpoons$	Ag
$H_2SO_3 + 4\ H^+ + 4e^-$	$\rightleftharpoons$	$S + 3\ H_2O$
$Cu^{2+} + 2e^-$	$\rightleftharpoons$	Cu
$SO_4^{2-} + 4\ H^+ + 2e^-$	$\rightleftharpoons$	$H_2SO_3 + H_2O$
$Sn^{4+} + 2e^-$	$\rightleftharpoons$	Sn^{2+}
$S + 2\ H^+ + 2e^-$	$\rightleftharpoons$	H_2S
$2\ H^+ + 2e^-$	$\rightleftharpoons$	H_2
$Pb^{2+} + 2e^-$	$\rightleftharpoons$	Pb
$Sn^{2+} + 2e^-$	$\rightleftharpoons$	Sn
$Ni^{2+} + 2e^-$	$\rightleftharpoons$	Ni

In the sample problem above, there are many other reactions that would occur but in every case the products can be oxidized by Cl_2 or reduced by Sn^{2+}. For example, Ag^+ can also oxidize I^- forming Ag and I_2 but this I_2 would then be reduced back to I^- by Sn^{2+} and the Ag would be oxidized back to Ag^+ by Cl_2. In every instance, the products would ultimately end up being those shown in the solution to the sample problem. Also keep in mind that if one species runs out, then the strongest remaining agent is "next up to bat."

Practice Problems 1.3.3 — Determining the Predominant Redox Reaction

Write the predominant redox reaction that will occur in each of the following mixtures:

1. Sn^{4+}, Br^-, Zn^{2+}, and Ni

2. $CuBr_2(aq)$ and $Al(s)$

3. Na^+, Cu^+, and F^-

4. Copper and bromine in a solution of iron(III) chloride

Redox Titrations

All the general principles of titrations apply to redox titrations. A chemist titrates an acid with a base or vice versa. Similarly, a chemist titrates an oxidizing agent with a reducing agent or vice versa. The chemist must choose a titrant that is a strong enough oxidizing agent to react with the reducing agent or a strong enough reducing agent to react with the oxidizing agent.

The indicator of an acid-base titration is itself a weak acid with a different color in its base form. Similarly, the indicator of a redox titration is itself a reducing agent with a different color in its oxidized form. Otherwise, redox indicators operate in a much simpler way than acid-base indicators. A chemist chooses a redox indicator that is a weaker oxidizing or reducing agent than the analyte (the chemical being analyzed) so that the indicator's reaction indicates that the analyte has been completely consumed.

In redox titrations it is not uncommon for the titrant to act as its own indicator. The purple permanganate ion is sometimes used as an oxidizing agent to titrate a chemical species. The permanganate ion is reduced to the very faint pink Mn^{2+} under acidic conditions. When the permanganate solution is slowly added to a reducing agent of unknown molarity, the permanganate ion is reduced, and the purple color disappears. Eventually a drop is added and the purple color remains. At this point, the chemist knows that the chemical species that was reducing the permanganate ion has been totally consumed, and the equivalence point has been reached.

Sample Problem 1.3.4 — Determining a Chemical's Concentration via Redox Titration

To titrate a 25.0 mL solution of Fe^{2+} to the equivalence point, 16.7 mL of 0.0152 M MnO_4^- in acidic solution was needed. What was the $[Fe^{2+}]$?

What to Think About	How to Do It
1. Write the balanced net ionic equation for the titration reaction.	$5\ Fe^{2+} + MnO_4^- + 8\ H^+ \rightarrow 5\ Fe^{3+} + Mn^{2+} + 4\ H_2O$
2. Calculate the moles of MnO_4^- reacted.	$0.0167\ L \times 0.0152\ \frac{mol}{L} = 2.54 \times 10^{-4}\ mol\ MnO_4^-$
3. Calculate the moles of Fe^{2+} reacted.	$2.54 \times 10^{-4}\ mol\ MnO_4^- \times \frac{5\ mol\ Fe^{2+}}{1\ mol\ MnO_4^-}$ $= 1.27 \times 10^{-3}\ mol\ Fe^{2+}$
4. Calculate the $[Fe^{2+}]$ in the original sample.	$[Fe^{2+}] = \frac{1.27 \times 10^{-3}\ mol}{0.0250\ L} = 0.0508\ M\ Fe^{2+}$ **Note:** Under basic conditions the permanganate ion is reduced to $MnO_2(s)$, as shown on the SRP table (+.60 V).

Practice Problems 1.3.4 — Determining a Chemical's Concentration via Redox Titration

1. Potassium dichromate is used to titrate a solution of iron(II) chloride. The dichromate ion acts as its own indicator. As the $Cr_2O_7^{2-}$ solution is added to the Fe^{2+} solution, the orange dichromate ion is reduced to green Cr^{3+} as it oxidizes the Fe^{2+} to Fe^{3+}. The equivalence point is evident when the orange color remains indicating that all the Fe^{2+} has reacted. An amount of 15.0 mL of 0.0200 M $Cr_2O_7^{2-}$ solution was required to titrate 20.0 mL of acidified $FeCl_2$.

   (a) Balance the redox equation for this titration: $Cr_2O_7^{2-} + Fe^{2+} \rightarrow Cr^{3+} + Fe^{3+}$

   (b) What was the $[FeCl_2]$?

2. A student uses 16.3 mL of an acidified $KMnO_4$ solution to titrate 1.00 g $Na_2C_2O_4$ to the equivalence point. The balanced equation is:

   $5\ C_2O_4^{2-} + 2\ MnO_4^- + 16\ H^+ \rightarrow 10\ CO_2 + 2\ Mn^{2+} + 8\ H_2O$

   Calculate the $[KMnO_4]$.

3. The following redox reaction occurs between the dichromate ion and ethanol:

   $3\ CH_3CH_2OH + 2\ Cr_2O_7^{2-} + 16\ H^+ \rightarrow 3\ CH_3COOH + 4\ Cr^{3+} + 11\ H_2O$

   ethanol, orange, ethanoic acid, green

   A chemist uses 26.25 mL of 0.500 M $Cr_2O_7^{2-}$ to titrate a 10.0 mL sample of wine to the equivalence point.

   (a) What is the $[CH_3CH_2OH]$ in the wine?

   (b) The concentration of ethanol in alcoholic beverages is expressed as percent by volume. If a wine is 10% alcohol, it means that there are 10 mL of ethanol for every 100 mL of the beverage. The density of ethanol is 0.789 g/mL. Convert your answer in part (a) into percent by volume.

1.3 Activity: Making an SRP Table

Question

How can you make a standard reduction potential table from a set of experimental data?

Background

Each redox reaction allows you to determine the relative position of its two half-reactions in the table. For example, from the following reaction in which L reduces M^{2+} you can infer that M^{2+} is a stronger oxidizing agent than L^+. M^+ is therefore above L^+ in the SRP table.

$L + M^{2+} \rightarrow 2\,L^+ + M$

reduction ½ reaction $\longrightarrow$

$M^{2+} + 2e^- \rightarrow M$

$L^+ + e^- \leftarrow L$

$\longleftarrow$ oxidation ½ reaction

Procedure

Use the following information to produce an SRP table with six half-reactions.

1. $L + M^{2+} \rightarrow 2\,L^+ + M$
2. P^- reduces D^{3+} to D^{2+}.
3. Element Q is the strongest oxidizing agent. ($Q + e^- \rightarrow Q^-$)
4. $M + 2\,P \rightarrow M^{2+} + 2\,P^-$
5. L^+ oxidizes C to C^{2+}.

Results and Discussion

1. Fill in the SRP table below:

Oxidizing Agents		Reducing Agents
______________	$\rightleftharpoons$	______________
______________	$\rightleftharpoons$	______________
______________	$\rightleftharpoons$	______________
______________	$\rightleftharpoons$	______________
______________	$\rightleftharpoons$	______________
______________	$\rightleftharpoons$	______________

2. Which chemical species is the weakest reducing agent? ______________

3. Which chemical species has the lowest reduction potential? ____________

1.3 Review Questions

1. Will iodine spontaneously oxidize: (a) Fe^{2+}? (b) Sn?

2. Identify a metal ion that will spontaneously oxidize I^- but not Cl^-.

3. For each of the following, state whether a spontaneous reaction will occur and if so, write the balanced equation for the reaction.
   (a) $Mg + Al^{3+} \rightarrow$

   (b) $Cl^- + I_2 \rightarrow$

   (c) $Hg^{2+} + Ag \rightarrow$

4. Complete the following table:

Metals	Non-metals
bottom right of SRP table	
	tend to take electrons
give e^- to chemicals above them on the left	

5. For each of the following, state whether a spontaneous reaction will occur and if so, write the balanced net ionic equation for the reaction.
   (a) $Fe + Sn(NO_3)_2 \rightarrow$

   (b) $F_2 + KBr \rightarrow$

   (c) $Cu + NaI \rightarrow$

6. (a) Write the net ionic equation for the reaction between KI and $FeCl_3$.

   (b) Write the net ionic equation for the reaction between Br_2 and $FeCl_2$.

7. When tin(II) nitrate dissolves in acid the two dissociated ions react with each other. Write the net ionic equation for this reaction.

8. Would it be practical to store a 0.5 M $FeCl_3$ solution in an aluminum container? Explain.

9. State whether the forward or the reverse reaction is spontaneous.
   (a) $Sn^{4+} + 2\ Fe^{2+} \leftarrow\ ?\ \rightarrow 2\ Fe^{3+} + Sn^{2+}$

   (b) $Cr_2O_7^{2-} + 14\ H^+ + 3\ Cu \leftarrow\ ?\ \rightarrow 2\ Cr^{3+} + 7\ H_2O + 3\ Cu^{2+}$

10. One characteristic of acids is that they react with magnesium, liberating hydrogen gas. Write the balanced redox equation for this reaction.

11. Explain why silver oxidizes and then dissolves in 1 M nitric acid but not in 1 M hydrochloric acid.

12. A few drops of phenolphthalein are added to a petri dish of water. A small piece of sodium reacts violently when placed in the water, leaving pink tracks as it skips across the water's surface. The air ignites above the sodium producing a small flame. Write the redox reaction that occurs and briefly explain the pink tracks and the flame.

13. (a) Which has the greatest reduction potential, I_2, Ag^+, or Mg^{2+}?

    (b) Which has the greatest oxidation potential, I^-, Ag, or Mg?

14. The surface of a sheet of aluminum is observed to darken after being placed in a solution of gallium nitrate. From this observation, determine which has the greater reduction potential, Al^{3+} or Ga^{3+}.

15. (a) What is the reduction potential of $Br_2(l)$?

    (b) What is the oxidation potential of Zn(*s*)?

16. Write the predominant redox reaction that will occur in each of the following mixtures:
    (a) Co^{2+}, Cu, Mn^{2+}, and Fe

    (b) Cu, Hg, Cu^+, and Cr^{2+}

    (c) $CuCl_2(aq) + SnI_2(aq)$

17. If a zinc sheet were placed into a solution of $Cu^{2+}(aq)$ and $Fe^{3+}(aq)$ what would the predominant reaction be?

18. Each of the following redox reactions is spontaneous in the forward direction:
    $A^{2+} + B \rightarrow B^{2+} + A$ $\quad$ $2\,C^{3+} + A \rightarrow 2\,C^{2+} + A^{2+}$ $\quad$ $B^{2+} + 2\,D \rightarrow 2\,D^{+} + B$
    Which of the chemical species involved in these reactions is:
    (a) the strongest oxidizing agent

    (b) the strongest reducing agent

19. A chemist titrates 15.0 mL of KI(*aq*) to the equivalence point with 32.8 mL of 0.200 M $Na_2Cr_2O_7$. What is the [KI]?
    $Cr_2O_7^{2-} + 14\,H^+ + 6\,I^- \rightarrow 2\,Cr^{3+} + 3\,I_2 + 7\,H_2O$

20. A $KMnO_4$ solution is standardized with oxalic acid. The equation for the redox reaction is:

    $5\,H_2C_2O_4 + 2\,MnO_4^- + 6\,H^+ \rightarrow 10\,CO_2 + 2\,Mn^{2+} + 8\,H_2O$

    What is the molar concentration of the $KMnO_4$ solution if 18.6 mL of the solution was required to titrate 0.105 g $H_2C_2O_4 \cdot 2H_2O$?

21. The legal limit for intoxication while driving in British Columbia had been a blood alcohol content (BAC) of 0.08% by mass for many years until it was reduced to 0.05% in September 2010. A 5.00 g sample of blood is titrated with 10.15 mL of 0.0150 M $K_2Cr_2O_7$. The dichromate ion acts as an oxidizing agent in the reaction of ethanol, C_2H_5OH, to form carbon dioxide and the Cr^{3+} ion.
    (a) Balance the equation for the reaction that occurs during the titration.

    (b) Calculate the percent alcohol by mass in the blood sample. Would this driver be considered legally impaired before September 2010? Now?

1.4 The Electrochemical Cell

Warm Up

1. A charged atom or group of atoms is called a(n) ______________.

2. The charged subatomic particle that travels around the nucleus is called a(n) ______________.

3. Current electricity is a steady flow of electric charge. A current of 1 amp means that one coulomb of charge is flowing past the point of measurement each second. The charge of a single electron is only 1.60×10^{-19} C. How many electrons does it take to make up one coulomb of charge?

The Standard Electrochemical Cell

Electrons are transferred from one chemical species to another in all redox reactions. An **electrochemical cell** is a portable source of electricity, in which the electricity is produced by a spontaneous redox reaction within the cell. Electrochemical cells are also referred to as voltaic cells and galvanic cells. The electrochemical cell is the most common application of redox reactions and is also the best tool for measuring the tendency of redox reactions to occur.

The basic design of an electrochemical cell isolates an oxidation half-reaction from a reduction half-reaction within the device. Electrons can travel only from the reducing agent to the oxidizing agent when the two agents are connected through an external circuit. The basic components of an electrochemical cell are two different conductive materials (electrodes immersed in the same or different electrolyte solutions. If each electrode is immersed in a separate solution then two half-cells are created. The two half-cells must be connected in some manner that allows ion migration between them. For example, a salt bridge is a U-tube filled with an electrolyte solution or gel that allows ion migration (Figure 1.4.1).

How does an electrochemical cell work? The chemical species in the two half-cells exert forces on each other's electrons through the wire that connects the two half-cells. Electrons spontaneously flow through the wire from the strongest available reducing agent to the strongest available oxidizing agent.

One type of half-cell consists of a metal electrode immersed in a solution containing ions of the same metal. Either the metal electrode gives electrons to the other half-cell or the metal ions receive electrons from the other half-cell. Let's consider a cell with two metal | metal ion half-cells. The cell in Figure 1.4.1 has one half-cell with a magnesium electrode immersed in a solution containing magnesium ions and another half-cell with a copper electrode immersed in a solution containing copper(II) ions. Although the metals are not in physical contact with the other half-cell's ions, they are electrically connected through the wire connecting the two half-cells.

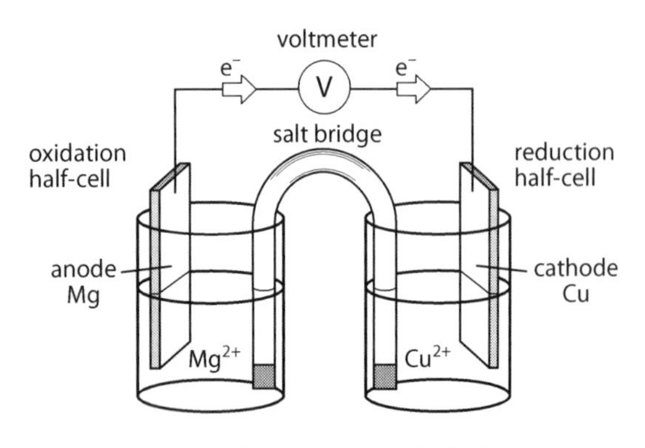

Figure 1.4.1 *A standard electrochemical cell*

The predominant redox reaction will be between the strongest available oxidizing agent and the strongest available reducing agent, just as though the chemicals were all in the same container. In fact, the SRP table (Table A7) specifically provides the tendency of redox reactions to occur between standard half-cells. A standard cell has ion concentrations of 1 M at 25°C as shown just below the heading of the SRP table. The SRP table thus allows us to predict the resulting direction of electron flow under standard conditions:

reduction ½ reaction

$$\begin{array}{lcl} Cu^{2+} + 2e^- & \rightarrow & Cu \\ Pb^{2+} + 2e^- & \rightleftharpoons & Pb \\ Co^{2+} + 2e^- & \rightleftharpoons & Co \\ Zn^{2+} + 2e^- & \rightleftharpoons & Zn \\ Mg^{2+} + 2e^- & \leftarrow & Mg \end{array}$$

oxidation ½ reaction

$$\begin{array}{rcl} Mg & \rightarrow & Mg^{2+} + \cancel{2e^-} \\ Cu^{2+} + \cancel{2e^-} & \rightarrow & Cu \\ \hline Cu^{2+} + Mg & \rightarrow & Mg^{2+} + Cu \end{array}$$

The **anode** is defined as the electrode where oxidation occurs. The **cathode** is defined as the electrode where reduction occurs.

> Oxidation occurs at the anode.
> Reduction occurs at the cathode.

Thus in the cells in Figure 1.4.1, the magnesium electrode is the anode and the copper electrode is the cathode. Note that although reduction occurs at the cathode, it isn't the cathode itself that is being reduced. In our example, it is the copper(II) ions (Cu^{2+}) that are being reduced and plating out as copper metal (Cu) at the cathode. In any cell where plating occurs, it will be at the cathode. While the cathode thus increases in mass, the anode decreases in mass as metal atoms donate electrons and become ions, which dissolve into solution.

A conductor doesn't increase in mass or become charged when an electric current flows through it. When electrons move into a copper wire, they displace or push the wire's free moving valence electrons ahead. Magnesium's two electrons need only move one atom toward the copper half-cell to displace electrons all the way through the wire and pop two electrons out the other end to the waiting Cu^{2+} ions. This is similar to what happens when water flows from a tap into a hose that is already full of water, immediately pushing some water out the other end of the hose.

The Salt Bridge

A salt bridge or a porous barrier allows ion migration that completes the circuit. In effect, the ion migration electrically counterbalances the electron flow. Without this ion migration, a charge build-up would occur: the reduction half-cell would become negative and the oxidation half-cell would become positive. This would create a polarization that would stop the electron flow. The natural ion migration prevents such a charge build-up. Consider a cell and its external circuit as one continuous loop with the negatively charged particles (electrons and anions) flowing in a continuous clockwise or counter-clockwise direction. In Figure 1.4.2, the negatively charged particles flow in a clockwise direction.

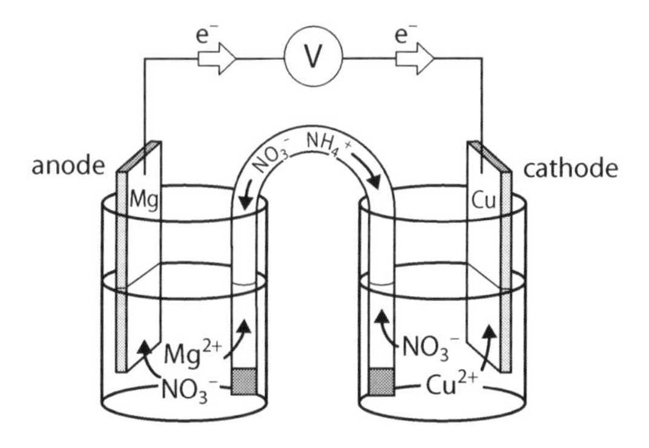

Figure 1.4.2 *Ion migration in an electrochemical cell*

> Anions migrate toward the anode.
> Cations migrate toward the cathode.

The oxidation half-cell above consists of a Mg electrode in $Mg(NO_3)_2(aq)$. The reduction half-cell consists of a Cu electrode in $Cu(NO_3)_2(aq)$. The salt bridge contains $NH_4NO_3(aq)$. The anion (NO_3^-) moves toward the anode while the cations (NH_4^+, Cu^{2+}, and Mg^{2+}) move toward the cathode.

Students sometimes ask whether the anode is the positive or the negative electrode. It is neither. The electrodes do not have any significant charge. Why then do commercial cells have a (–) label and a (+) label on them? The anode and the cathode each have a (–) and a (+) terminal or end, just as a magnet has a north and a south pole. Electrons flow externally from the (–) terminal of the anode to the (+) terminal of the cathode while internally anions migrate from the (–) terminal of the cathode to the (+) terminal of the anode (Figure 1.4.3).

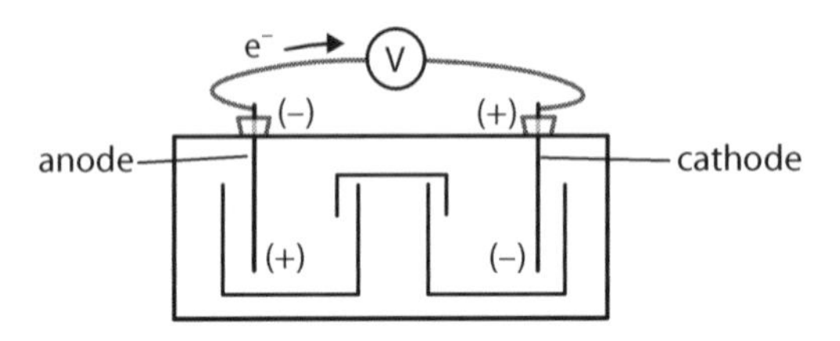

Figure 1.4.3 *Electrons move the through the wire connecting the electrodes while ions move through the salt bridge.*

Non-metal | Non-metal Ion Half-Cells

Another type of half-cell consists of a non-metal electrode immersed in a solution containing ions of the same non-metal. What does a non-metal electrode such as a chlorine electrode look like? Obviously, a gas or a liquid electrode can't simply be a piece of the substance. They are essentially an inverted test tube filled with the liquid or gas (Figure 1.4.4). A platinum (inert metal) wire runs through the liquid or gas and connects at the bottom, open end of the tube to a piece of porous platinum foil where most of the electron transfer occurs. The gas is fed into the tube at 1 atm pressure through a side arm at the closed, top end of the tube. There are several variations on this design. Sometimes, an inert electrode is simply suspended above the open end of a tube that feeds gas bubbles into the solution. Many of the bubbles make contact with and even adhere to the electrode as they rise up through the solution.

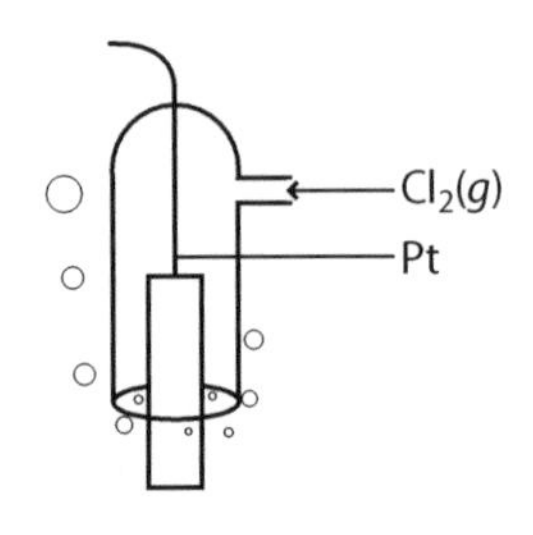

Figure 1.4.4 *A chlorine electrode*

A chlorine electrode immersed in a solution containing chloride ions is an example of a non-metal | non-metal ion half-cell. Either the non-metal electrode receives electrons from the other half-cell or the non-metal ions give electrons to the other half-cell when the electrochemical cell is operating. Hydrogen cells are an exception. Either the hydrogen electrode gives electrons to the other half-cell or the hydrogen ions receive electrons from the other half-cell. If a hydrogen | hydrogen ion half-cell were connected to a chlorine | chloride ion half-cell then electrons would flow from the hydrogen half-cell to the chlorine half-cell. The hydrogen gas would be oxidized and the chlorine gas would be reduced.

reduction ½ reaction →

$$Cl_2 + 2e^- \rightarrow 2\,Cl^-$$
$$Br_2 + 2e^- \rightleftharpoons 2\,Br^-$$
$$I_2 + 2e^- \rightleftharpoons 2\,I^-$$
$$Cu^{2+} + 2e^- \rightleftharpoons Cu$$
$$2\,H^+ + 2e^- \leftarrow H_2$$

← oxidation ½ reaction

$$H_2 \rightarrow 2\,H^+ + \cancel{2e^-}$$
$$Cl_2 + \cancel{2e^-} \rightarrow 2\,Cl^-$$
$$\overline{Cl_2 + H_2 \rightarrow 2\,H^+ + 2\,Cl^-}$$

Predicting Standard Cell Potentials (Voltages)

The simple design of the standard electrochemical cell makes it ideal for measuring redox potentials. The redox potential is the tendency of a redox reaction to occur. Standard cell potentials are measured in volts. Voltage can be thought of as the difference in electrical pressure that causes the flow of electrons in much the same way that a difference in air pressure causes a flow of air (wind). Cell voltages measure the net tendency for electron transfer between one redox tandem (oxidizing agent–reducing agent) and another. Cell voltages do not apply outside the context of standard

Quick Check

For the cell shown on the right:

1. Which electrode is the anode? ____________

2. In which direction do the electrons flow through the wire?

   ____

3. In which direction do the cations flow through the salt bridge?

   ____

4. Which electrode gains in mass? ________________

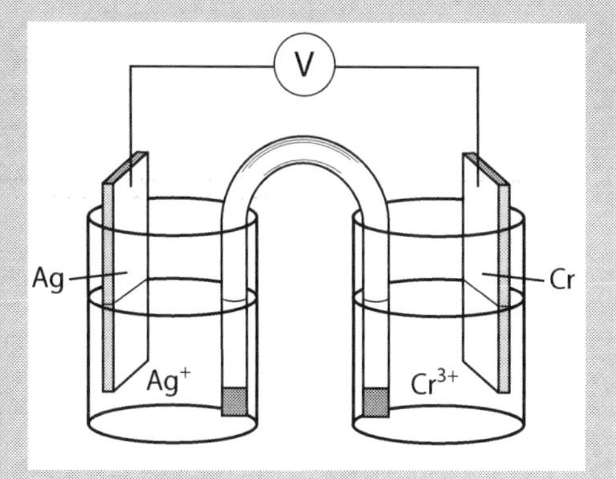

electrochemical cells. However, they can still be useful for predicting the spontaneity of a reaction between these species in other circumstances.

By now you are discovering that answering redox questions is all about knowing how to use the SRP table (Table A7). The SRP table not only allows us to predict the direction of electron flow in standard cells, it also allows us to predict the tendency of electron flow. All E° values in this table are reported relative to the $H_2(g)$ half-cell. The hydrogen electrode is thus referred to as a *reference* electrode. The result of any other "competition" can be determined by a third-party comparison against what might be considered their common enemy, H^+. This is like predicting the result of a football game by comparing how the two teams did against a common opponent. If Team A defeats Team B by 14 points and Team B defeats Team C by 10 points then we would predict that Team A would defeat Team C by 24 points. Third party comparisons are not always valid in sports, but they do work for predicting the voltages of half-cell combinations in electrochemical cells.

The half-reactions highlighted below show that, under standard conditions, a Ni | Ni^{2+} half-cell would lose to a hydrogen half-cell by 0.26 V. However an I_2 | I^- half-cell would win against a hydrogen half-cell by 0.54 V. It's predictable that, when a Ni | Ni^{2+} half-cell and a I_2 | I^- half-cell are connected, the result would be a 0.80 V victory for the I_2 | I^- half-cell.

reduction ½ reaction	$I_2 + 2e^-$	$\rightarrow$	$2\,I^-$	+0.54 V
	$Cu^+ + e^-$	$\rightleftharpoons$	Cu	+0.52 V
	$H_2SO_3 + 4\,H^+ + 2e^-$	$\rightleftharpoons$	$S + 3\,H_2O$	+0.45 V
	$Cu^{2+} + 2e^-$	$\rightleftharpoons$	Cu	+0.34 V
	$SO_4^{2-} + 4\,H^+ + 2e^-$	$\rightleftharpoons$	$H_2SO_3 + H_2O$	+0.17 V
	$Cu^{2+} + e^-$	$\rightleftharpoons$	Cu^+	+0.15 V
	$Sn^{4+} + 2e^-$	$\rightleftharpoons$	Sn^{2+}	+0.15 V
	$S + 2\,H^+ + 2e^-$	$\rightleftharpoons$	H_2S	+0.14 V
	$2\,H^+ + 2e^-$	$\rightleftharpoons$	H_2	0.00 V
	$Pb^{2+} + 2e^-$	$\rightleftharpoons$	Pb	−0.13 V
	$Sn^{2+} + 2e^-$	$\rightleftharpoons$	Sn	−0.14 V
oxidation ½ reaction	$Ni^{2+} + 2e^-$	$\leftarrow$	Ni	−0.26 V

Voltage is also called *potential difference* because it measures the difference in electrical potential energy between two points in a circuit. The difference between the reduction potentials of Ni^{2+} and I_2 is 0.54 V – (–0.26 V) = 0.80 V. Perhaps the easiest way to determine standard cell voltages is to write each half-reaction the way it occurs and then add the half-cell potentials together. When a half-reaction is written in the opposite direction as that shown in the SRP table then its half-cell potential is also changed from (+) to (–) or vice versa.

Sometimes it is necessary to multiply one or both of the half-reactions by an integer in order to balance the transfer of electrons. A half-cell potential (E°) doesn't change when its half-reaction is multiplied by an integer. One volt is one joule of energy per coulomb of charge. One coulomb of charge represents 6.2×10^{18} electrons. Tripling the half-reaction does not affect the half-cell potential since the energy *per electron* (voltage) is unchanged. Changing the size of metal electrodes does not affect the cell voltage.

Sample Problem 1.4.1 — Determining Standard Cell Potentials (Voltages)

Determine the voltage of a standard cell consisting of a Ni | Ni^{2+} half-cell and an I_2 | I^- half-cell.

What to Think About	How to Do It
1. Write each half-reaction and its standard potential. The oxidation potential of Ni is +0.26 V because it is the reverse of the reduction potential of Ni^{2+} provided in the SRP table (Table A7).	$Ni \rightarrow Ni^{2+} + 2e^-$ $E° = 0.26$ V $I_2 + 2e^- \rightarrow 2I^-$ $E° = 0.54$ V
2. Add the reduction potential to the oxidation potential.	$I_2 + Ni \rightarrow Ni^{2+} + 2I^-$ $E° = 0.80$ V

A positive E° indicates that the reaction is spontaneous. A negative E° indicates that the reverse reaction is spontaneous. In the context of an electrochemical cell, a negative E° means that you wrote the half-reactions backwards. The beauty of the SRP table is that it displays the strength of oxidizing and reducing agents, while also allowing you to quickly calculate the standard cell voltage of hundreds of half-cell combinations. A two-dimensional table could also be used to directly display the standard cell voltages of a limited number of half-cell combinations. Table 1.4.1 shows an example.

Table 1.4.1 *Example of Table to Display Half-cell Combinations*

		Reduction Half-cell		
		$2H^+ + 2e^- \rightarrow H_2$	$Ni^{2+} + 2e^- \rightarrow Ni$	$I_2 + 2e^- \rightarrow 2I^-$
Oxidation Half-cell	$H_2 \rightarrow 2H^+ + 2e^-$		–0.26 V	0.54 V
	$Ni \rightarrow Ni^{2+} + 2e^-$	0.26 V		0.80 V
	$2I^- \rightarrow I_2 + 2e^-$	–0.54 V	–0.80 V	

Practice Problems 1.4.1 — Determining Standard Cell Potentials (Voltages)

Determine the standard cell potential of each of the following combinations of half-cells. Show the oxidation and reduction half-reactions as well as the overall redox reaction occurring in each cell.

1. Ni | Ni^{2+} and Br_2 | Br^-

2. Cu | Cu^{2+} and Al | Al^{3+}

3. Au | Au^{3+} and I_2 | I^-

Non-Standard Conditions

A cell's conditions usually change as it operates. The voltages predicted using the SRP table are cell voltages under standard conditions (1 M, 25°C). As a cell operates, its voltage drops. Recall the Cu | Cu^{2+} || Mg | Mg^{2+} cell from the original examples in this section.

$$Cu^{2+} + Mg \rightarrow Mg^{2+} + Cu$$

For the purposes of this discussion let's consider Cu^{2+} to be having an electron tug-of-war with Mg^{2+} in this cell. Both Cu^{2+} and Mg^{2+} are, after all, oxidizing agents. The Cu^{2+} pulls Mg's valence electrons toward the Cu | Cu^{2+} half-cell while Mg^{2+} pulls Cu's valence electrons toward the Mg | Mg^{2+} half-cell. These are opposing forces even though they are pulling on different electrons because electrons cannot simultaneously flow in two directions through a wire. Just as water can, at any given time, flow only in one direction through a hose, electrons can at any given time flow only in one direction through a wire. If you connected two taps with a hose, the water would flow from the tap with the greatest pressure to that with the least pressure. The tap with the greatest pressure would win the "push-of-war," but the water pressure in the opposite direction would act as a resistance to that flow. Similarly, electrons flow from the Mg | Mg^{2+} half-cell to the Cu | Cu^{2+} half-cell and the electrical pressure in the opposite direction acts as a resistance. In other words, Cu^{2+} wins the electron tug-of-war against Mg^{2+}.

Now let's consider how the cell's conditions change as it operates and how those changes affect the cell's voltage. As the cell operates, Mg transfers electrons to Cu^{2+}, thereby decreasing the $[Cu^{2+}]$ and increasing the $[Mg^{2+}]$. The increased $[Mg^{2+}]$ increases its pulling force while the decreasing $[Cu^{2+}]$ decreases its pulling force. Eventually the pulling forces of the Mg^{2+} and Cu^{2+} become equal and the cell now has 0 V so it is "dead." As an analogy, consider a tug-of-war between 20 grade 12s and 20 grade 8s. Naturally the grade 12s would win. But what would happen if every time the rope moved one foot, the grade 12s lost one of their pullers and the grade 8s gained another puller? Eventually the grade 8s' pulling force and the grade 12s' pulling force would be equal and the contest would come to a draw.

Cell Equilibrium

A "dead" cell is often said to be at equilibrium. The equilibrium referred to in the context of an electrochemical cell is a static equilibrium of forces. It is **not** a dynamic chemical equilibrium because electrons cannot travel simultaneously in two directions through the same wire. This same redox reaction could develop a chemical equilibrium if the reactants were both present in the same solution. Just as protons (H^+) are passed back and forth in Brønsted-Lowry acid-base equilibria, electrons are passed back and forth in redox equilibria. A reaction's E° indicates essentially the same thing as its K_{eq}. A formula called the *Nernst equation* converts E°s into K_{eqs}. Even small cell voltages generally correspond to large equilibrium constants. The reactions go almost to completion before establishing equilibrium. Small negative cell voltages therefore correspond to small equilibrium constants for reactions that establish equilibrium with little product. Chemists use cell voltages and the Nernst equation to determine equilibrium constants that would be virtually impossible to determine by direct chemical analysis.

We have seen that changes to a cell's conditions will affect its voltage. If the reactant concentrations are greater than 1 M or the product concentrations are less than 1 M then the cell's potential will be greater than the standard cell potential because the forward reaction has to proceed further to achieve the equilibrium of forces. Conversely if the reactant concentrations are less than 1 M or the product concentrations are greater than 1 M, the cell's potential will be less than the standard cell potential. This is because the forward reaction has less reactant to consume before achieving the equilibrium of forces. The concentration of an ion may be lowered in a half-cell by precipitating some ions out of solution. For example, if some sodium sulfide were added to a $Cu \mid Cu^{2+}$ half-cell then some Cu^{2+} ions would precipitate out with S^{2-} ions. This would cause the voltage in our $Cu \mid Cu^{2+} \parallel Mg \mid Mg^{2+}$ cell to drop.

The Nernst Equation

The Nernst equation is useful for converting E°_{cell} into *K* and vice versa. It can also be used to determine how E°_{cell} will change when non-standard ion concentrations are introduced into an electrochemical cell. Two different equations, both of which describe free energy, may be used to derive the Nernst equation. The first is from Chapter 3, featuring thermodynamics:

$$\Delta G = \Delta G^\circ + RT \ln Q \qquad \text{Equation I}$$

The second will be worked with in detail in section 1.6.

$$\Delta G^\circ = -nFE^\circ \qquad \text{Equation II}$$

The symbol *F* in the second equation is called the Faraday constant. It has a numerical value of 96 500 C/mol e⁻. Substitution of Equation II into Equation I gives this new equation:

$$-nFE = -nFE^\circ + RT \ln Q \qquad \text{Equation III}$$

Division of both sides of Equation III by $-nF$ results in the following equation.

$$\frac{-\cancel{nF}E}{-\cancel{nF}} = \frac{-nFE^\circ + RT\ln Q}{-nF} = \frac{-\cancel{nF}E^\circ}{-\cancel{nF}} + \frac{RT\ln Q}{-nF}$$

Canceling of $-nF$ wherever possible results in an initial version of the Nernst equation:

$$\mathbf{E = E^\circ - \frac{RT}{nF} \ln Q} \qquad \text{Equation IV}$$

At 25°C, substitution of known values such as

$R = 8.31$ J/mol·K
$T = 298$ K
$\ln Q = 2.303 \log Q$
$F = 96\,500$ C/mol e⁻

results in: $E = E^\circ - \frac{(8.31\,J/\cancel{mol\cdot K})(298\,\cancel{K})\,2.303}{n(96\,500\,C/\cancel{mol}\,e^-)} \log Q$

Combining numerical values, and remembering that a joule/coulomb is equivalent to a volt, gives the final form of the Nernst equation. Note that n is the number of moles of electrons transferred.

$$E = E^{\circ} - \frac{0.0592}{n} \log Q$$

This equation allows us to calculate the cell voltage for an electrochemical cell whose half-cells contain any concentration of reactants and products. When a cell is at equilibrium, E = 0 and $Q = K$. This means that $0 = E^{\circ} - \frac{0.0592}{n} \log K$ or

$$E^{\circ} = \frac{0.0592}{n} \log K$$

The Danielli Cell

The historically important Danielli cell is often anglicized as the "Daniels cell." It involves copper and zinc electrodes in solutions of copper(II) and zinc ions (Figure 1.4.5).

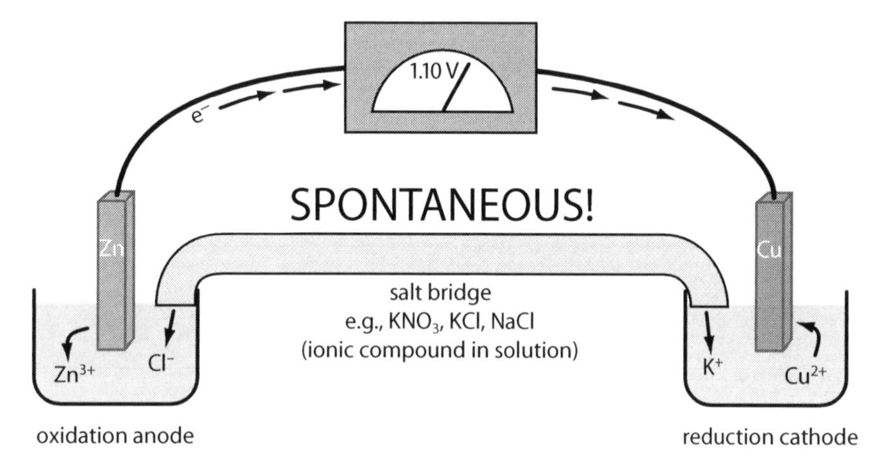

Figure 1.4.5 *The Danielli cell is made of zinc and copper half-cells.*

Zinc is the stronger reducing agent so it is oxidized and is the anode. Copper(II) ions are reduced at the cathode. The overall reaction is:

$$Zn(s) + Cu^{2+}(aq) \rightarrow Zn^{2+}(aq) + Cu(s)$$

Assuming the concentrations of both half-cells are standard, that is 1.0 *M*, the voltage for the cell is determined as explained earlier in section 7.4.

Oxidation (at the anode):	$Zn(s) \rightarrow Zn^{2+}(aq) + 2e^-$	$E^{\circ}_{ox} = 0.76$ V
Reduction (at the cathode):	$Cu^{2+}(aq) + 2e^- \rightarrow Cu(s)$	$E^{\circ}_{red} = 0.34$ V
	$Zn(s) + Cu^{2+}(aq) \rightarrow Zn^{2+}(aq) + Cu(s)$	$E^{\circ}_{cell} = 1.10$ V

The E°_{cell} value and E_{cell} are the same as long as the concentrations of the ions in both half-cells are the same, since Q will equal 1 and the log of 1 equals zero:

$$E = E^{\circ} - \frac{0.0592}{n} \log Q = 1.10\text{ V} - \frac{0.0592}{2} \log \frac{[Zn^{2+}]}{[Cu^{2+}]} = 1.10\text{ V} - \frac{0.0592}{2} \log \frac{\cancel{1.0 M}}{\cancel{1.0 M}}$$

$$\text{Now, } 1.10\text{ V} - \frac{0.0592}{2}\log 1.0 = 1.10\text{ V} - \frac{0.0592}{2} \times 0 = 1.10\text{ V}$$

If, on the other hand, the concentration of one of the ions is made non-standard, the ratio of $[Zn^{2+}]/[Cu^{2+}]$ becomes greater or less than one. This leads to a $\log([Zn^{2+}]/[Cu^{2+}])$ with a positive or negative value. The consequence is an E_{cell} value larger or smaller than E°_{cell}.

Sample Problem 1.4.2(a) — The Nernst Equation

A Danielli cell is assembled with a standard half-cell for zinc, and one-tenth of the standard concentration of copper(II in the copper half-cell. Determine the cell voltage.

What to Think About	How to Do It
1. Determine the balanced chemical equation.	$Zn(s) + Cu^{2+}(aq) \rightarrow Zn^{2+}(aq) + Cu(s)$
2. Determine the voltage for this reaction.	$E^\circ_{cell} = 0.76 + 0.34 = 1.10\text{ V}$
3. Use the Nernst equation.	$E = E^\circ - \frac{0.0592}{n}\log Q$, where $n = 2$ and $Q = \frac{[Zn^{2+}]}{[Cu^{2+}]} = \frac{(1.0\text{ M})}{(0.10\text{ M})}$
4. Proper substitution into the Nernst equation will lead to the correct cell voltage.	$E = 1.10\text{ V} - \frac{0.0592}{2}\log\frac{(1.0\text{ M})}{(0.10\text{ M})}$ $= 1.10\text{ V} - \frac{0.0592}{2}\log(10)$
5. Always think about whether the answer makes sense. Although electrochemical cells are not at equilibrium, they are certainly driving toward equilibrium, which they will reach when the cell stops functioning and produces a voltage of zero. In this sense, the application of Le Chatêlier's principle may assist the prediction of how the voltage of a cell may be affected by changing molarities in half-cells.	$= 1.10\text{ V} - \frac{0.0592}{2} \times 1 = 1.07\text{ V}$ Decreasing the concentration of a reactant ion (Cu^{2+}) would be expected to decrease the frequency of reactant particle collisions and hence to decrease the rate of the forward reaction. The result would be a left shift and a decrease in electron transfer. Hence the decrease in voltage makes sense.

Sample Problem 1.4.2(b) — The Nernst Equation

What is the equilibrium constant for the Danielli cell under standard conditions?

$Zn(s) + Cu^{2+}(aq) \rightarrow Zn^{2+}(aq) + Cu(s)$

What to Think About	How to Do It
1. Use the standard-conditions form of the Nernst equation.	$E = E^\circ - \frac{0.0592}{n}\log Q$
2. When *Q* becomes *K*, E becomes 0. This represents equilibrium conditions.	$0 = 1.10\text{ V} - \frac{0.0592}{2}\log K$

Continued

Sample Problem 1.4.2(b) *(Continued)*

3. Solve for log *K*.

$$1.10 \text{ V} = \frac{0.0592}{2} \log K$$

$$\text{Thus } \log K = \frac{1.10 \text{ J/C}}{\frac{0.0592}{2}} = 37.2$$

4. Solve for *K*.

$$K = 10^{37.2} = 1.45 \times 10^{37} = 1 \times 10^{37.162}$$

Practice Problems 1.4.2 — The Nernst Equation

1. A standard-conditions iron-nickel cell is assembled to determine the voltage and equilibrium constant for the system. Determine E° and *K* for the cell. How does the voltage change when the concentration of Fe^{2+} ions is decreased to 0.05 M? Predict whether it will increase or decrease, and then calculate the new value.

2. A standard Zn^{2+}/Ni^{2+} cell is adjusted by the addition of nickel(II) ions to increase their concentration to 5.0 mol/L from 1.0 mol/L. Calculate the voltage for this cell.

3. Given a voltage of 0.45 V for an Fe^{2+}/Cu^{2+} cell, if the concentration of the iron(II) half-cell is standard, what is the reaction quotient for the cell? What is the concentration of the copper(II) half-cell?

Common Cells and Batteries

With the proliferation of handheld electronic devices, worldwide battery sales now top $70 billion annually. You obviously cannot put a standard electrochemical cell into a portable electronic device. The cells used in electronic devices are called *dry* cells because their electrolytes are in gels or pastes rather than ordinary aqueous solutions that would be more likely to leak. Most commercial cells have only one electrolyte and thus need no barrier at all between the locations of the two half-reactions.

Alkaline Dry Cell

A **battery** is a group or battery of cells. The common household 1.5 V battery that we use to power portable electronics is actually an individual alkaline dry cell. Two or more of them connected end to end are a battery. The modern alkaline cell was invented by Canadian engineer Lewis Urry in the 1950s. Over 500 million alkaline cells are purchased annually in Canada.

An alkaline cell's anode consists of zinc powder packed around a brass pin in the middle of the cell (Figure 1.4.6). Its cathode is a paste of solid manganese dioxide (MnO_2) and powdered carbon. The two electrodes are separated by a fibrous fabric. The alkaline cell is so named because its electrolyte is a moist paste of the base KOH.

The alkaline dry cell lasts longer and generates a steadier voltage than its predecessor, the Leclanché cell, which instead had a moist paste of the acidic salt, ammonium chloride (NH_4Cl) and zinc chloride ($ZnCl_2$). The alkaline cell's half-reactions are:

Anode	$Zn + 2\,OH^- \rightarrow ZnO(s) + H_2O + 2e^-$
Cathode	$2\,MnO_2 + H_2O + 2e^- \rightarrow Mn_2O_3(s) + 2\,OH^-$

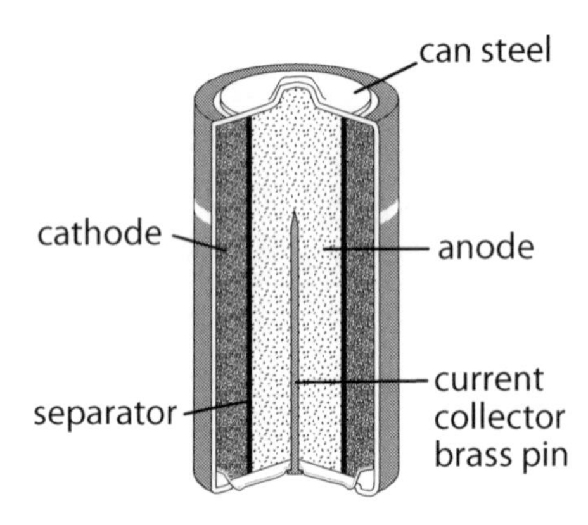

Figure 1.4.6 *An alkaline dry cell*

Other related cells include the button batteries used in calculators and watches, nickel-cadmium (Ni-Cad batteries, and lithium ion batteries. Lithium ion batteries are a type of rechargeable battery used in everything from cellphones to electric vehicles.

Lead-Acid Storage Battery

A 12 V lead storage battery consists of six cells connected in series (Figure 1.4.7). This type of battery is most commonly used in cars. The anodes are lead alloy grids packed with spongy lead. The cathodes are lead alloy grids packed with lead oxide (PbO_2 The lead storage battery consists of true "wet" cells

because its electrolyte is an aqueous solution of sulfuric acid. The cell doesn't have separate anode and cathode compartments because the oxidizing and reducing agents are both solids (PbO_2 and Pb and both are immersed in the same electrolyte (HSO_4^-)

Anode	$Pb(s) + HSO_4^{-2} \rightarrow PbSO_4(s) + H^+ + 2e^-$
Cathode	$PbO_2(s) + 3\,H^+ + HSO_4^- + 2e^- \rightarrow PbSO_4(s) + 2\,H_2O$

The product $PbSO_4(s)$ adheres to the electrodes' surfaces. When a car's engine is running, an alternator continuously recharges the battery. The alternator supplies an electric current to the battery, operating it "backwards" as an electrolytic cell (section 1.5) to restore the original reactants.

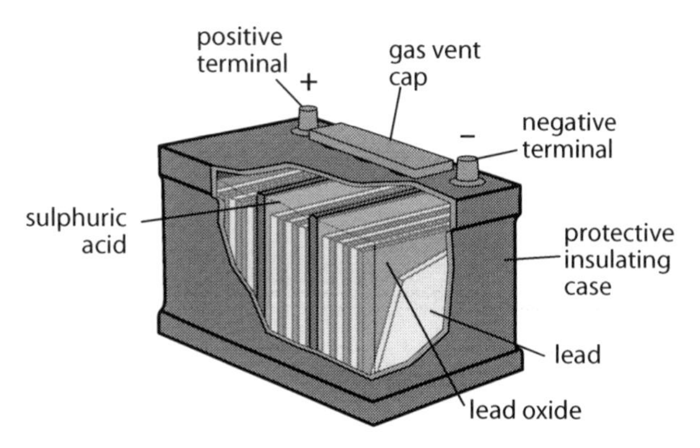

Figure 1.4.7 *A lead-acid storage battery*

For a cell to be classified as rechargeable, the redox reaction that occurs during the cell's operation must be "efficiently reversed" when the opposite electric potential is applied across the cell so that hundreds of recharging cycles are possible. Standard alkaline batteries are non-rechargeable cells because, in addition to the required reverse reactions, other reactions occur when the opposite electric potential is applied across the cell. Since not all of the original reactants are reformed during the reverse operation, the number of recharging cycles is very limited, with the cell lasting for a shorter period of time with each successive recharge. More importantly, recharging a standard alkaline battery is not safe because one of the side-products formed during the reverse operation is hydrogen gas, which can ignite and cause the battery to explode. (Non-rechargeable cells are also called primary cells.)

Fuel Cells

A **fuel cell** is a cell that has its reactants continuously resupplied from an external source as they are consumed. Fuel cells are used to power electric cars and buses as well as provide electricity for vehicles used in space travel. Fuel cells are also being used to provide backup, supplemental, and even mainstream power for industrial complexes and isolated communities. The most common fuel cell is the hydrogen-oxygen fuel cell (Figure 1.4.8). Hydrogen (the fuel) is oxidized at the anode while oxygen (the oxidizer) is reduced at the cathode. Both electrodes are composed of a porous carbon material.

Ballard Power Systems of Burnaby, Canada, is a world leader in fuel cell technology. In Ballard's current cell, the electrodes are bonded to a "cellophane-like" proton exchange membrane (PEM) that is coated with a very thin layer of platinum. The platinum catalyzes the half-reaction at the anode. The proton exchange membrane acts as an electrolyte medium conducting the hydrogen ions (protons) from the anode to the cathode.

Anode	$2\,H_2(g) \rightarrow 4\,H^+ + 4e^-$
Cathode	$O_2(g) + 4\,H^+ + 4e^- \rightarrow 2\,H_2O$

The overall reaction is: $2\,H_2 + O_2 \rightarrow 2\,H_2O$. The water produced at the cathode is vented out the bottom half of the cell as steam. The same reaction occurs when hydrogen burns or explodes in oxygen. The heat released from burning hydrogen could be converted into electricity in a variety of ways but the vast majority of that energy would be lost during the conversion from heat to electrical energy. By contrast, fuel cells' conversions of chemical energy directly into electrical energy are 40% to 60% efficient.

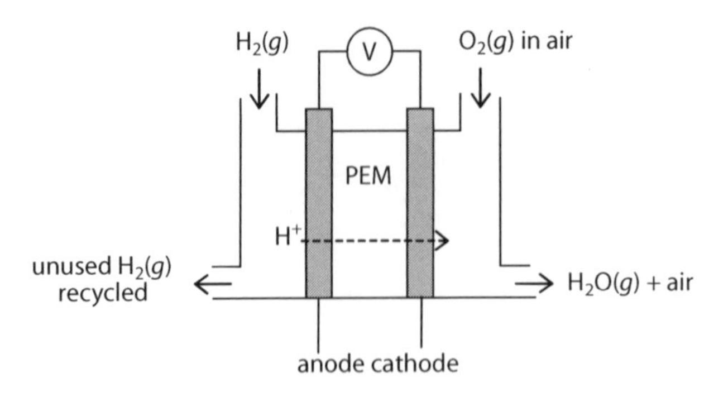

Figure 1.4.8 *A hydrogen fuel cell*

Quick Check

1. Complete the following table:

Type	Anode Material	Cathode Material	Electrolyte Medium	Use
Alkaline cell				
Lead-acid storage battery				
Fuel cell				

Corrosion

Corrosion is a term people use for *unwanted oxidation*, much like we use the term *weed* for an unwanted plant. **Rusting**, the corrosion of iron, is the most familiar and commercially important type of corrosion. Repairing rust damage to buildings, bridges, ships, cars, etc. costs billions of dollars each year.

Let's look at a simplified description of the rusting process. Droplets of water act as an electrolyte to create tiny voltaic cells on iron surfaces (Figure 1.4.9). Iron is more readily oxidized in some surface regions than others due to factors such as impurities and physical stresses such as being bent. When a water droplet forms over one of these "anode" regions, a pit forms as the iron is oxidized to Fe^{2+}:

Anode $\quad Fe(s) \rightarrow Fe^{2+} + 2e^-$

The lost electrons are passed through the iron itself to oxygen molecules at the edge of the droplet:

Cathode $\quad \frac{1}{2} O_2(g) + 2\,H^+ + 2e^- \rightarrow H_2O$ and/or

$\frac{1}{2} O_2(g) + H_2O + 2e^- \rightarrow 2\,OH^-$

Migrating Fe^{2+} ions are further oxidized to Fe^{3+} as they react with dissolved O_2 near the droplet's edge. The Fe^{3+} then readily reacts with water to form rust (hydrated iron (III) oxide), which, having low solubility, deposits on the iron's surface:

$$2\,Fe^{3+}(aq) + 4\,H_2O(l) \rightarrow \underset{\text{(rust)}}{Fe_2O_3 \cdot H_2O(s)} + 6\,H^+(aq)$$

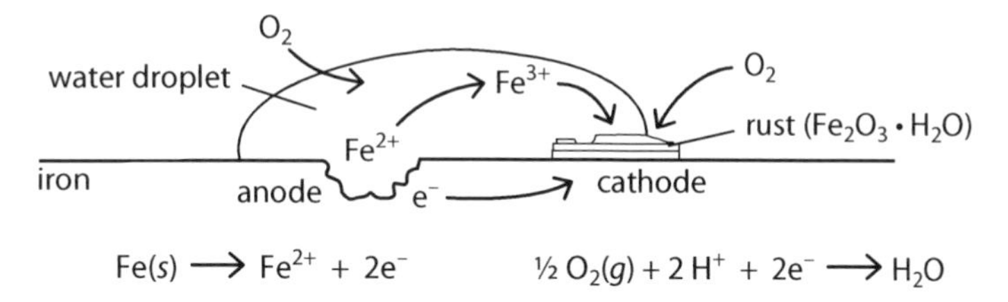

$Fe(s) \longrightarrow Fe^{2+} + 2e^-$ $\quad\quad$ $\frac{1}{2} O_2(g) + 2\,H^+ + 2e^- \longrightarrow H_2O$

Figure 1.4.9 *Voltaic mechanism for rusting*

Dissolved salts in the water droplet increase its conductivity, thus increasing the corrosion rate. This is why cars generally rust faster in eastern Canada where more road salt is used in the winter than in western Canada.

The tarnishing of silver is another example of corrosion. The black color typical of tarnishing results from silver reacting with sulfur compounds in the air or in materials that it touches.

Oxygen is capable of oxidizing most metals but most other metal oxides such as aluminum oxide, chromium oxide, and zinc oxide form hard, impenetrable coatings that protect their metals from further corrosion. By contrast, rust is porous and flaky and unable to shield the underlying metal from further oxidation.

The Prevention of Corrosion

Iron can be protected from rusting by coating it with paint or grease, by cathodic protection, or by galvanizing it.

One way to prevent a reaction from occurring is to prevent the reactants from coming into contact (collision theory). Rusting is commonly prevented by painting the iron's surface so that it is not directly exposed to water or air. To prevent a redox reaction from occurring, the paint must electrically insulate the iron as well as coat it. If the paint can conduct electrons to the oxidizing agent then its physical coating offers no protection from rusting.

Cathodic protection is another way to prevent rusting. In one form of cathodic protection, a metal is protected from corrosion by attaching a metal to it that is a stronger reducing agent. The attached metal gets oxidized instead of the metal you are protecting. The oxidizing agent draws electrons from the sacrificial metal through the metal being protected. As electrons from the oxidized metal move into the conductor, they displace or push the conductor's valence electrons through to the oxidizing agent. The exposed metal thus remains intact, acting only as a conductor for the electrons. Because the metal that is protected acts as a cathode, this process is called *cathodic protection*.

Cathodic protection is used to protect structures such as underground pipelines, steel reinforcing bars in concrete, deep-sea oil rigs, and ship hulls. Steel is an alloy consisting primarily of iron. Without protection, the steel hulls of ships would be quickly corroded by ocean water because of its salt content. Zinc bars are welded to ships' hulls. The cations in the ocean water preferentially oxidize the zinc through the steel hull and leave the steel alone. The zinc saves the iron from corrosion but the combination of the two metals causes the zinc to be oxidized much more quickly than if it had been exposed to the oxidizing agent alone. This is due to the increased surface area exposed to the oxidizing agent via conduction of its electrons through the iron. In a well-documented example of this phenomenon, the Statue of Liberty's internal support structure of iron ribs was corroded quickly by the moist sea air through the statue's copper skin.

Some iron materials are coated with zinc in a process known as **galvanizing**. Any chemical mixture that can oxidize iron can more easily oxidize zinc so how does the zinc coating offer the iron any protection? If the zinc is oxidized it forms zinc oxide. Zinc oxide forms a hard, impenetrable coating. Should the zinc or the zinc oxide coating be scratched off in some areas, the remaining zinc coating still provides cathodic protection.

Quick Check

1. What is the chemical name for rust? ______________________

2. Identify the reduction half-reaction responsible for rusting.

3. List three factors that influence the corrosion rate of iron.

   (a) ______________________

   (b) ______________________

   (c) ______________________

4. What are two methods that could be used to reduce the corrosion rate of iron?

   (a) ______________________

   (b) ______________________

1.4 Review Questions

1. Complete the following table for an electrochemical (metal electrode/metallic ions) cell.

Anode	Cathode
	reduction occurs
mass decreases	
	attracts cations
electrons flow away	

2. The electrochemical cell below consists of a strip of iron in 1.0 M $Fe(NO_3)_2$ and a strip of nickel in 1.0 M $Ni(NO_3)_2$. A salt bridge containing 1.0 M NH_4NO_3 connects these half-cells. A voltmeter connects the two electrodes. (Make sure your answers to the following questions refer specifically to the cell below. Generic responses that are true for any cell, such as "oxidation occurs at the anode," will not be marked correct.)

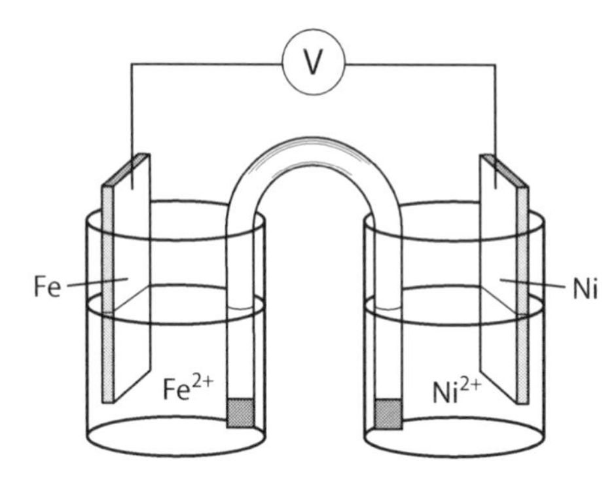

(a) Show the direction of electron flow on the diagram.
(b) In which half-cell does oxidation occur?

(c) Write the half-cell reactions involved.

(d) Label the anode and the cathode.
(e) What is the expected initial voltage?

(f) Describe the flow of the NH_4^+ and NO_3^- ions within the cell.

(g) Describe how the mass of each electrode changes as the cell operates.

3. Elemental bromine does not exist in nature. Bromine is a corrosive, red-brown liquid at room temperature. Draw and label a bromine half-cell.

Use the following diagram for questions 4 and 5.

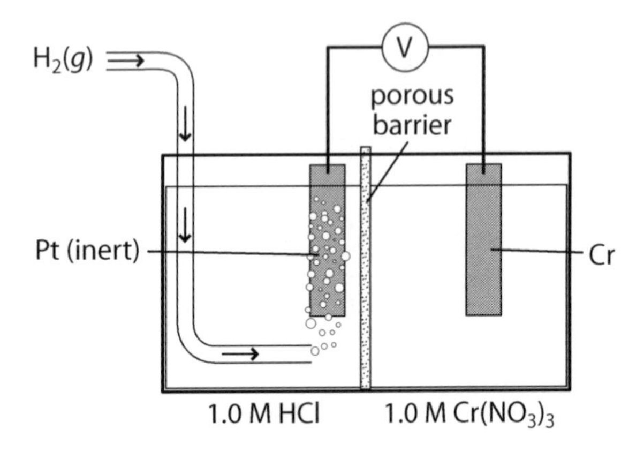

4. (a) Show the direction of electron flow on the above diagram.
   (b) In which half-cell does reduction occur?
   (c) Write the half-cell reactions involved.

5. (a) Label the anode and the cathode.
   (b) What is the expected initial voltage?
   (c) Describe the flow of ions within the cell.
   (d) Describe how the mass of each electrode changes as the cell operates.

6. (a) Draw a Zn | Zn^{2+} || F_2 | F^- electrochemical cell with the following labels:
   - electrodes (Zn, F_2)
   - solutions (1 M $ZnCl_2$, 1 M NaF)
   - anode and the cathode

   (b) Show the direction of electron flow on your diagram.
   (c) Show the direction of anion and cation flow on your diagram.
   (d) Write the cell's two half-reactions and overall redox reaction.
   (e) Calculate the cell's initial voltage.

7. What is the purpose of a salt bridge in an electrochemical cell?

8. Calculate the standard cell potential for the reaction: $Br_2 + 2\ Fe^{2+} \rightarrow 2\ Br^- + 2\ Fe^{3+}$

9. Suppose that the silver-silver ion electrode were used as the reference for E° values, instead of the hydrogen electrode. What would be the standard reduction potentials, E°, for these half-cell reactions?
   (a) $F_2(g) + 2e^- \rightleftharpoons 2\ F^-$

   (b) $Mg^{2+} + 2e^- \rightleftharpoons Mg(s)$

10. The standard cell potential for the following reaction is 2.33 V.
$$Sr + Cr^{2+} \rightarrow Sr^{2+} + Cr$$
Write the reduction half-reaction and determine its standard reduction potential (E°).

11. Given:
$$Pd^{2+} + Cu \rightarrow Pd + Cu^{2+} \qquad E° = 0.49\ V$$
$$2\ Np + 3\ Pd^{2+} \rightarrow 2\ Np^{3+} + 3\ Pd \qquad E° = 2.73\ V$$

   (a) What is the standard reduction potential (E°) of Pd^{2+}?

   (b) What is the standard reduction potential (E°) of Np^{3+}?

12. In the table below, fill in the missing cell voltages by using the voltages provided for other combinations of half-cells.

		Reduction Half-Cell	
		$Cd^{2+} + 2e^- \rightarrow Cd$	$Pt^{2+} + 2e^- \rightarrow Pt$
Oxidation Half-cell	$Pt \rightarrow Pt^{2+} + 2e^-$		0 V
	$Ni \rightarrow Ni^{2+} + 2e^-$	- 0.17 V	+ 1.43 V
	$Ce \rightarrow Ce^{3+} + 3e^-$	+ 1.93 V	

13. In an Fe | Fe^{2+} || Pb | Pb^{2+} standard cell, electrons are transferred from the Fe half-cell to the Pb half-cell.
   (a) What would be the effect on the voltage if $Pb(NO_3)_2$ were added to the lead half-cell?

   (b) What is the voltmeter reading when the cell reaches "equilibrium"?

   (c) What would be the effect on the voltage if sulfide ions (S^{2-}) were added to the Fe^{2+} ion compartment?

   (d) What would be the effect on the voltage if the size of the Fe electrode were doubled?

14. Sony demonstrated a paper cell at the Eco-Products 2011 Exhibition in Tokyo. Sony's bio-cell uses cellulase enzymes to hydrolyze paper into glucose, which is then oxidized. What features of this cell make it eco-friendly when compared to current commercial cells?

15. Describe how cathodic protection could be used to protect a steel stairway exposed to an ocean spray. Explain how this works.

16. Some steel nails are galvanized. Zinc is easier to oxidize than iron so how can coating a steel nail with zinc prevent it from corroding?

17. What adaptation to collision theory is necessary for redox reactions occurring in electrochemical cells?

18. Explain the graphic relationship shown here for the Danielli cell:

$Zn(s) + Cu^{2+}(aq) \rightarrow Zn^{2+}(aq) + Cu(s) \quad E^\circ_{cell} = 1.10\ V$

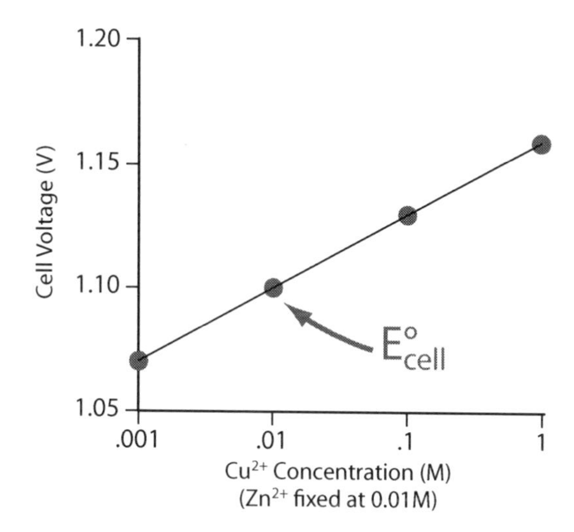

19. Use Table A7 Standard Reduction Potential of Half-Cells in the appendix to determine E° and *K* for the following reaction performed under standard conditions:

$I_2(s) + 5\ Cu^{2+}(aq) + 6\ H_2O(l) \rightarrow 2\ IO_3^-(aq) + 5\ Cu(s) + 12\ H^+(aq)$

20. (a) Calculate the voltage of the cell described by the following reaction. Then determine *K*. Assume standard temperature.

$2\ Al(s) + 3\ I_2(s) \rightarrow 2\ Al^{3+}(aq)\ (0.0040\ M) + 6\ I^-(aq)\ (0.010\ M)$

(b) How do these values compare to those for the cell operating under standard conditions? Explain.

21. Consider a cell in which the following reaction occurs at 25°C:

$Zn(s) + 2\ H^+(aq) \rightarrow Zn^{2+}(aq) + H_2(g)$

(a) Calculate E°_{cell}.

(b) If the $[Zn^{2+}]$ is 0.10 M and $[H_2]$ is 1.0 M and the measured cell voltage is 0.542 V, what is the hydrogen ion concentration?

(c) What is the pH?

22. Examine the electrochemical cell shown here.

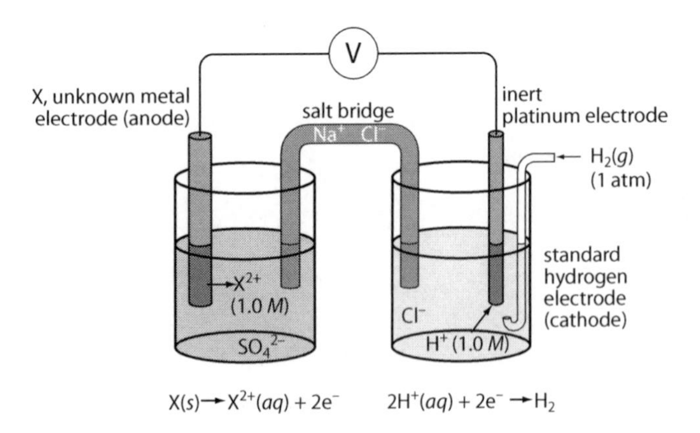

Under standard conditions, the equilibrium constant *K* for the cell's reaction is 6.1×10^8.

(a) What is E°_{cell}?

(b) What is the oxidation potential for the unknown metal?

(c) Identify the unknown metal.

1.5 The Electrolytic Cell

Warm Up

Complete the following table showing pairs of devices that perform opposite energy transformations. Each pair of devices transforms a different form of energy to and from electrical energy.

Device	Energy Conversion	
	From	To
light bulb	electrical energy	light energy
	light energy	electrical energy
speaker	electrical energy	
		electrical energy
heating element	electrical energy	
		electrical energy
motor	electrical energy	
		electrical energy
electrolytic cell	electrical energy	chemical energy
		electrical energy

The Structure and Function of the Electrolytic Cell

Current electricity is a flow of electrical charge. Although electrical charge is always carried by a particle, that particle is not always an electron. In solutions, ions are the particles responsible for carrying the charge. A chemical is an **electrolyte** if its aqueous solution conducts electricity. Whenever electricity is conducted through a molten electrolyte or an electrolyte solution, the process is called **electrolysis** and the apparatus is called an **electrolytic cell**.

For an electric current to exist, there must be a continuous path from the source's anode to its cathode. This continuous path is called a circuit. It would be simple if there were a chemical species in the electrolytic cell solution that picked up the electrons from one electrode and ferried them over to the other electrode but this is not the case. Instead, an oxidizing agent picks up the electrons from one electrode while an entirely different chemical species, a reducing agent, donates electrons at the other electrode. The circuit is complete. It doesn't matter that the electrons being removed from one electrode are not the same ones being released at the other electrode. "If you've seen one electron you've seen them all." It's like a con game where the electrons are being switched and the source never suspects.

In an electrolytic cell, oxidation occurs at the anode and reduction occurs at the cathode just like in an electrochemical cell. Figure 1.5.1 shows an electrolytic cell.

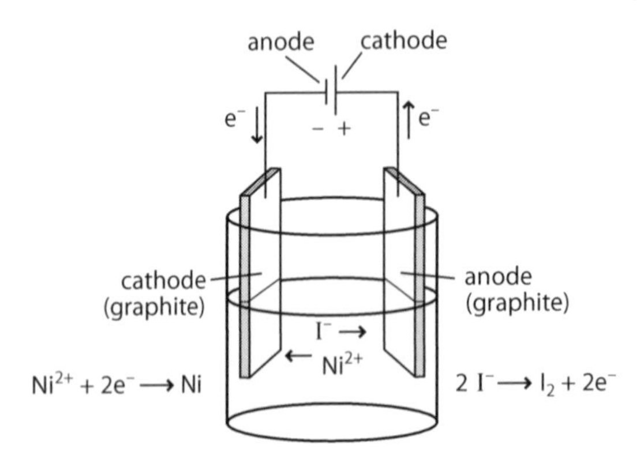

Figure 1.5.1 *An electrolytic cell*

The schematic symbol $|\!|$ at the top of Figure 1.5.1 represents the electrochemical cell that serves as the source of direct current (DC) driving the electrolytic cell. Note that the electrochemical cell's anode is connected to the electrolytic cell's cathode. This makes sense if you think it through. Oxidation (electron loss) occurs at the anode; therefore, this is where the voltaic cell emits electrons. In the electrolytic cell, those electrons are accepted by a chemical species, which is thereby reduced. The site of reduction is the cathode. Likewise, the electrochemical cell's cathode is connected to the electrolytic cell's anode.

An electrolytic cell may superficially resemble an electrochemical cell but it performs the reverse energy transformation. In other words, an electrochemical cell generates electricity whereas an electrolytic cell uses electricity.

> Electrolytic cells transform electrical energy into chemical energy.

The non-spontaneous reactions of electrolytic cells "read" in the reverse direction in the SRP table (Table A7) as the spontaneous reactions of electrochemical cells. In electrolytic cells, the oxidation half-reaction is above the reduction half-reaction. Try the following trick to remember which direction electrons are passed in the SRP table. Electrons are very "light" so they spontaneously float upward in the table but they must be pushed downward.

oxidation ½ reaction $\longleftarrow$

$I_2 + 2e^-$	$\leftarrow$	$2\ I^-$	+0.54 V
$H_2SO_3 + 4\ H^+ + 2e^-$	$\rightleftharpoons$	$S + 3\ H_2O$	+0.45 V
$Cu^{2+} + 2e^-$	$\rightleftharpoons$	Cu	+0.34 V
$SO_4^{\ 2-} + 4\ H^+ + 2e^-$	$\rightleftharpoons$	$H_2SO_3 + H_2O$	+0.17 V
$2\ H^+ + 2e^-$	$\rightleftharpoons$	H_2	0.00 V
$Sn^{2+} + 2e^-$	$\rightleftharpoons$	Sn	−0.14 V
$Ni^{2+} + 2e^-$	$\rightarrow$	Ni	−0.26 V

$\longrightarrow$ reduction ½ reaction

$$2\ I^- \rightarrow I_2 + 2e^-$$
$$Ni^{2+} + 2e^- \rightarrow Ni$$
$$\overline{Ni^{2+} + 2\ I^- \rightarrow I_2 + Ni}$$

The net E° for the non-spontaneous reactions that occur in electrolytic cells is negative. The net E° gives us an estimation of how much voltage will be required to drive this electrolytic cell. In other words, the SRP table not only allows you to determine how much voltage an electrochemical cell will generate but also allows you to determine how much voltage an electrolytic cell will require to operate. This value will normally be less than the voltage actually required. The difference between the voltages the SRP table predicts will be necessary to drive electrolytic cells and the voltages actually required to drive those cells is referred to as **overpotential**.

The standard reduction potentials in the SRP table are derived solely from thermodynamic data. They represent the difference between the chemical potential energy of the reactants and the chemical potential energy of the products. However, the voltages required to drive electrolytic cells are also influenced by kinetic factors such as the reaction's activation energy and the reactants' localized concentrations at the electrodes. A cell's overpotential thus depends on the specific reactions involved and the cell's design.

Sample Problem 1.5.1 — Predicting the Voltage Required to Operate an Electrolytic Cell

Predict the voltage required to operate the electrolytic cell in Figure 1.5.1.

What to Think About	How to Do It
1. Write each half-reaction and its standard potential. The oxidation potential of I^- is – 0.54 V because it is the reverse of the reduction potential of I_2 provided in the SRP table.	$2I^- \rightarrow I_2 + 2e^-$ $E° = -0.54$ V $Ni^{2+} + 2e^- \rightarrow Ni$ $E° = -0.26$ V $Ni^{2+} + 2I^- \rightarrow I_2 + Ni$ $E° = -0.80$ V
2. Add the reduction potential to the oxidation potential.	A voltage of at least 0.80 V would be required to operate this cell.

Practice Problems 1.5.1 — Predicting the Voltage Required to Operate an Electrolytic Cell

Predict the voltage required to operate each of the following electrolytic cells given the pair of half-reactions occurring within each cell.

1. $Ag \rightarrow Ag^+ + e^-$ and $Ni^{2+} + 2e^- \rightarrow Ni$

2. $2F^- \rightarrow F_2 + 2e^-$ and $Cu^{2+} + 2e^- \rightarrow Cu$

3. $Sn \rightarrow Sn^{2+} + 2e^-$ and $Al^{3+} + 3e^- \rightarrow Al$

Comparing Electrochemical and Electrolytic Cells

In electrochemical cells, the strongest available reducing agent (lowest on the right in the SRP table) passes electrons *up* to the strongest available oxidizing agent (highest on the left in the SRP table). Thus, the half-reactions that occur in electrochemical cells are the ones that are farthest apart in the SRP table and generate the greatest possible voltage.

In electrolytic cells, the strongest available reducing agent (lowest on the right in the SRP tablepasses electrons *down* to the strongest available oxidizing agent (highest on the left in the SRP table. Thus, the half-reactions that occur in electrolytic cells are the ones closest together in the SRP table and require the least voltage to drive them (Figure 1.5.2). Table 1.5.1 summarizes the differences between an electrochemical cell and an electrolytic cell.

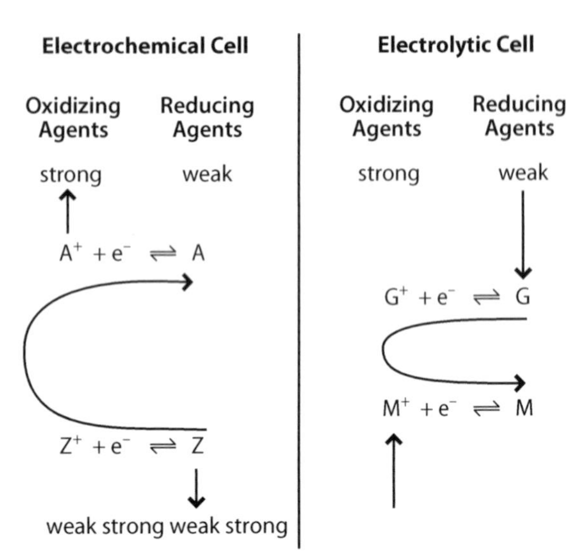

Figure 1.5.2 *Using the SRP table for electrochemical and electrolytic cells*

Table 1.5.1 *Contrasting the Electrochemical Cell and the Electrolytic Cell*

Electrochemical Cell	Electrolytic Cell
• exothermic • "makes" electricity • transforms chemical energy into electrical energy	• endothermic • "takes" electricity • transforms electrical energy into chemical energy
• is a DC voltage source	• requires a DC voltage source
• 2 half-cells	• 1 cell
• spontaneous redox reaction • E° is positive	• non-spontaneous redox reaction • E° is negative
• salt bridge or equivalent	• no salt bridge
V	DC
The oxidation half-reaction is below the reduction half-reaction in the SRP table. Think of the electrons floating upward.	The oxidation half-reaction is above the reduction half-reaction in the SRP table. Think of the electrons being pushed downward.
The half-reactions that are farthest apart in the SRP table will occur, generating the greatest possible voltage.	The half-reactions that are closest together in the SRP table will occur, requiring the least possible voltage to drive the cell.

Quick Check

What am I (an electrochemical cell, an electrolytic cell, or both)?

1. I have two half cells. ____________________
2. My oxidation half-reaction is $Ni \rightarrow Ni^{2+} + 2e^-$.
   My reduction half-reaction is $Fe^{2+} + 2e^- \rightarrow Fe$. ____________________
3. Oxidation occurs at my anode. ____________________
4. I transform chemical energy into electricity. ____________________
5. In order to flow, the electrical charge requires a complete path or circuit. ____________________
6. You can use the SRP table to calculate how much voltage it "takes" to operate me. ____________________
7. My E° is + 0.94 V. ____________________

Electrolytic Cell Types

In this textbook, we will categorize electrolytic cells into three types.

- In type 1 cells, inert electrodes are immersed in a molten ionic compound. Only the molten ions (*1 type of thing*) can be oxidized and reduced.
- In type 2 cells, inert electrodes are immersed in an aqueous ionic solution. Only the ions or H_2O (*2 types of things*) can be oxidized and reduced.
- In type 3 cells, non-inert electrodes are immersed in an aqueous ionic solution. The ions, H_2O, or the anode itself (*3 types of things*) can be oxidized and the ions or H_2O can be reduced. Metals never form anions so the cathode itself is never reduced.

Type 1 Cells

Type 1 cells consist of inert electrodes (typically carbon or platinum) immersed in a molten ionic fluid. Electrolysis (electro-lysis) literally means *separation by electricity*. In a type 1 cell, the cations pick up the electrons and are reduced at the cathode, while the anions drop off electrons and are oxidized at the anode. In that way, the cations and anions are separated.

Consider an electrolytic cell having carbon electrodes immersed in molten magnesium chloride. The half-reactions occurring at the electrodes are:

Cathode $Mg^{2+}(l) + 2e^- \rightarrow Mg(l)$
Anode $2\,Cl^-(l) \rightarrow Cl_2(g) + 2e^-$

Magnesium chloride has a higher melting point than magnesium so the magnesium formed at the cathode is also liquid.

Type 2 Cells

Type 2 cells consist of inert electrodes immersed in an aqueous ionic solution. The first question generally asked about an electrolytic cell is, "What half-reactions occur within this cell?" A type 1 cell has only one type of chemical species that can react, the molten ions. In type 2 cells, either the dissolved ions or the water can react. A chemist uses the SRP table to determine whether a dissolved ion or water is reduced and whether a dissolved ion or water is oxidized.

The oxidation and the reduction of water have particularly high overpotentials. Under electrolytic conditions, these half-reactions must be moved relative to the others as shown on the SRP table. This is significant as type 2 and type 3 electrolytic cells conduct currents through aqueous solution. Because of the overpotential effect, water is a weaker reducing agent in electrolytic cells than Br^- and Cl^- ions, and a weaker oxidizing agent in electrolytic cells than Zn^{2+}, Cr^{3+}, and Fe^{2+} ions.

Water doesn't usually react in the spontaneous reactions of electrochemical cells but frequently reacts in the non-spontaneous reactions of electrolytic cells. Water can act as both a weak reducing agent (low oxidation potential) and as a weak oxidizing agent (low reduction potential). Since it is high on the right side of the SRP table, there are not many species above it on the left that it will reduce spontaneously. However, there are many below it that it will reduce non-spontaneously. Likewise, since it is low on the left side of the table, there are not many species below it on the right that it will oxidize spontaneously, but there are many species above it on the right that it will oxidize non-spontaneously.

Sample Problem 1.5.2(a) — Predicting the Half-Reactions That Will Occur in a Type 2 Electrolytic Cell

Identify the half-reactions that occur in the electrolysis of an aqueous solution of manganese(II) bromide.

What to Think About

1. Identify the oxidizing agent(s) and the reducing agent(s).
2. Use the SRP table to determine which species is the strongest oxidizing agent and which species is the strongest reducing agent.
3. The lowest available species on the right will pass electron(s) down to the highest available species on the left. Be mindful of the overpotential effect!
4. Write the two half-reactions balancing the transfer of electrons if necessary.

How to Do It

Mn^{2+} and H_2O are oxidizing agents.
Br^- and H_2O are reducing agents.

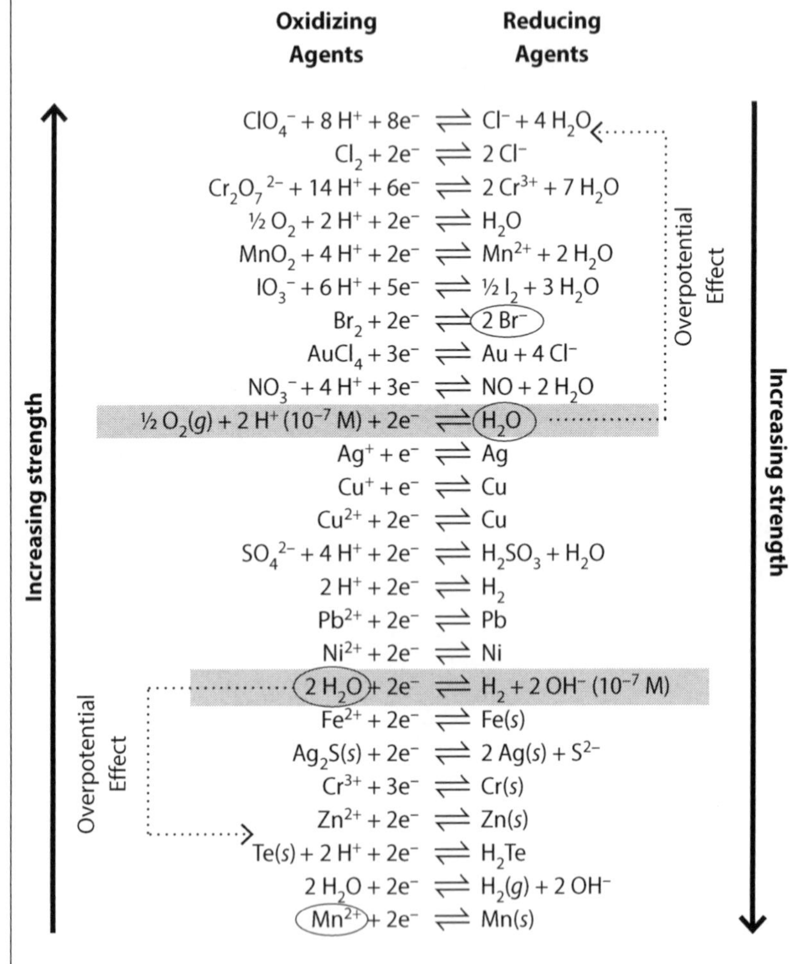

Br^- is a stronger reducing agent than H_2O (overpotential effect).
H_2O is a stronger oxidizing agent than Mn^{2+}.

$$2\,Br^- \rightarrow Br_2 + 2e^-$$
$$2\,H_2O + 2e^- \rightarrow H_2 + 2\,OH^-$$
$$2\,Br^- + 2\,H_2O \rightarrow Br_2 + 2\,OH^-$$

Type 3 Cells

Type 3 cells consist of non-inert electrodes immersed in an aqueous ionic solution. A type 3 cell adds the possibility that a metal anode itself could be oxidized.

Sample Problem 1.5.2(b) — Predicting the Half-Reactions That Will Occur in a Type 3 Electrolytic Cell

Identify the half-reactions that occur in an electrolytic cell consisting of copper electrodes in a solution of $CrBr_3$.

What to Think About

1. Identify the oxidizing agent(s) and the reducing agent(s).

How to Do It

Cr^{3+} and H_2O are oxidizing agents.
Br^-, H_2O and Cu are reducing agents.

2. Use the SRP table to determine which species is the strongest oxidizing agent and which species is the strongest reducing agent.

Oxidizing Agents		Reducing Agents
$ClO_4^- + 8H^+ + 8e^-$	⇌	$Cl^- + 4H_2O$
$Cl_2 + 2e^-$	⇌	$2Cl^-$
$Cr_2O_7^{2-} + 14H^+ + 6e^-$	⇌	$2Cr^{3+} + 7H_2O$
$\frac{1}{2}O_2 + 2H^+ + 2e^-$	⇌	H_2O
$MnO_2 + 4H^+ + 2e^-$	⇌	$Mn^{2+} + 2H_2O$
$IO_3^- + 6H^+ + 5e^-$	⇌	$\frac{1}{2}I_2 + 3H_2O$
$Br_2 + 2e^-$	⇌	$2Br^-$ (circled)
$AuCl_4 + 3e^-$	⇌	$Au + 4Cl^-$
$NO_3^- + 4H^+ + 3e^-$	⇌	$NO + 2H_2O$
$\frac{1}{2}O_2(g) + 2H^+(10^{-7}\,M) + 2e^-$	⇌	H_2O (circled)
$Ag^+ + e^-$	⇌	Ag
$Cu^+ + e^-$	⇌	Cu
$Cu^{2+} + 2e^-$	⇌	Cu (circled)
$SO_4^{2-} + 4H^+ + 2e^-$	⇌	$H_2SO_3 + H_2O$
$2H^+ + 2e^-$	⇌	H_2
$Pb^{2+} + 2e^-$	⇌	Pb
$Ni^{2+} + 2e^-$	⇌	Ni
$2H_2O$ (circled) $+ 2e^-$	⇌	$H_2 + 2OH^-(10^{-7}\,M)$
$Fe^{2+} + 2e^-$	⇌	$Fe(s)$
$Ag_2S(s) + 2e^-$	⇌	$2Ag(s) + S^{2-}$
Cr^{3+} (circled) $+ 3e^-$	⇌	$Cr(s)$
$Zn^{2+} + 2e^-$	⇌	$Zn(s)$
$Te(s) + 2H^+ + 2e^-$	⇌	H_2Te
$2H_2O + 2e^-$	⇌	$H_2(g) + 2OH^-$
$Mn^{2+} + 2e^-$	⇌	$Mn(s)$

Increasing strength (oxidizing agents, upward) · Increasing strength (reducing agents, downward) · Overpotential Effect (both sides)

3. The lowest available species on the right will pass electron(s) down to the highest available species on the left.

4. Write the two half-reactions balancing the transfer of electrons if necessary.

Cu is a stronger reducing agent than Br^- or H_2O.
Cr^{3+} is a stronger oxidizing agent than H_2O (overpotential effect).

$$3\,Cu \rightarrow 3\,Cu^{2+} + 6e^-$$
$$2\,Cr^{3+} + 6e^- \rightarrow 2\,Cr$$
$$3\,Cu + 2\,Cr^{3+} \rightarrow 3\,Cu^{2+} + 2\,Cr$$

Practice Problems 1.5.2 — Predicting the Half-Reactions That Will Occur in an Electrolytic Cell

1. For each of the following, identify the type of electrolytic cell and the half-reactions occurring within it:
   (a) carbon electrodes in $MgI_2(l)$

   (b) platinum electrodes in $CaSO_4(aq)$

   (c) iron electrodes in $NaCl(aq)$

2. Draw an electrolytic cell having carbon electrodes in $NiBr_2(aq)$. Label the DC source, its terminals, and the anode and cathode of the electrolytic cell. Show each ion in the solution migrating toward the appropriate electrode. Write the half-reaction that occurs at each electrode and predict the voltage required to operate this cell.

Applications: Electrowinning, Electroplating, Electrorefining

Electrolytic cells are used extensively in mining and other metallurgy-related industries. **Electrowinning** is a metallurgical term for the electrolytic recovery of a metal from a solution containing its ions. The metal ions are reduced at the cathode where they deposit as metal. The world's largest zinc and lead smelter is the Cominco plant at Trail, B.C., Canada, Cominco electrowins zinc from zinc sulfate at this smelter.

Electroplating is a form of electrowinning in which a conductive material, usually a metal, is coated with a thin layer of a different metal. Electroplating is usually performed to provide a surface property such as wear resistance, corrosion protection, or lustre to a surface that lacks these properties. The technique is used widely in the manufacture of electronic and optic components and sensors, and to chrome plate bathroom fixtures and automobile parts.

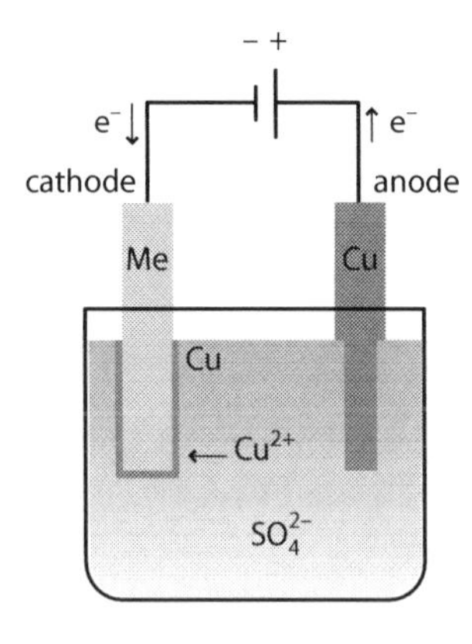

Figure 1.5.3 *Electroplating a metal (Me) with copper*

Consider an electrolytic cell having a metal object as its cathode, a copper anode, and a solution of $CuSO_4$ (Figure 1.5.3). Cu is a stronger reducing agent than SO_4^{2-} or H_2O. Cu^{2+} is a stronger oxidizing agent than H_2O (or SO_4^{2-} under acidic conditions). The half-reactions that occur in this cell are therefore:

$$Cu \rightarrow Cu^{2+} + 2e^-$$
$$Cu^{2+} + 2e^- \rightarrow Cu$$

Note that no net reaction occurs in this electrolytic cell. Copper ions from the solution are reduced at the cathode and plate out as metallic copper. Those copper ions are replaced by the oxidation of the copper anode. In effect, copper is simply being transferred from the anode to the cathode. This process can continue indefinitely as long as the anode is replaced after it has been consumed.

Electrorefining is another application of electrowinning. **Electrorefining** is the electrolytic purification of a metal. The metal of an impure anode is oxidized to ions that then migrate to the pure cathode where they are reduced back to the metal. The impurities remain behind. Sample Problem 1.5.2(b) would be an example of electrorefining if the anode were composed of impure copper and the cathode composed of pure copper. An impurity is anything that makes something impure. In chemistry, impurities are minority substances within a majority substance. Just because a substance is present in a material as an impurity doesn't mean that it isn't valuable. Many rare and valuable metals are recovered from the impurities left behind as *anode mud* during electrolysis. The electrorefining of lead by the Betts process, pioneered by Cominco's Trail Operations in 1902, is still the last step of lead production at the Trail complex. Significant quantities of silver and gold are recovered from the anode mud in this process. The cell voltage used is insufficient to oxidize silver or gold, which are much weaker reducing agents than lead.

Applications: The Héroult-Hall Process for Producing Aluminum

In 1885, aluminum was more valuable than gold. The most common mineral of aluminum is bauxite ($Al_2O_3 \cdot 3\ H_2O$. Aluminum cannot be produced from bauxite by electrowinning because water is a stronger oxidizing agent than Al^{3+}. Producing aluminum from the electrolysis of molten Al_2O_3 (type 1 cellis very expensive because Al_2O_3's melting point is over 2050°C. In 1886, two 23-year-olds, Paul Hroult of France and Charles Hall of the USA independently discovered that aluminum oxide dissolves in molten cryolite ($Na_3AlF_6(l)$). This aluminum oxide-cryolite mixture melts at about 1000°C, making it much more economical to electrolyze than aluminum oxide alone. The Héroult-Hall process still consumes a tremendous amount of energy, both to melt the aluminum oxide-cryolite mixture and to electrolyze it. The aluminum produced in the electrolytic cell is also molten at 1000°C. Molten aluminum is denser than the aluminum oxide-cryolite mixture so it runs off through openings at the bottom of the cell where it collects.

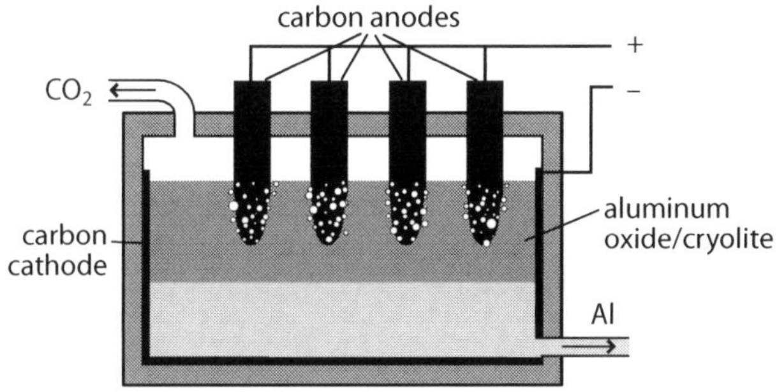

Figure 1.5.4 *The Héroult-Hall process*

Applications: The Chloralkali Industry

Sodium hydroxide and chlorine are both produced by the electrolysis of aqueous sodium chloride. The chemical industry based on this process is known as the chloralkali industry. Both sodium hydroxide and chlorine are among the world's top 10 chemicals (by mass) produced annually. Between 12 and 14 million tonnes of each are produced annually in the United States alone, for sales of approximately $4 billion. Sodium hydroxide and chlorine are used in the manufacture of a tremendous variety of everyday products from pharmaceuticals to plastics.

In the electrolysis of an aqueous sodium chloride solution, chloride ions are oxidized:

$$2\ Cl^- \rightarrow Cl_2 + 2e^-$$

and water molecules are reduced:

$$2\ H_2O + 2e^- \rightarrow H_2 + 2\ OH^-$$

The net reaction is:

$$2\ NaCl + 2\ H_2O \rightarrow Cl_2 + H_2 + 2\ NaOH$$

The sodium ions are uninvolved spectators in this process. They are dissolved with chloride ions in the reactants and with hydroxide ions in the products. Note that hydrogen gas is also produced in this process but it is generated more easily by other means.

Applications: Impressed Current Cathodic Protection

The form of cathodic protection described in section 1.4 is called "galvanic" cathodic protection because the reactions involved are spontaneous (positive E° like those of a galvanic cell. Another form of cathodic protection called *impressed current* cathodic protection involves non-spontaneous (negative E° reactions like those of an electrolytic cell. In this form of cathodic protection, the structure to be protected is connected to the negative terminal of a direct current source such as a rectifier or a battery. The positive terminal is usually connected to an inert electrode that must also be immersed in the solution or buried in the material containing the oxidizing agent(s. In this arrangement, the protected structure becomes the cathode in an electrolytic cell. Impressed current systems are generally less expensive and more effective than galvanic systems (particularly when used in combination with protective coatings. Despite the advantages of impressed current systems, galvanic systems continue to be more commonly used.

Quick Check

1. What is *electrowinning*?

____

2. What discovery was the key to designing an economical process for refining aluminum?

____

3. What two chemicals are produced in the chloralkali industry?

____

4. In what form of cathodic protection does the metal being protected act as the cathode in an electrolytic cell?

____

1.5 Review Questions

1. Specialty sports drinks are called electrolyte drinks because they replenish the water and solutes, including electrolytes, that athletes lose in sweat during exercise. Which of the following ingredients of a typical sports drink are electrolytes: water, sucrose, dextrose, citric acid, sodium chloride, sodium citrate, and potassium dihydrogen phosphate?

2. Draw a type 1 electrolytic cell electrolyzing molten NaCl. Label the DC source, its terminals, and the anode and cathode of the electrolytic cell. Show each ion in the molten NaCl migrating toward the appropriate electrode. Write the half-reaction that occurs at each electrode and predict the voltage required to operate this cell.

3. Sodium is commercially produced by the electrolysis of molten NaCl in an apparatus called a Downs cell. A Downs cell directs the products into separate chambers to prevent them from coming into contact with each other. Why is it important to keep the two products physically separated as the cell operates?

4. Complete the following table:

	Cell Type (1,2,3)	Electrolyte	Anode/Cathode	Products	
				Anode	Cathode
(a)		$NaCl(l)$	Pt/Pt		
(b)		$NaCl(aq)$	Pt/C		
(c)		$CuBr_2(aq)$	C/C		
(d)		$AlF_3(aq)$	C/C		
(e)		$CuCl_2(aq)$	Cu/Cu		

5. An electrolytic cell contains inert electrodes in a solution of acidified copper(II) nitrate.
   (a) Write the half-reactions occurring at the anode and cathode.

   (b) Predict the voltage required to operate this cell.

6. Electrolysis is also used as a technique for the permanent removal of individual hairs. A very thin metal probe is inserted alongside the hair into the follicle beneath the skin's surface from which the hair emerges. This probe is the cathode of an electrolytic cell. Hydroxide ions formed at the cathode kill the cells that produce the hair. Write the half-reaction that produces the hydroxide ions.

7. How is electrorefining a special kind of electrowinning?

8. Why is it uneconomical to produce metallic aluminum by electrolyzing $Al_2O_3(l)$ and impossible to produce metallic aluminum by electrolyzing $Al_2O_3(aq)$?

9. Describe how impressed current cathodic protection is electrochemically different than galvanic cathodic protection.

10. Draw a type 3 electrolytic cell electroplating an aluminum spoon with silver. Label the DC source, its terminals, and the anode and cathode of the electrolytic cell. Predict the voltage required to operate this cell.

11. An electrolytic cell containing inert electrodes is used to electrolyze pure water.
    (a) What type of cell is this? Explain.

    (b) Identify a salt that could be added to water to increase its conductivity without the salt reacting.

12. What is the minimum voltage theoretically required to operate an electrolytic cell consisting of inert electrodes in an aqueous solution of $CuBr_2$?

1.6 The Stoichiometry of Electrochemistry – Faraday's Constant and Free Energy

Warm Up

Coulomb's law helps explain some of the trends in the periodic table. The coulomb is the SI unit of charge named after the great French physicist, Charles Augustin de Coulomb. One coulomb is the charge on 6.24×10^{18} electrons. For this Warm Up, write an equation using the number of electrons in 1 coulomb and Avogadro's number to determine the charge (in coulombs) on 1 mole of electrons.

Stoichiometry and Electrolysis

Michael Faraday was an English scientist who contributed a great deal to our understanding of electrochemistry. He was the first to describe a quantitative relationship, called **Faraday's law**, between the number of amperes used and the quantity of product formed or reactant consumed during an electrochemical process.

> The amount of substance produced (or consumed) at each electrode is directly proportional to the coulombs of charge flowing through an electrolytic cell.

In the warm-up exercise, you derived a conversion factor that represents the number of coulombs in each mole of electrons. The equation below outlines the process for this derivation. The number of coulombs in each mole of electrons is Faraday's constant and has the symbol *F*.

$$\frac{6.02 \times 10^{23}\ \cancel{\text{electrons}}}{\text{mole } e^-} \times \frac{1\ \text{coulomb}}{6.24 \times 10^{18}\ \cancel{e^-}} = 96\,500\ \text{C/mol } e^-$$

Using Faraday's law and the number of amperes, we can calculate the mass of product formed or reactant consumed in an electrochemical process. The ampere, named after the French physicist André-Marie Ampère, is the SI unit of electrical current. The symbol for amperes or amps is A. One ampere is equal to the number of coulombs of electrons flowing past a particular point in a conducting path each second.

> Faraday constant (F): $\frac{96\,500\ \text{C}}{\text{mole } e^-}$ = 1 faraday = the charge on 1 mol of electrons
>
> $1\ \text{amp} = \frac{1\ \text{coulomb}}{\text{second}}$ or 1 A = 1 C/s

Sample Problem 1.6.1(a) — Conversion of Reaction Time ⟷ Mass of Product

What mass of solid nickel can be deposited on a graphite cathode by passing 15.00 A of current through a solution of $NiCl_2$ for 2.25 h?

What to Think About

1. Determine the balanced chemical equation. This is the first step in any stoichiometry problem. In this case, it is a half-reaction.
2. Perform the following conversions:
   hours → seconds (the unit in the denominator of amps)
   time → charge (use the current in amps expressed as C/s)
   charge → mol e^- (use the constant *F*)
   mole e^- → mol Ni (use the half reaction)
   mole Ni → mass Ni (use the molar mass)

How to Do It

Nickel will be produced by the reduction of the nickel(II) ion:

$$Ni^{2+}(aq) + 2e^- \rightarrow Ni(s)$$

$$2.25\ \text{h} \times \frac{3600\ \text{s}}{1\ \text{h}} \times \frac{15.00\ \text{C}}{1\ \text{s}} \times \frac{1\ \text{mol}\ e^-}{96\,500\ \text{C}} \times \frac{1\ \text{mol Ni}}{2\ \text{mol}\ e^-} \times \frac{58.7\ \text{g Ni}}{1\ \text{mol Ni}} = 37.0\ \text{g Ni}$$

Sample Problem 1.6.1(b) — Calculation of Current

What current is required to deposit 5.00 g of gold in 1.50 h from a solution containing gold(III ions?

What to Think About

1. As always, determine the balanced chemical equation.
2. Convert 5.00 g of gold into coulombs using the following series of conversions:
   mass → moles (use the molar mass)
   moles → mol e^- (use the half reaction)
   mole e^- → coulombs (use the constant *F*)
3. Divide the coulombs by the time (in seconds) to determine the current in amperes.

How to Do It

The reduction half reaction is:

$$Au^{3+}(aq) + 3e^- \rightarrow Au(s)$$

$$5.00\ \text{g} \times \frac{1\ \text{mol Au}}{197.0\ \text{g}} \times \frac{3\ \text{mol}\ e^-}{1\ \text{mol Au}} \times \frac{96\,500\ \text{C}}{1\ \text{mol}\ e^-}$$

= 7347.7 C (note there are three significant figures)

$$\text{Current} = \frac{7347.7\ \text{C}}{1.50\ \text{h}} \times \frac{1\ \text{h}}{3600\ \text{s}} = 1.36\ \text{A}$$

Practice Problems 1.6.1 — Stoichiometry and Electrolysis

1. Figure 7.5.4 in section 7.5 depicts a Hall-Héroult cell used in the production of aluminum metal from bauxite ore, $Al_2O_3(s)$. What mass of aluminum is produced if 15.0 A of current passes through molten bauxite for 24.0 h?

Continued opposite

Practice Problems 1.6.1 (*Continued*)

2. Calculate the current required to deposit 15.0 g of silver metal in 2.5 h from a solution containing silver ions.

3. The peroxydisulphate ion forms during the electrolysis of a cold concentrated solution of potassium sulfate. The half reaction is:

   $2\ SO_4^{2-}(aq) \rightarrow S_2O_8^{2-}(aq) + 2e^-$

   (a) At which electrode does this reaction take place? Explain your answer.

   (b) Calculate the time required to produce 2.00 kg of $K_2S_2O_8$ with a current of 125 A.

Free Energy and Electrochemistry

Moving electrons through a wire requires work. What is the source of the energy to do this work? The work done when electrons move from one point to another on a conducting path depends on the electrical potential difference between the two points. The free energy of an oxidation-reduction reaction drives electrons through a circuit. As long as a reacting mixture is not at equilibrium, its free chemical energy ($\Delta G°$) provides electrical energy to do the work to move a given number of moles of electrons (n) across an electrical potential difference (E°).

As indicated earlier in this section, the unit of electrical potential difference (sometimes referred to as *electromotive force* or *emf*) is the **volt (V)**. One volt is equivalent to 1 joule of work per coulomb of charge transferred.

$$\textbf{potential difference (V)} = \frac{\textbf{work (J)}}{\textbf{charge (C)}}$$

When 1 coulomb of charge moves between two points in a circuit that differ by 1 volt of electrical potential, the chemical system produces or requires 1 joule of work. A simple algebraic manipulation of the equation above shows that work is the product of potential difference and charge. A review of the derivation of Faraday's constant shows that the charge transferred during a redox reaction, q, is equivalent to the product of the number of moles of electrons, n, and the constant, F. Substitution of $\Delta G°$ for maximum work provides the connection between thermodynamics and electrochemistry as $\Delta G° = -nFE°$. The equation is derived as follows:

$$\text{work (J)} = \text{potential difference} \left(\frac{J}{C}\right) \times \text{charge (C)} \quad or \quad w_{max} = -E_{max}q$$

$$\text{Since } q = nF$$

$$w_{max} = -nFE° = \Delta G° \text{ thus:}$$

$$\boldsymbol{\Delta G° = -nFE°}$$

Spontaneous processes are never one hundred percent efficient. Some energy is always wasted in the form of heat. The values calculated for w_{max} and E_{max} assume 100% efficiency and are simplified to w and E° (assuming standard conditions) in this equation. The experimentally determined values of w and E° would likely be lower than the calculated values because the process is less than 100% efficient. The free energy is *produced by* the chemical system, therefore convention requires the insertion of a negative sign.

> Spontaneous processes always result in a (+) E° value and a (–) ΔG° value.

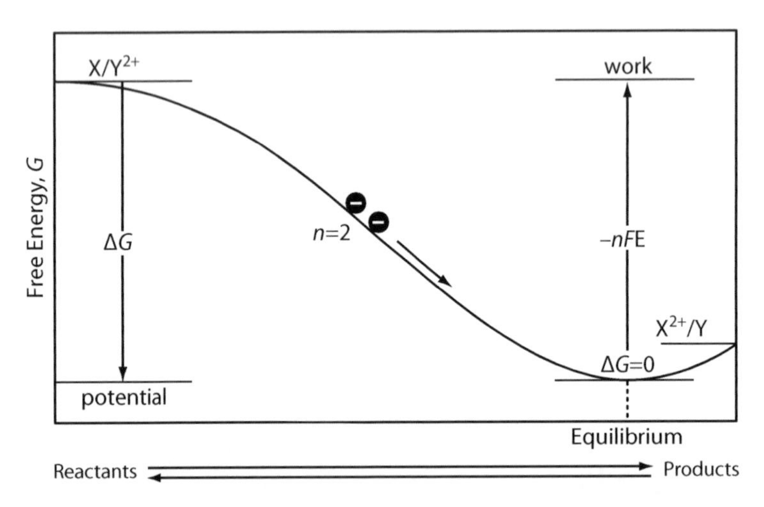

Figure 1.6.1 *This curve depicts the change in free energy when the reducing agent X transfers two electrons to the oxidizing agent Y^{2+} to form X^{2+} and Y. The change in free energy (ΔG°) is the amount of energy available to do electrical work. The maximum work available equals –nFE. This is a spontaneous process, and the negative sign indicates the work is done by the system.*

Sample Problem 1.6.2 — Free Energy and Electrochemistry: ΔG° ⇔ E°

Use Table A7 Standard Reduction Potentials of Half-Cells in the appendix to calculate E°_{cell} and ΔG° and to predict whether the following reaction is spontaneous:

$$Cl_2(g) + 2\,Br^-(aq) \rightarrow 2\,Cl^-(aq) + Br_2(l)$$

What to Think About	How to Do It
1. Calculate E° for the cell exactly as explained in section 7.4 (see sample problem 7.4.1).	Red: $Cl_2 + 2e^- \rightarrow 2\,Cl^-$ $E^\circ = 1.36$ V Ox: $2\,Br^- \rightarrow Br_2 + 2\,e^-$ $E^\circ = -1.09$ V Redox: $Cl_2 + 2\,Br^- \rightarrow 2\,Cl^- + Br_2$ $E^\circ = +0.27$ V
2. Substitute E° into the equation ΔG° = –nFE° taking care with the signs. Remember that a volt is equivalent to a joule/coulomb.	$\Delta G^\circ = -\frac{2\ \text{mol e}^-}{\text{mol}_{rxn}} \times \frac{96\,500\ \text{C}}{\text{mol e}^-} \times \frac{0.27\ \text{J}}{1\ \text{C}} \times \frac{1\ \text{kJ}}{10^3\ \text{J}}$ $= -52\ \text{kJ/mol}_{rxn}$
3. Consider the sign of each value as it relates to spontaneity. Ensure the signs of E° and ΔG oppose one another.	Both (+) E° and (–) ΔG° indicate the reaction is spontaneous!

Practice Problems 1.6.2 — Free Energy and Electrochemistry: $\Delta G°$ ⇔ E°

1. Calculate E° and $\Delta G°$ when silver metal dissolves in nitric acid. Is this process thermodynamically favorable?

2. Cadmium metal spontaneously reduces copper(II) ions to copper metal, producing Cd^{2+} ions as well. $\Delta G°$ for this reaction is –143 kJ/mol_{rxn}. Determine the standard reduction potential for Cd^{2+}. Hint: Begin by finding E° for the redox reaction.

3. The reaction $6X^- + 2\,Al^{3+} \rightarrow 3\,X_2 + 2\,Al$ has a $\Delta G°$ value of 1270 kJ/mol_{rxn}.
   (a) Calculate E° for the reaction.

   (b) Use Table A7 Standard Reduction Potentials of Half-Cells in the appendix to determine the identity of the element X_2.

1.6 Review Questions

1. Electroplating metals makes them more resistant to corrosion and may make them more attractive.
   (a) A motorcycle's exhaust pipe is plated with chromium by passing 55 A of current through a cell containing chromium(III) ions for 0.75 min. What mass of chromium is deposited on the pipe?

   (b) Steel screws for use in kitchen cabinetry are plated with nickel from a nickel(II) ion solution. If 125 mg of nickel are required for each screw and a current of 0.50 A is used, how long will it take to plate 32 screws for a set of kitchen cabinets?

   (c) An antique teapot requires a new silver surface with a mass of 12.0 g. If the plating process requires 1.50 h, what current should be used?

2. "Tin" cans are prepared by plating a steel can with tin.
   (a) What is the advantage of placing a layer of tin against the steel, which is mainly composed of iron?

   (b) The steel can is connected at the cathode in an electrolytic cell containing 1.00 L of 3.75 mol/L $SnCl_2(aq)$. A current of 2.50 A passes through the cell for 1.25 h.
   (i) What mass of tin is deposited on the steel can?

   (ii) What concentration of $SnCl_2(aq)$ remains in the cell once the plating is complete?

3. Pure bismuth is produced by the electrolysis of a solution containing BiO^+ ions. How long would it take to produce 15.0 g of bismuth using 10.0 A of current? Begin by writing a balanced reduction half reaction.

4. An aqueous solution of CoF_2 is electrolyzed with 3.50 A for 1.40 h. Both electrodes are made of graphite.
   (a) What mass of cobalt metal is collected?

   (b) What volume of oxygen gas evolves at the other electrode? Determine the volume at STP conditions.

   (c) Give two chemical tests to determine that the gas is, indeed, oxygen.

5. Calculate the standard cell potential E° *and* the change in free energy $\Delta G°$ for each of these reactions. Which reaction is spontaneous?
   (a) $2\,H_2O(l) \rightarrow 2\,H_2(g) + O_2(g)$ *decomposition of water*

   (b) $2\,Fe(s) + O_2(g) + 4\,H^+(aq) \rightarrow 2\,Fe^{2+}(aq) + 2\,H_2O(l)$ *rusting of Fe*

6. The reaction $Ag_2O(s) + Zn(s) + H_2O(l) \rightarrow 2\,Ag(s) + Zn^{2+}(aq) + 2\,OH^-(aq)$ occurs in some "button" batteries producing a cell potential of 1.104 V.
   (a) Calculate the standard reduction potential for the cathodic half reaction.

   (b) Calculate $\Delta G°$ for the spontaneous redox reaction.

7. The reaction $CH_4(g) + 2\ O_2(g) + 2\ OH^-(aq) \rightarrow CO_3^{2-}(aq) + 3\ H_2O(l)$ occurs in a methane-oxygen fuel cell producing energy at nearly 70% efficiency (compared to the 25% efficiency of a normal combustion reaction to produce steam in an electricity generating plant). E°_{cell} is 0.23 V for this reaction.

   (a) Calculate ΔG° for this reaction.

   (b) Given $E^\circ = 0.40$ V for $O_2(g) + 2\ H_2O(l) + 4\ e^- \rightarrow 4\ OH^-(aq)$, write the balanced oxidation half-reaction and determine E° for the anodic reaction.

8. If 0.40 g of a metal is deposited on a cathode by 5.0 A of current in 0.50 h, what mass of the *same* metal would be deposited by 1 faraday? Recall: 1 faraday is equivalent to 1 mole of electrons *or* 96 500 C.

9. Scientists and engineers have designed a wide variety of new rechargeable cells during the decade 2004 to 2014. A popular, though expensive, example is the silver-cadmium cell. The overall reaction is:
   $2\ AgO(s) + H_2O(l) + Cd(s) \rightarrow Ag_2O(s) + Cd(OH)_2(s)\ \Delta G^\circ = -257\ kJ/mol_{rxn}$
   What is the voltage for a silver-cadmium cell?

10. Scientists designed the first "transistor battery" shown here in the 1950s. It was commonly used to power the first portable transistor radios. Today, devices such as remote control cars, alarm systems, motion sensors, and smoke detectors use this same battery. The battery is actually a system of *six cells* each involving the standard dry cell reaction shown here:

$$2\ MnO_2(s) + H_2O(l) + Zn(s) \rightarrow Mn_2O_3(s) + 2\ OH^-(aq) + Zn^{2+}(aq)$$

$\Delta G°$ for this reaction is –299 kJ/mol$_{rxn}$. What is the overall voltage for a transistor battery?

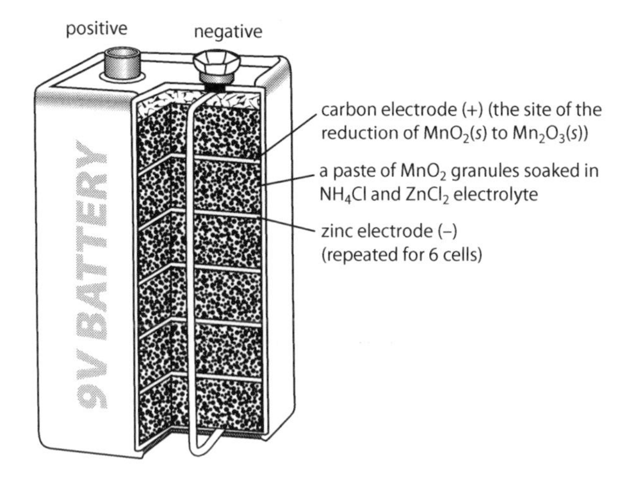

A transistor battery consists of six cells stacked vertically and connected in series.

11. The Hall-Héroult cell requires a low-voltage DC source (approximately 4.53 V) that applies current across inert graphite electrodes through molten bauxite (Al_2O_3) ore. The addition of cryolite (Na_3AlF_6) lowers the melting point of bauxite.

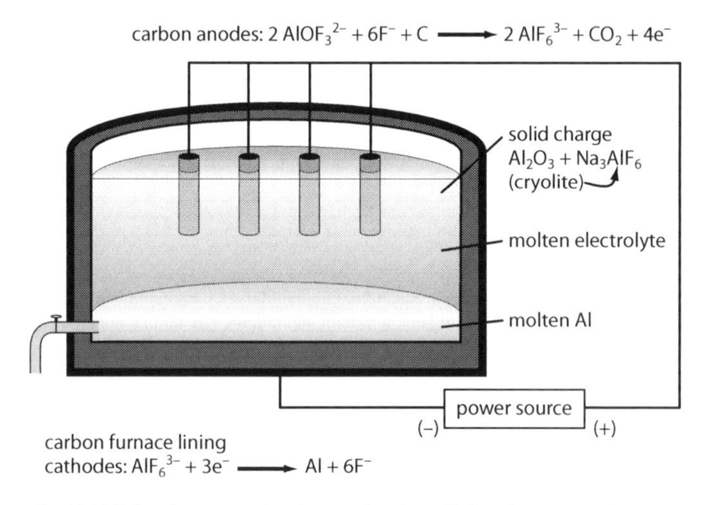

The Hall-Héroult process for the production of aluminum metal.

(a) Combine the anode and cathode half-reactions to give the overall equation for the Hall-Héroult process.

(b) Calculate the $\Delta G°$ value for the process.

2 Structure and Properties of Matter

Big Ideas

- The nature of the attractive forces that exist between particles in a substance determines the properties and limits the uses of that substance.
- Technological devices that are based on the principles of atomic and molecular structures can have societal benefits and costs.

Overall Expectations

By the end of this course, students will

C1. assess the benefits to society and evaluate the environmental impact of products and technologies that apply principles related to the structure and properties of matter;

C2. investigate the molecular shapes and physical properties of various types of matter;

C3. demonstrate an understanding of atomic structure and chemical bonding, and how they relate to the physical properties of ionic, molecular, covalent network, and metallic substances.

Learning Goals	Success Criteria
Relating Science to Technology, Society and the Environment	*Relating Science to Technology, Society and the Environment*
□ Assess the benefits to society of technologies that are based on the principles of atomic and molecular structures	□ I can identify several technologies based on atomic molecular structure e.g. magnetic resonance imaging [MRI], infrared spectroscopy, X-ray crystallography, nuclear energy, medical applications of spectroscopy and mass spectrometry □ I can provide a research-based explanation of how these technologies depend on atomic and molecular structure □ I can assess the social, environmental and scientific benefits and drawbacks of these technologies
□ evaluate the benefits to society, and the impact on the environment, of specialized materials that have been created on the basis of scientific research into the structure of matter and chemical bonding	□ I can identify several materials developed from research into matter and chemical bonding (e.g. nanoparticles, adhesive technologies, Kevlar, Mylar, other polymers, superconductors) □ I can explain how the structure of matter and chemical bonding led to these new development and observations □ I can assess the social, environmental and technological benefits and drawbacks of these materials
Developing Skills of Investigation and Communication	*Developing Skills of Investigation and Communication*
□ Articulate and understand the terms and processes related to the structure and properties of matter	□ I can properly describe the history of human understanding of the atomic model, the quantum mechanical model, orbitals, emission spectra, energy levels, photons, and dipoles
□ Use quantum principles to write electron configurations	□ I can use Hund's Rule, the Aufbau Principle, the Pauli Exclusion Principle and the correct quantum mechanical notation to write the electron configurations of atoms □ I understand why there are some exceptions to the Aufbau Principle □ I can correctly predict if an exception to the Aufbau Principle might apply to an electron configuration
□ Use VSEPR theory correctly to predict the shape of molecules and ions	□ I understand the VSEPR theory and can apply it to predict molecular shapes □ I can draw correct Lewis Dot diagrams of molecules □ I can correctly predict the bond angle(s) within a molecule □ I can construct correct VSEPR models for molecules using a molecular model kits □ I can use molecular models kits to explain bonding angles

☐ Use an understanding of molecular shape, electronegativity and symmetry to predict the polarity of a molecule	☐ I can use molecular models kits to explain molecular dipoles ☐ I can explain how symmetry and asymmetry affect molecular dipoles ☐ I can explain how molecular dipoles can affect the physical properties of a substance
☐ Classify the four types of solids (molecular, ionic, network, metallic)	☐ I can explain why covalent network solids are generally hard, good thermal insulators that have high melting points ☐ I can explain why metallic solids are generally good conductors of heat and electricity, have a wide range of melting points, are shiny, malleable, ductile and easily form alloys ☐ I can explain why ionic solids have high melting points, are brittle and conduct electricity only when molten or in solution ☐ I can explain why molecular solids generally have lower melting points and are not expected to conduct electricity
☐ Conduct an inquiry to observe and analyze physical properties and use the analysis to predict the type of chemical bonding present in compounds	☐ I can design an experiment with several tests of physical properties to distinguish between molecular and ionic compounds ☐ I can predict whether a substance is molecular or ionic based on experimental evidence
☐ Understand Valence Bond (VB) Theory and use it to explain bonding in molecules (AP)	☐ I understand how the VB Theory explains molecular chemical bonding ☐ I can use VB Theory to describe molecular bonding ☐ I can differentiate between the sp, sp^2, sp^3, sp^3d and sp^3d^2 hybrid orbitals ☐ I can correctly identify the type of hybrid orbital(s) formed between atoms in a molecule (AP)
☐ Use Coulomb's Law to qualitatively explain the structure of the atom and chemical bonding (AP)	☐ I understand how Coulomb's Law explains the magnitude of the force of attraction between protons and electrons ☐ I understand how Coulomb's Law explains the magnitude of the force of repulsion between protons ☐ I understand how Coulomb's Law explains the magnitude of the force of repulsion between electrons ☐ I understand how Coulomb's Law explains the strength of intermolecular attractions ☐ I can use Coulomb's Law to explain (AP)
☐ Understand how Mass, Ultraviolet and visible radiation (UV vis), Photoelectron (PES), nuclear magnetic resonance (NMR) and infrared (IR) spectroscopy provide information used to identify compounds (AP)	☐ I understand how different types of spectroscopy provided evidence to contradict earlier models of the atom ☐ I understand how mass spectroscopy can be used to distinguish between isotopes of the same atom ☐ I understand how spectroscopy can be used to determine the composition of an unknown compound in general terms (you will not have to use NMR, UV vis or IR spec in the determination of an unknown) ☐ I understand how to use Beer's Law to calculate the absorption of a solution (AP)
☐ Use PES to identify unknown compounds (AP)	☐ I can use PES spectra to identify unknown atoms ☐ I understand how electrons within the atom form the peaks on PES spectra ☐ I understand and can explain the different heights of the peaks on PES spectra ☐ I can sketch the expected PES spectrum for a given atom (AP)
☐ Conduct an investigation to better understand the physical properties of alloys (AP)	☐ I understand the difference between interstitial and substitution alloys ☐ I can predict whether an alloy is likely to be an interstitial or a substitutional alloy ☐ I understand how different percent compositions of an alloy can affect the physical properties of the alloy ☐ I can determine the eutectic point of an alloy by experiment (AP)

Understanding Basic Concepts	*Understanding Basic Concepts*
☐ Explain how experimental observations and inferences made by Ernest Rutherford and Niels Bohr contributed to the development of the planetary model of the hydrogen atom	☐ I understand the historical development of various models of the atom and the strengths of each of the models in the context of the time in which they were developed ☐ I understand how limitations of each of the previous models led to further development of the model of the atom ☐ I can explain wave particle duality using the development in scientific understanding (e.g. Newton, Thomas Young, Einstein's Photoelectric Effect) ☐ I understand how to use Planck's Law to calculate the energy of a photon ☐ I can use the Universal Wave Equation to calculate the wavelength or frequency of a photon ☐ I can calculate the expected amount of energy released during an energy level transition in a hydrogen atom according to Bohr's Model ☐ I understand the significance and the energy difference between electron transitions in the Balmer, Lyman and Paschen series ☐ I understand how the DeBroglie equation applies to wave particle duality and how to solve problems using the DeBroglie relation ☐ I understand how probability applies qualitatively to the quantum mechanical model and can qualitatively explain why Heisenberg's Uncertainty Principle and Schrodinger's Equation are important
☐ Describe the electron configurations of a variety of elements in the periodic table using quantum mechanical principles	☐ I understand how to assign the four quantum numbers to define an electron in an atom ☐ I understand the correct notation associated with each of the quantum numbers ☐ I understand how to use the correct notation to write the quantum mechanical electron configuration of an atom ☐ I can use orbital diagrams to depict electron configurations ☐ I can use energy level diagrams to depict electron configurations
☐ Identify the characteristic properties of elements in each of the s, p, and d blocks of the periodic table ☐ Explain the relationship between the position of an element in the periodic table, its properties, and its electron configuration	☐ I can identify the s, p, d and f blocks on the periodic table and understand the connection between each block and the associated electron configuration ☐ I understand how the position of an element on the periodic table provides information about the chemical and physical properties of that element
☐ Explain how the physical properties of a solid or liquid depend on the particles present and the types of intermolecular and intramolecular forces	☐ I can explain when ionic bonding, hydrogen bonding, dipole-dipole forces and London dispersion forces occur ☐ I can differentiate between inter and intra-molecular forces ☐ I can quantify the relative strength of inter and intra molecular forces in molecular and ionic compounds ☐ I understand how the physical properties of a compound or element provides information about the inter and intra molecular bonding
☐ Use the Kinetic Molecular Theory (KMT), mathematical relationships and intermolecular forces to explain the behaviour of Gases (AP)	☐ I can correctly apply all of the Gas Laws to solve problems ☐ I can use the KMT to explain the behaviour of Ideal Gases ☐ I understand the limitations of the KMT ☐ I understand why gases sometimes exhibit non-ideal behaviour (AP)
☐ Describe a Canadian contribution to the field of atomic and molecular theory	☐ I can identify and describe Canadian contributions to atomic and molecular theory (e.g. Bader, LeRoy, Gillespie)

In the AP curriculum, these topics relate to AP Big Idea 1: The chemical elements are fundamental building materials of matter, and all matter can be understood in terms of arrangements of atoms. These atoms retain their identity in chemical reactions and AP Big Idea 2: Chemical and physical properties of materials can be explained by the structure and the arrangement of atoms, ions, or molecules and the forces between them.

2.1 Describing Chemical Bonding

Warm Up

1. What term do we give to an atom's outer electrons that take part in chemical bonding?
____
2. Define electronegativity.
____
3. In which region of the periodic table are elements located that tend to
(a) lose outer electrons most easily during chemical changes?
____
(b) gain outer electrons most easily during chemical changes?
____

An Introduction to Chemical Bonding

All matter is composed of atoms, and those individual atoms are far too small to see. From that, it seems reasonable to conclude that matter must be made up of large numbers of atoms connected or bonded together. In this section, we will investigate the nature of the bonds between atoms and how those bonds determine important properties in compounds.

Atoms are electrical species with a negative cloud of electrons surrounding and attracted to a positive nucleus. As you have learned, the electrostatic forces of attraction and repulsion within atoms influence properties such as atomic size, ionization energy, and electronegativity. Those same forces and properties also play a role whenever atoms bond together.

When two atoms approach each other, all of the electrostatic interactions associated with equally and oppositely charged particles occur. The negative electron clouds of the atoms exert repulsive forces on each other, as do the positive nuclei of each atom. This repulsion slows the approaching atoms and converts some of their kinetic energy to potential energy. In addition, each nucleus also begins to attract the approaching atom's outer electron cloud. These attractive forces are most intense in the region of space where the electron clouds "overlap" between the adjacent nuclei. If the attractive forces between the atoms are stronger than the repulsive forces, the two atoms together are in a state of lower energy than when they were apart. Thus, a chemical bond forms between them.

Types of Chemical Bonds

The events described above apply to the formation of all chemical bonds. But recall that we have classified elements as metals and non-metals based on a number of physical and chemical properties that correlate to different positions on the periodic table. These properties and the three possible ways that these two varieties of elements can combine give rise to three different *types* of chemical bonds, which are listed in Table 2.1.1. In this course, we will cover ionic and covalent bonds.

Table 2.1.1 *Types of Chemical Bonds*

Atoms Involved in Chemical Bond	Type of Chemical Bond
1. metal bonded to non-metal	ionic bond
2. non-metal bonded to non-metal	covalent bond
3. metal bonded to metal	metallic bond

Table 2.1.1 is a simplified summary of chemical bonds because the bonds between atoms in most chemical compounds have varying proportions of both ionic and covalent characteristics. We will begin with clear examples of each type of bond to introduce the concepts involved.

Ionic Bonds

Ionic bonds form between two atoms with large differences in their ionization energies and electronegativities. Recall that such combinations typically occur when relatively large metal atoms located on the far left side of the periodic table in groups 1 or 2 combine with smaller non-metal atoms on the far right side of the table belonging to groups 16 or 17.

Look again at the electronegativities on your periodic table. Imagine a "collision," for example, between an alkali metal atom such as sodium and a halogen atom such as chlorine. These elements are located at opposite ends of the 3rd period of the periodic table and therefore exhibit significant differences in size, ionization energy, and electronegativity.

Compared to an atom of sodium, a chlorine atom is smaller with a higher ionization energy and electronegativity. As a result, when the outer electron clouds of these two atoms encounter each other, sodium's lone valence electron will be closer to chlorine's nucleus than to its own. It will therefore feel a stronger attraction from chlorine's nucleus than from its own. In fact, because the difference in the electronegativities of these two elements is *greater than 1.7*, the probability of finding sodium's outer electron near chlorine's nucleus is so great that the sodium atom can be considered to *transfer* that valence electron to the chlorine atom. Electronegativity difference is often abbreviated as **ΔEN**.

The large sodium atom, having lost the only electron in its 3rd energy level, is now a much smaller positively charged sodium cation (Na^+). The relatively small chlorine atom, having gained an extra electron, becomes a larger negatively charged chloride anion (Cl^-). These two oppositely charged ions are now bound together by an electrostatic attraction called an **ionic bond**.

An **ionic bond** is the electrostatic attractive force between the oppositely charged ions produced when a metal atom transfers one or more electrons to a non-metal atom.

The electron transfer from sodium to chlorine and the resulting ionic bond is shown in Figure 2.1.1. These diagrams are **Bohr model** diagrams, showing the number of electrons in the shells surrounding the nuclei of the atoms and ions.

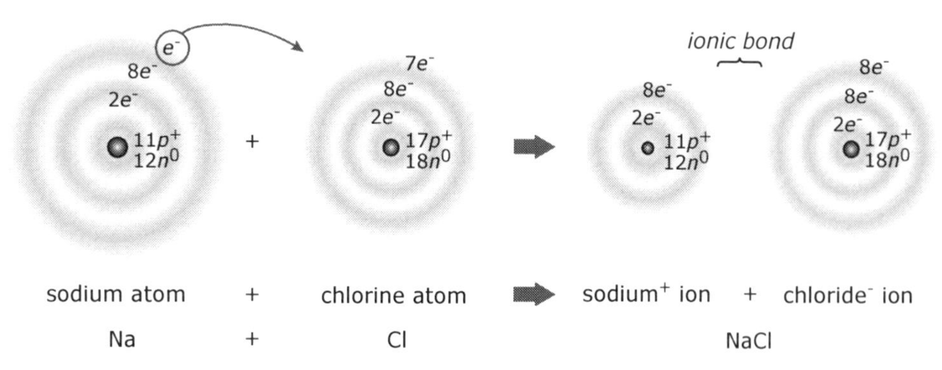

Figure 2.1.1 *An electron transfers from sodium atom to a chlorine atom, resulting in the formation of an ionic bond between the ions.*

The Ionic Crystal Lattice

Obviously, when any macroscopic sample of chlorine gas and sodium metal react together, countless atoms will transfer electrons to form countless oppositely charged ions. These oppositely charged species being produced in close proximity are drawn together into an ordered, solid, three-dimensional array of cations and anions called a **crystal lattice** (Figure 2.1.2). The smallest whole number cation-to-anion ratio in this structure represents the chemical formula for the ionic compound, in this case, NaCl.

Figure 2.1.2 *NaCl crystal lattice*

The vast number of interionic forces present in a crystal lattice locks all of the ions into place. This helps explain why all ionic compounds are solids with high melting temperatures (e.g., sodium chloride melts at 801°C.)

Ionic compounds form a number of different crystal structures depending on the relative sizes and ratios of their ions. Those ratios in turn depend on the charges on the ions in the compound.

Recall that the representative elements in groups 1, 2, 13, 15, 16, and 17 of the periodic table tend to form stable ions by losing or gaining sufficient electrons to become isoelectronic with the nearest noble gas. This results in the common ion charges shown in Table 2.1.2 for those groups.

Table 2.1.2 *Common Ion Charges in Groups 1, 2, 13, 15, 16, and 17*

Group Number	1	2	13	15	16	17
Most Common Ion Charge	1+	2+	3+	3-	2–	1–

We can think of ionic bond formation as a case of *extremely unequal electron sharing*. Both metal and non-metal nuclei attract the valence electrons between them when their atoms meet. However, the non-metal pulls those electrons so close to its own nucleus that it effectively captures the metal's valence electrons and forms the metal cation and non-metal anion. An accurate analogy might be a grossly mismatched tug-of-war, except that in this case, the smallest competitor wins.

Several important points should be mentioned when summarizing ionic bonding:

1. Ionic compounds form between metals and non-metals whose ΔEN exceed 1.7. They typically form when metals from groups 1 or 2 react with non-metals from groups 16 or 17 of the periodic table.
2. During the formation of an ionic bond, metal atoms will transfer one or more valence electrons to the more electronegative non-metal atoms. This occurs because of the metal's relatively low ionization energies and electronegativities. In the process, metal cations and non-metal anions form and are attracted to each other by ionic bonds.
3. Ionic compounds form structures known as crystal lattices. The vast number of attractive forces present in such lattices account for the high melting temperatures of ionic compounds.
4. The formulas for ionic compounds represent the smallest whole number ratios of cations-to-anions that are electrically neutral.

Quick Check

1. What event occurs when atoms of metals and non-metals react to become cations and anions?

____

2. Identify the three types of chemical bonds based on the different elements involved.

____

____

____

3. Which chemical families in the periodic table are typically associated with ionic bond formation?

____

Sample Problem — Ionic Bond Formation

Write formulas for the compounds formed when the following elements combine and justify that the bonds present are ionic by determining the ΔEN in each case.

(a) Ca and Br (b) Al and O (c) Be and O (d) Rb and N (e) Ba and Cl

What to Think about	How to Do It
1. Write the element symbols with their charges and criss-cross the numbers.	(a) Ca^{2+} Br^{-} → $CaBr_2$ ΔEN = 1.8 (ionic bond)
2. Reduce formulas to smallest whole number ratios	(b) Al^{3+} O^{2-} → Al_2O_3 ΔEN = 2.0 (ionic bond)
3. Determine ΔEN values using the table above. Values above 1.7 represent ionic bonds.	(c) Be^{2+} O^{2-} → BeO ΔEN = 2.0 (ionic bond)
	(d) Rb^{+} N^{3-} → Rb_3N ΔEN = 2.2 (ionic bond)
	(e) Ba^{2+} Cl^{-} → $BaCl_2$ ΔEN = 2.1 (ionic bond)

Practice Problems — Ionic Compounds

1. Write formulas for the ionic compounds formed when the following elements combine:

   (a) Ba and Br
   (b) Be and O
   (c) Sr and N
   (d) Mg and Cl
   (e) Fr and F

2. Justify that the bonds in the following compounds are ionic by calculating the ΔEN values for each.

   (a) RbF
   (b) $RaCl_2$
   (c) KBr
   (d) Na_2O

3. Write formulas for the ionic compounds formed when the following elements combine. Using the ΔEN values, arrange the compounds in order of the increasing ionic character of the bonds in each compound.

   (a) Na and N (b) Sr and Br (c) Li and Cl (d) Cs and F (e) Rb and O

Covalent Bonds

Now let's look at the formation of a bond between two atoms of the same non-metal element, such as hydrogen (Figure 2.1.3). Obviously, the electronegativities of these or any two identical atoms would be the same.

As mentioned above, bond formation begins with atoms "colliding." As the two hydrogen atoms approach each other, their kinetic energy increases as each electron cloud is attracted to the other's approaching positive nucleus. The two atoms continue moving together until the repulsive forces of the two negative electron clouds and the two positive nuclei slow the atoms and convert their kinetic energy into potential energy.

As the atoms get close to each other, their electron clouds may overlap enough to cause attractive forces to exceed repulsive ones. The two valence electrons will move into the region of space between the adjacent nuclei because this is where they experience the most attractive force from those two centres of positive charge. The two atoms will settle into a position next to each other with the pair of valence electrons in a cloud of negative charge between the two nuclei. As the electron clouds of each hydrogen atom overlap, the two valence electrons experience the maximum attractive force between the two adjacent nuclei. This force of attraction of a pair of valence electrons between two adjacent nuclei constitutes a single **covalent bond**. In our example, the result of this covalent bond is a molecule of hydrogen, H_2

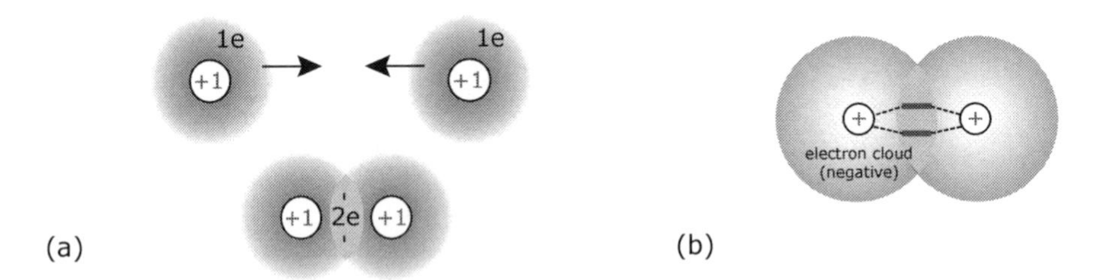

Figure 2.1.3 *(a) Two hydrogen atoms collide and two valence electrons move into the space between the nuclei. (b) The valence electrons experience a force of attraction from the two nuclei. This attraction holds the two atoms together to form H_2.*

Because this bond has formed between two atoms of hydrogen, the electronegativity difference associated with the atoms in the bond must be zero. This tells us that, on average, the pair of bonded electrons will spend the majority of their time equidistant between the two hydrogen nuclei. Stated another way, this means that the density of the electron charge cloud is greatest in the region of space halfway between the two adjacent nuclei. This is true whenever two atoms of the same element form covalent bonds. The "equal sharing" of valence electrons is sometimes referred to as a "pure covalent" or non-polar covalent bond.

Although both ionic and covalent bond formation involves only valence electrons, there are several important differences between the two events:

1. Covalent bonds typically form between two non-metal atoms rather than between metal atoms and non-metal atoms.
2. Because no electron transfer occurs and no ions form, all of the species prior to and following covalent bond formation between two atoms are electrically neutral.
3. The force of attraction in a covalent bond is between a pair of electrons and two adjacent positive nuclei, rather than between a cation and an anion as in an ionic bond. Electrons in covalent bonds are *always associated into pairs.*
4. Covalent compounds often exist as independent molecules rather than large crystal structures.

Polar Covalent Bonds

We have discussed above the two extreme cases of bonding: complete electron transfer and completely equal electron sharing. Between these extremes are covalent bonds involving *unequal* electron sharing.

When atoms with different electronegativities form covalent bonds, those ΔEN values may be minimal or significant. If ΔEN is less than 0.4, the bonding electrons between the two atoms spend no more of their time nearer one nucleus than the other. Such bonds are designated as being mostly covalent because ΔEN appears to be insignificant. Another way to characterize this is to say that these bonds have very little "ionic character."

However, as ΔEN increases beyond 0.4, the pair of bonding electrons will be drawn closer and closer to the nucleus of the atom with the higher electronegativity. This unequal distribution of electron density will give that end of the bond a partially negative "pole" and the other a partially positive "pole." A bond "dipole" is said to exist and the bond itself is known as a **polar covalent bond**.

As the ΔEN increases and the bonds become more and more polar, we could say that the amount of ionic character in those bonds increases (Table 2.1.3).

Table 2.1.3 *Relationship of ΔEN and Bond Designation*

ΔEN	Bond Designation
0	non-polar covalent
< 0.4	mostly covalent
0.4 – 1.7	polar covalent
> 1.7	ionic

Let's look at an example of a polar covalent bond. When a hydrogen atom having an electronegativity of 2.1 bonds to a chlorine atom with an electronegativity of 3.0, the ΔEN = 0.9. The electron density will be concentrated near chlorine giving that end of the bond a partial negative charge and leaving the hydrogen end with a partial positive charge. The bond dipole is said to be in the direction of chlorine and we can designate this polar covalent bond in several ways. Two are shown in Figure 2.1.4. The lower case Greek deltas (δ) indicate that there are slight or *partial* charges associated with each end of the HCl molecule. Note also that more electron density is associated with chlorine. Another depiction of this polar covalent bond simply shows the hydrogen chloride bond as a straight line between the element symbols. Beneath this is an arrow facing in the direction of the highest electron density or the negative end of the bond dipole.

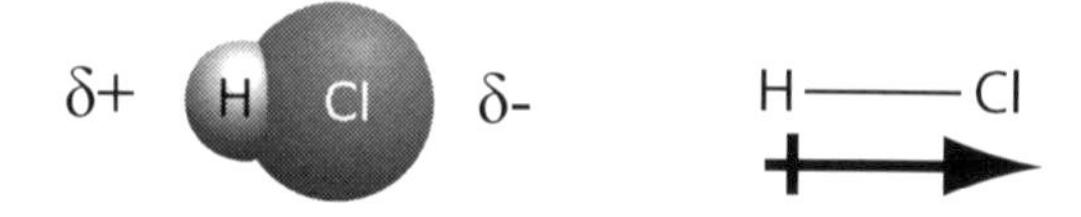

Figure 2.1.4 *Polar covalent bond depictions. The bond dipole is in the direction of the chlorine.*

Atoms That Form More Than One Bond

So far we have considered the formation of only one bond per atom in two different molecules, namely H_2 and HCl. Notice that hydrogen and chlorine each require a single electron to become isoelectronic with their nearest noble gas. In hydrogen's case, one more electron will complete its first energy level. When chlorine acquires another electron it achieves a stable octet in its valence shell.

In each example, the sharing of a pair of valence electrons, whether equal or not, gives each atom in the bond the benefit of that extra electron in its valence shell. The bond also allows both atoms to have *all of their valence electrons paired,* which is a very stable configuration from a quantum mechanical perspective.

Of course, non-metals sometimes require more than one electron to achieve a stable outer electron shell and have all of their valence electrons paired. Consider several non-metals in groups 14, 15, and 16. To achieve a stable octet containing four electron pairs in each of their valence shells, carbon requires four electrons, nitrogen needs three, and oxygen needs two.

This tells us that the number of electrons required by an atom to achieve the stable outer electron configuration of the nearest noble gas also represents the number of covalent bonds that the atom must form.

We can use Table 2.1.4 to predict formulas for compounds formed between elements in these families. For example, when phosphorus and chlorine react together, phosphorus requires three electrons to complete its octet, while chlorine requires only one.

Table 2.1.4 *Electrons Needed to Achieve a Stable Octet for Non-metals*

Periodic Table Group Number	14	15	16	17
Electrons Needed to Achieve Stable Octet	4	3	2	1

The element with the lower electronegativity, in this case phosphorus, normally requires the most electrons and is written first in a chemical formula. Place the number of electrons it requires above its symbol on the right (similar to a charge without the sign). Then do the same for chlorine as follows: P^3 Cl^1 Now criss-cross those numbers to give the formula: PCl_3.

The process is similar to writing ionic formulas except no charges exist and you don't always reduce the formula to the smallest ratio of atoms. This is because a covalent formula does not represent a ratio. Rather, it tells us the actual number of atoms that exist in the molecule. Assume at this point, however, that you *can* reduce covalent formulas unless told otherwise by your teacher.

There are also numerous examples where more than one pair of electrons is shared between the same two atoms. Two pairs of shared valence electrons results in a double covalent bond and three pairs will produce a triple covalent bond. We will discuss multiple bonds in detail in the next section. For now, we will only mention that as the number of electron pairs shared between two adjacent nuclei increases, so does the strength of the covalent bond.

Sample Problem — Covalent Bond Formation

Predict the formulas for the compounds formed when the following elements combine and determine whether the bonds present are non-polar covalent or polar covalent.
(a) N and F (b) C and H (c) Si and N (d) C and S (e) O and O

What to Think about

1. Determine how many electrons each atom requires to complete its valence shell and write that number above the symbol.
2. Criss-cross those numbers and reduce ratios if possible (for now).
3. Determine the ΔEN for each and classify the bonds present.

How to Do It

(a) N^3 F^1 → NF_3 $\Delta EN = 1.0$ (polar covalent)
(b) C^4 H^1 → CH_4 $\Delta EN = 0.4$ (polar covalent)
(c) Si^4 N^3 → Si_3N_4 $\Delta EN = 1.2$ (polar covalent)
(d) C^4 S^2 → CS_2 $\Delta EN = 0$ (non-polar covalent)
(e) O^2 O^2 → O_2 $\Delta EN = 0$ (non-polar covalent)

Practice Problems — Comparing Types of Chemical Bonds

1. Consider the ΔEN values and pair up the elements Al, Cl, N, and Na to write the formula for the types of compounds identified below. Justify each choice by showing the appropriate ΔEN value next to each formula.
   (a) A compound with an ionic bond

   (b) A compound with a polar covalent bond

   (c) A compound with a non-polar covalent bond

2. Calculate the ΔEN values for the bonds in the following compounds. Then arrange the compounds in order from those containing bonds in which the electrons are shared most equally to those in which the electrons are shared most unequally.
   (a) H_2O (b) PCl_3 (c) Cl_4 (d) SiO_2 (e) AlN

3. Complete the following table:

Elements Present	Formula	ΔEN Value	Nature of Bonds	Atom Possessing Greater Electron Density
C and S				
B and Cl				
Al and O				
N and I				
Ca and F				

The Strength of Ionic vs. Covalent Bonds

Remember that ionic compounds are solids at room temperature and have high melting points. This results from the vast number of interionic forces locking all of the ions together in place in the crystal lattice. As mentioned earlier, the common ionic compound NaCl melts at 801°C.

Covalent compounds, however, usually exist as individual molecules and in any of the three states of matter: solid, liquid, or gas. We shouldn't conclude from this, however, that covalent bonds are any weaker than ionic bonds. Consider, for example, the molecule methane, CH_4, the main component of natural gas.

Although the melting point of methane (–182°C) is very low compared to sodium chloride, this physical property does not reflect the strength of the C – H bonds in methane or indicate that the bonds are weak compared to those in NaCl.

This is because no chemical bonds are broken when methane or any molecular covalent compound melts. Instead, weak intermolecular forces *between* the molecules are overcome. The result is that molecules are separated *from each other* rather than breaking the bonds between the atoms within those molecules.

The energy required to separate the bonded carbon and hydrogen atoms within the molecules from each other is far more than that required to simply pull the molecules apart.

Compelling evidence of the strength of covalent bonds can be seen by studying compounds called **network covalent solids**. Rather than consisting of individual molecules, these substances are held together by covalent bonds that extend throughout the entire sample. In the same way that melting an ionic solid requires overcoming all of the attractive forces between the oppositely charged ions in the crystal lattice, melting a network covalent solid involves breaking all of the covalent bonds within what is effectively a giant molecule literally as big as the sample.

Consider quartz, for example, which is a network covalent solid having the formula SiO_2 (Figure 2.1.5). The fact that no separate molecules exist in a quartz crystal means that the melting point is very high: 1550°C. The melting point does reflect the strength of the bonds in the compound. It shows us that covalent bonds can be as strong as ionic bonds.

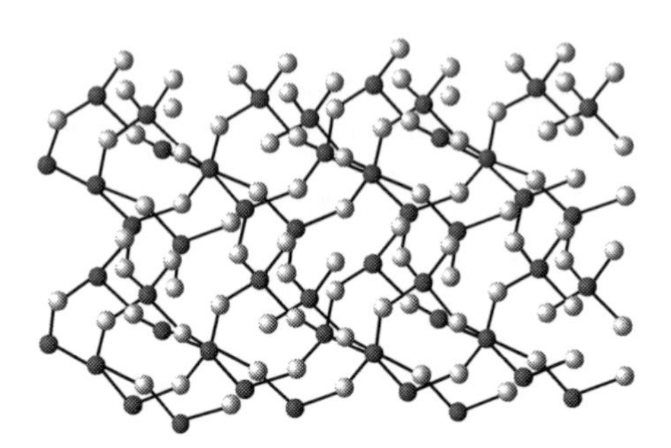

Figure 2.1.5 *A quartz crystal*

2.1 Activity: The Colors of Chemical Bonds

Question

Can one primary color blending into another be used to depict the transition from pure covalent bonding to ionic bonding?

Materials

Either blue, green, and yellow colored pencils or blue, green, and yellow watercolor paint and brushes.

Procedure

1. Use the three grids below, (A), (B), and (C). In each of the blank spaces, write the correct formula for the compound resulting from the combination of the two elements that intersect at that space. Remember to write the least electronegative atom symbol first.

2. Consult the electronegativities of the elements on your periodic table given earlier (Figure 6.2.6). Determine the electronegativity difference for each pair of elements to determine the type of bonds present in those compounds. Then shade in the spaces around each formula according to these directions: Shade in the spaces around the compounds containing ionic bonds yellow, covalent bonds blue and polar covalent bonds green.

(A)

	Li	**Be**	**B**	**C**	**N**	**O**	**F**
F							

(B)

	Na	**Mg**	**Al**	**Si**	**P**	**S**	**Cl**
Cl							

(C)

	K	**Ca**	**Ga**	**Ge**	**As**	**Se**	**Br**
Br							

Results and Discussion

1. Does every metal-non-metal combination result in an ionic bond?

2.1 Review Questions

1. (a) For a chemical bond to form between two atoms, how must the energy associated with the bonded atoms compare to the energy when the atoms are apart?

   (b) What does this tell us about the attractive forces compared to the repulsive forces between them?

2. What is an ionic crystal lattice and how does it explain the high melting points of ionic compounds?

3. Use your answer to question 2 to explain why formulas for ionic compounds do not represent neutral independent molecules of those compounds.

4. Identify the attractive forces associated with
   (a) ionic bonds

   (b) covalent bonds

5. (a) Identify two similarities between ionic and covalent bonds.

   (b) Identify two differences between ionic and covalent bonds.

6. Complete the following table by writing in the formulas of the compounds formed from the pairs of elements. Determine the ΔEN value for each and then classify the bonds as non-polar covalent, polar covalent, or ionic.

Elements	Compound Formula	ΔEN Value	Nature of Bonds Present
(a) rubidium and oxygen			
(b) strontium and bromine			
(c) carbon and sulfur			
(d) silicon and chlorine			

7. Magnesium is a metal and sulfur is a non-metal. Compare the ΔEN value for these elements in the compound MgS to the ΔEN value for the non-metals hydrogen and oxygen in water, H_2O. Which of the two compounds possesses a greater amount of ionic character in its bonds?

8. Glucose is a covalent compound with the molecular formula $C_6H_{12}O_6$. This and many other covalent formulas aren't reduced to the smallest whole-number ratios of atoms in the compound. Why not?

9. Many covalent compounds have much lower melting points than ionic compounds. Why does this not mean that covalent bonds are weaker than ionic bonds?

10. Diamond is a form of pure carbon containing only covalent bonds. It is the hardest substance known and has a melting point of about 3550°C. What name do we give to this type of covalent substance? Suggest a reason for its very high melting point.

11. Consider the nature of the covalent bonds present in HCl and in N_2. Which substance would you expect to have the higher melting point? Give a reason for your answer.

2.2 Lewis Structure Diagrams

Warm Up

1. Why do elements in the same chemical family display similar chemical behaviour?

 ____

2. How can you determine the number of valence electrons in each of the representative or main group elements?

 ____

3. Define the term "stable octet."

 ____

Depicting Atoms, Ions, and Molecules in Two Dimensions

As you learned earlier, an atom's valence electrons are the outermost electrons. These are the electrons involved in chemical bonding. This means that, in chemical behaviour, the valence electrons of an atom are really the only electrons that matter.

In 1916, the American chemist Gilbert N. Lewis devised a system of representing the atoms of the elements based on the number of valence electrons they possess. This notation system uses each element symbol to represent the nucleus and all of the inner electrons of an atom (Lewis called this the "kernel" of an atom). It then surrounds that symbol with a series of dots representing that atom's valence electrons. These **electron dot diagrams** are called **Lewis structures**.

The notation is a simple and useful way to represent atoms and serves as a foundation to help us understand and predict chemical behaviours and compound structures without the need for sophisticated bonding theories. Our discussion of Lewis structures and diagrams will be confined to the representative or main group elements in the periodic table, that is, groups 1, 2, 13, 14, 15, 16, 17, and 18.

We will begin by discussing Lewis structures for individual atoms and ions, and then expand that discussion to include Lewis diagrams for molecular compounds and polyatomic ions.

Lewis Structures for Atoms

To write a Lewis structure for an atom, you need only determine the number of an atom's valence electrons. Recall from our discussion of the periodic table that this process is straightforward for the main group elements. For any period, beginning at the alkali metals, we see that atoms of this family have one valence electron. As we move across the period, each main group family has atoms with one additional valence electron up to the stable octet of four electron pairs present in each noble gas (except helium) (Table 2.2.1).

Table 2.2.1 *Valence Electrons in Main Group Atoms*

Main Group Number	1	2	13	14	15	16	17	18
Valence Electrons	1	2	3	4	5	6	7	8
Valence Electron Configuration	ns^1	ns^2	$ns^2 np^1$	$ns^2 np^2$	$ns^2 np^3$	$ns^2 np^4$	$ns^2 np^5$	$ns^2 np^6$

To write Lewis structures for the atoms, follow these steps:

1. Write the element symbol.
2. For hydrogen place a single dot next to the symbol. For helium place a pair of dots.
3. For 2nd period elements and beyond: for each valence electron present, place one dot around that symbol at one of the four positions of the compass: west, east, north, or south.
4. If more than four valence electrons are present, begin pairing the dots only after the four compass positions are filled.

The relative placement of the paired and unpaired dots is not as important as how many of each is present. Figure 2.2.1 shows the Lewis structures for the main group elements of the first three periods.

Group Number	1	2	13	14	15	16	17	18
	H·							He:
	Li·	Be·	B·	·C·	·N:	·O:	·F:	:Ne:
	Na·	Mg·	Al·	·Si·	·P:	·S:	·Cl:	:Ar:

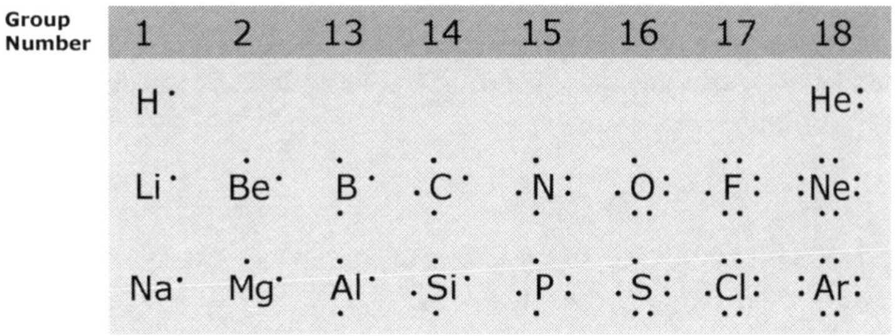

Figure 2.2.1 *Lewis structures for main group elements of the first three periods*

As you view Figure 2.2.1, consider the following important points:

1. As each element in a family has the same number of valence electrons, the Lewis structure for those elements has the same number of dots.
2. For the metals, the *total number of dots* represents the number of electrons that each atom loses when forming a cation.
3. In a correctly drawn Lewis structure for a non-metal, the number of *unpaired* dots shown represents either the number of electrons that atom *must gain* when forming an anion, or the number the electrons the atom *must share* to complete its octet when forming covalent bonds.

Lewis Structures for Monatomic Ions

From points 2 and 3 above, we can see that writing Lewis structures for monatomic ions is straightforward.

For the metals in groups 1, 2, and 13, the Lewis structure for their *stable ions* does not include any dots. The element symbol is usually enclosed in square brackets with the cation's charge written outside the brackets on the upper right. The magnitude of that positive charge simply equals the number of dots (which represent electrons) that were removed from the neutral atom's Lewis structure. Remember that because the number of protons in the nucleus has not changed, a loss of any number of electrons will result in that amount of positive charge on the cation.

For the non-metals in groups 15, 16, and 17, the Lewis structures for their anions all include four pairs of dots surrounding the element symbol enclosed in square brackets with the appropriate negative charge written outside the brackets on the upper right. The magnitude of the negative charge written outside the brackets equals the number of *unpaired* dots that were originally present in the parent atom's Lewis structure. This also equals how many electrons were required to generate the four pairs resulting in a stable octet.

The Lewis structures are shown for the sodium and chloride ions in Figure 2.2.2. Note that the chlorine atom originally had one unpaired dot. This required one electron for four pairs resulting in the charge of 1– on the anion. The sodium has had its one dot removed to form a 1+ cation.

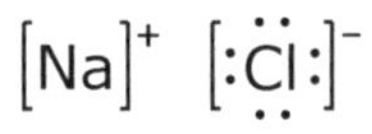

$[Na]^{+}$ $[:\ddot{\underset{..}{Cl}}:]^{-}$

Figure 2.2.2 *Lewis structures for sodium ions and chloride ions*

Quick Check

1. What do the "dots" in a Lewis structure for an atom or an ion represent?

   ____

2. What do the total number of dots present in the Lewis structures for the metals in groups 1, 2, and 13 tell us about the cations these atoms will form during a chemical change?

   ____

3. The Lewis structures for nitrogen, phosphorus, and antimony include one pair of dots and three unpaired dots. How many electrons do these atoms require to form a stable octet?

   ____

Sample Problem — Drawing Lewis Structures

Draw the Lewis structures for the representative elements belonging to period 4 of the periodic table.

What to Think about

1. Elements in the same chemical family have the same number of valence electrons.
2. Those electrons are represented by placing dots around each element symbol.
3. Consider Figure 6.4.1. Begin at group 1 and give potassium 1 valence electron. Continue to the right placing the same number of dots around each symbol in the same way that the dots appear for the other members of each group.

How to Do It

Group Number

1	2	13	14	15	16	17	18
K·	Ca·	Ga·	·Ge·	·As:	·Se:	:Br:	:Kr:

Practice Problems — Building Lewis Structures

1. Write the Lewis structures for the main group elements in period 5 of the periodic table.

2. Write the Lewis structures for the following atoms and ions.

   (a) Ba (b) Al^{3+} (c) Bi (d) I^- (e) Te

3. Convert the following atomic symbols to the Lewis structures for the ions of those elements:

   (a) Ca (b) Se (c) Ga (d) As

Lewis Structures for Molecules

Each of the pages in this book is a flat surface and any diagrams or images that you see on these pages can only be two-dimensional representations of the real three-dimensional world. Of course, the ionic and molecular compounds that make up that world are also three-dimensional. Understanding their shapes is a very important part of explaining and predicting their behaviour.

Recall that ionic compounds normally exist as ordered, three-dimensional arrays of cations and anions called crystal lattices. The arrangement of ions in these crystals maximizes the attractions between the oppositely charged ions within the lattices and minimizes the repulsions between ions with the same charges.

When molecules form, their three-dimensional shapes are also governed by the attractive and repulsive forces that exist within them. The first step toward visualizing the three-dimensional shape of a molecule is to convert its molecular formula into a two-dimensional Lewis structure.

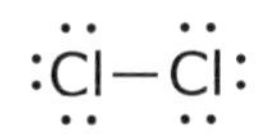

:Cl—Cl:

Figure 2.2.3 *Lewis structure of Cl_2*

One of the simplest examples of a Lewis structure is a diatomic halogen molecule such as Cl_2 (Figure 2.2.3). The single line between the atoms represents one pair of shared electrons. The other pairs of electrons are referred to as non-bonding or **lone pairs** of electrons. Note that all 14 of the valence electrons possessed by the 2 chlorine atoms are accounted for in the Lewis structure. Note also that each chlorine atom now has the benefit of an extra valence electron and thus has a stable octet.

As with any new procedure, learning to draw Lewis diagrams for molecules is easier if you follow a series of steps. Let's begin with a simple example: the Lewis structure for a molecule of nitrogen trichloride, NCl_3.

Step 1: Determine the total number of valence electrons in the molecule.
A correctly drawn Lewis structure must account for all of the valence electrons present. In this case, nitrogen has five valence electrons and each chlorine atom has seven. Therefore the total number of valence electrons is given by: $5 + (3 \times 7) = 26$.

Note that this is an even number, which will be true for all of the examples you will see. There are a few cases where odd numbers of electrons exist, but the vast majority of molecules (and polyatomic ions) possess even numbers of valence electrons. All bonding electrons exist in pairs.

Step 2: Construct the "skeleton" of the molecule using lines to indicate single covalent bonds between the atoms.

To generate the most likely skeleton of the molecule, the following set of guidelines will be of great help. The guidelines are based on numerous empirical observations and hold true for the vast majority of molecules. They also correspond to what we would expect given the electron configurations and electronegativities of the atoms involved. They may seem difficult to remember at first, but you won't need to use all of them for every molecule you draw. As with any new skill, the steps will become more familiar with practice.

Guidelines for Generating Molecule "Skeletons"

1. If the general formula for the compound is of the form "AX_n," then the central atom "A" will be the one with the lower group number, which also usually corresponds to the lower electronegativity. Obviously, if only two atoms exist in the molecule, then no central atom exists.
2. Hydrogen atoms form only one bond and so do not achieve an octet of electrons.
3. Fluorine atoms always form only one bond, and the other halogen atoms *usually* form only one bond. Exceptions to this occur if those halogens are central atoms and are bonded to other smaller halogens or to oxygen.
4. (a) Oxygen atoms normally form two bonds and don't often bond to each other in compounds with other elements. (An exception to this is hydrogen peroxide.)
   (b) Nitrogen atoms normally form three bonds.
   (c) Carbon atoms normally form four bonds.
5. Avoid creating rings or cyclic structures when you draw skeletons.

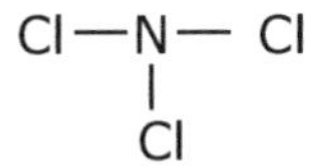

Figure 2.2.4 *Molecular skeleton for NCl_3*

Using the above rules, we see that a central atom exists and that nitrogen is most likely that central atom. We can therefore sketch the molecular skeleton for NCl_3 shown in Figure 2.2.4. The relative orientation of each chlorine atom around the nitrogen atom isn't that important because Lewis structures do not depict shape or 3-D geometry. All the matters at this stage is that nitrogen is in the centre and each chlorine atom is a peripheral or surrounding atom.

Step 3: Subtract the number of valence electrons used to construct the skeleton from the total number of valence electrons available from step 1 to determine the number of valence electrons remaining.

Consider that each line drawn in the skeleton represents a pair of bonding valence electrons, so, in this case, the number of valence electrons remaining is:
$26 - (3 \times 2) = 20$.

Step 4: Assume that all of the atoms in the molecule obey the octet rule (except hydrogen). Determine the number of additional valence electrons required (beyond those already present as a result of the bonds drawn) to give all of those atoms the required eight valence electrons.

In this case, because each peripheral chlorine atom has one bond and is therefore associated with two valence electrons, each chlorine atom needs six more electrons to complete its octet. The central nitrogen has three bonds and so has the benefit of six valence electrons. This means that the nitrogen atom needs only two more valence electrons to complete its octet. The calculation to determine the total number of required valence electrons is: $(3 \times 6) + 2 = 20$

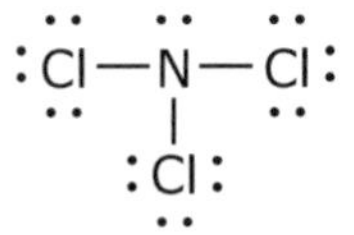

Figure 2.2.5 *Lewis structure for NCl_3*

Step 5: Compare the number of valence electrons available (from step 3) to the number of valence electrons needed to complete the octets of the atoms (from step 4). If those two numbers match, pair up the electrons. Beginning with the peripheral atoms and ending with the central atom, place those electron pairs where they're needed to satisfy the octets. In this case, the two numbers do indeed match and so the resulting Lewis structure is shown in Figure 2.2.5. If the numbers don't match, there is a procedure we'll discuss later.

At this point, consider the following:

Criteria Governing the Octet Rule in a Lewis Structure

(a) A peripheral or surrounding atom must not violate the octet rule in a Lewis structure. If an atom does violate the octet rule, then it must be a central atom in the molecule. This doesn't apply to hydrogen, which is associated with only two electrons in molecules.

(b) ***Exception (i)*** Atoms belonging to the second period in the periodic table will not have expanded octets in Lewis structures. An expanded octet (more than eight valence electrons) is only possible for elements belonging to the 3rd period or higher because only those atoms have access to d orbital electrons. These electrons are unavailable below the third energy level.
Exception (ii) The atoms Be, B, and Al will often have incomplete octets such that only two or three pairs of valence electrons will be associated with these central atoms in Lewis structures for molecules.

Step 6: If the numbers in step 5 above agree, then as a final step, check that the total number of valence electrons represented in the diagram matches the total number of valence electrons you began with in step 1.

In this example, the number of valence electrons in the diagram matches the number in the molecule.

Quick Check

1. Suggest a reason why the elements Be, B, and Al are not able to achieve a valence octet when they form covalent compounds.

   ____

2. Hydrogen sulfide, H_2S, is a poisonous, foul-smelling, and flammable gas. Why is the molecular skeleton "S – H – H" incorrect for this molecule?

   ____

3. Determine the total number of valence electrons present in each of the following molecules:
   (a) H_2Se _____ (b) CCl_4 _____ (c) NF_3 _____ (d) PCl_5 _____ (e) SF_6 _____

Sample Problem — Drawing a Lewis Structure for a Molecule

Draw the Lewis structure for a molecule of water, H_2O.

What to Think about	How to Do It
1. Each hydrogen atom will form one bond and the oxygen will form two. The oxygen must therefore be the central atom even though it has a higher electronegativity than hydrogen. Oxygen has six valence electrons and hydrogen has one.	
2. Use the steps listed above:	
Step 1: Determine the total number of valence electrons in the molecule.	$6 + (2 \times 1) = 8$ valence electrons present in molecule
Step 2: Construct the "skeleton" of the molecule.	H – O – H
Step 3: Determine the number of valence electrons remaining.	Electrons available: 8 Electrons used in skeleton: 4 Electrons remaining: $8 - 4 = 4$
Step 4: Assume that all of the atoms in the molecule obey the octet rule (except hydrogen).	Electrons required to complete oxygen's octet: 4
Step 5: Compare the number of valence electrons available to the number of valence electrons needed to complete the octets of the atoms. Pair up remaining electrons and place them where needed to satisfy oxygen's octet.	
Step 6: Available electrons match electrons in the diagram. Note that in the final structure, oxygen is associated with two bonding pairs and two non-bonding (or lone pairs).	H—$\ddot{\underset{\cdot\cdot}{O}}$—H

Practice Problems – Drawing Lewis Structures for Molecules

1. Construct the Lewis structure for a molecule of carbon tetrachloride, CCl_4.

2. (a) Draw the Lewis structure for a molecule of ammonia, NH_3.

   (b) When you're finished drawing the structure, determine how many bonding pairs and how many lone pairs of electrons are associated with the central atom.

3. (a) Draw the Lewis structure for a molecule of boron trichloride, BCl_3.

   (b) Consider the central atom in your structure. Does it possess a stable octet of eight electrons?

Drawing Lewis Structures for Molecules Containing Multiple Bonds

We have seen that one pair of valence electrons shared between two adjacent nuclei constitutes a single covalent bond. There are also many cases where the covalent bonds between two atoms involve more than one pair of shared electrons. These are known as **multiple bonds.** If two pairs of electrons are shared between the same two atoms, the bond is called a double bond and if three pairs exist, the bond is a triple bond.

As you might expect, as multiple bonds involve more attractive forces between two atoms than single bonds do, multiple bonds are stronger. Bond strengths are usually measured by the amount of energy required to break a mole of those bonds and are thus represented by the unit kJ/mol. The greater attraction between the atoms in a multiple bond also draws those bonded atoms closer together, which means that multiple bonds are also shorter than single bonds. Table 2.2.2 compares some single and multiple bond strengths and lengths.

Table 2.2.2 *Single and Multiple Bond Strengths and Lengths*

Bond	Bond Energy (kJ/mol)	Bond Length (pm)
C – C	347	154
C = C	614	134
C ≡ C	839	120
N – N	160	145
N = N	418	125
N ≡ N	941	110
C – O	358	143
C = O	799	123
C ≡ O	1072	113

Let's follow the steps outlined above to draw the Lewis structure for a molecule that contains double bonds, such as carbon dioxide, CO_2.

Step 1: The total number of valence electrons is given by: $4 + (2 \times 6) = 16$

Step 2: Carbon has the lower group number and electronegativity, and oxygen doesn't usually bond to itself in compounds with other elements. Therefore the following skeleton is likely:

O – C – O

Step 3: As four electrons were used to construct the above skeleton, 12 of the original 16 electrons remain to complete each atom's octet.

Step 4: Each of the oxygens in the skeleton requires six electrons and the carbon atom requires four electrons to complete their valence shells. This gives a total of:
$(2 \times 6) + 4 = 16$ electrons.

Step 5: Notice that 16 electrons are required but only 12 electrons are available to complete the octets of the atoms. We are therefore lacking four electrons. This means that we must return to step 2 and re-draw the molecular skeleton such that we incorporate one *multiple bond* for each pair of electrons that we lack to complete the octets._

Because we are four electrons short, we can consider either of the following modified skeletons:

skeleton 1: **O = C = O** or skeleton 2: **O ≡ C – O**

Although both skeletons above show carbon forming a total of 4 bonds, as oxygen normally forms two bonds, we would choose skeleton 1, showing each oxygen atom participating in a double bond as being the most likely skeleton. Note also the symmetry associated with this choice as opposed to skeleton 2. Molecules will often possess a high degree of symmetry and that also makes this choice more likely: **O = C = O**

Now we again return to following the steps:

Step 3: Each line in the skeleton represents a pair of shared electrons, so each double bond indicates two electron pairs or four electrons. Therefore eight electrons have been used in constructing the skeleton, so the number of electrons remaining is given by: $16 - (2 \times 4) = 8$

Step 4: The two oxygen atoms each need four more electrons to complete their octets, but the carbon atom now has the benefit of eight valence electrons and so requires no more. This means that only eight electrons are needed to complete the octets of the atoms in the skeleton.

Step 5: As the number of electrons we need now matches the number available, we pair up those electrons to give the Lewis structure for carbon dioxide. Figure 2.2.6 shows two possible ways of representing that structure.

:Ö=C=Ö: :Ö::C::Ö:

Figure 2.2.6 *Lewis structures for* CO_2

As a final step we see that all 16 valence electrons have been accounted for in the Lewis structure. The construction of this molecule can be understood by considering how the valence electrons present in each individual atom are reorganized as the two double bonds form:

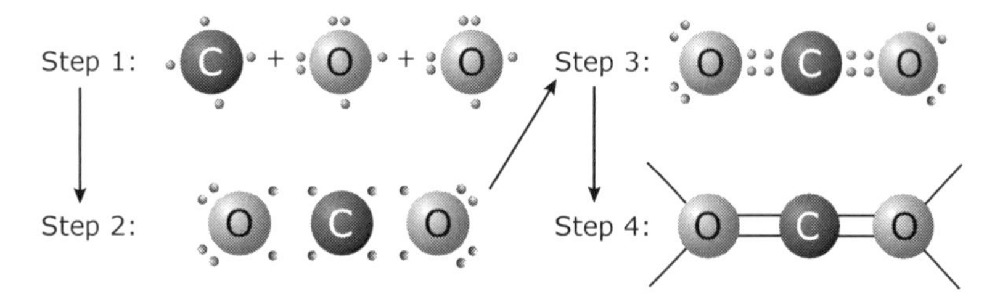

Figure 2.2.7 *Constructing the molecule from the Lewis structures*

Drawing Lewis Structures Containing Atoms With Expanded Octets

Sometimes we discover that fewer electrons are available than needed to complete the octets of the atoms in a molecule. At other times, we might encounter situations where more electrons are available than needed. This normally results in **expanded octets** associated with the central atom in a Lewis structure. Remember that an expanded octet is only possible for an atom if d orbital electrons are available. That is only possible for elements belonging to period 4 or higher in the periodic table.

Let's investigate this by drawing the Lewis structure for one of the few compounds involving noble gases, namely XeF_4. To do this, we follow the steps below:

F
|
F — Xe — F
|
F

Figure 2.2.8 *Molecular skeleton for XeF4*

Step 1: Total number of valence electrons = 8 + (4 × 7) = 36

Step 2: Molecular skeleton: See Figure 6.5.8.

Step 3: Electrons used in skeleton: 4 × 2 = 8
Electrons remaining: 36 – 8 = 28

Step 4: Electrons required to complete octets: 4 × 6 = 24

Note that xenon needs no electrons but each fluorine atom needs six electrons to complete its octet.

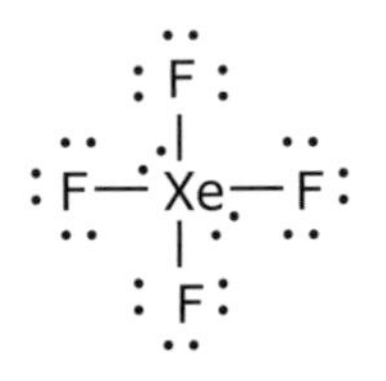

Figure 2.2.9 *Lewis structure for XeF_4*

Step 5: We have 28 electrons available but only need 24. At this point, we first place the 24 electrons where they're needed in pairs around each peripheral fluorine atom. We then place the remaining two pairs of electrons around the central xenon. The orientation of the lone pairs on the central atom is not important. Simply placing two pairs at any two locations available on xenon is all that matters. Note that xenon has an "expanded octet" of 12 valence electrons.

Step 6: All 36 valence electrons are accounted for in the Lewis structure (Figure 2.7.9).

Sample Problem — Drawing a Lewis Structure Containing a Multiple Bond

Draw the Lewis structure for a molecule of hydrogen cyanide, HCN.

What to Think about	How to Do It
1. Calculate the total valence electrons present in the molecule.	Total of 10 valence electrons available
2. Determine the most likely molecular skeleton.	H – C – N
3. Determine electrons used in skeleton and those remaining.	4 electrons used to construct the skeleton, 6 electrons remaining.
4. Determine electrons needed to complete octets.	The carbon needs 4 more electrons and the nitrogen needs 6 to complete their respective octets.
5. Compare the number of valence electrons available to the number of valence electrons needed to complete the octets of the atoms.	Only 6 electrons are left: 4 electrons short
6. The original skeleton must be changed to incorporate multiple bonds.	
7. Hydrogen only forms one bond and so cannot be the central atom. The two extra bonds must be added between the nitrogen and carbon atoms in the form of a triple bond. Of the remaining two atoms, carbon has the lower group number and electronegativity. Carbon is therefore the most likely central atom. Carbon normally forms four bonds and nitrogen forms three.	H – C ≡ N
8. We see that 8 valence electrons (4 × 2) have been used in this new skeleton, leaving only 2 of the original 10. Pair up those final 2 electrons and place them on nitrogen. As carbon's octet is now satisfied and nitrogen only needs 2 more electrons, the number of available electrons matches the number required.	H—C≡N:
9. A final check shows us that all 10 valence electrons are accounted for.	

Practice Problems – Lewis Structures Containing Multiple Bonds and Expanded Octets

1. Formaldehyde is used as a disinfectant, an embalming agent, and as a component in many organic synthesis reactions. Draw the Lewis structure for a molecule of formaldehyde, CH_2O. (Hint: Carbon is the central atom.)

2. Carbon monoxide is an invisible, odorless, and toxic gas that renders hemoglobin unable to transport oxygen to body tissues. Draw the Lewis structure for a molecule of CO.

3. Bromine trifluoride is a very reactive and toxic liquid that explodes on contact with water and organic compounds. Draw the Lewis structure for a molecule of BrF_3.

Drawing Lewis Structures for Polyatomic Ions

Many polyatomic ions contain non-metal atoms bonded covalently to each other. To draw a Lewis diagram for a polyatomic ion, we follow the same steps discussed above but must be careful to count the correct number of valence electrons present when we begin. Remember that the magnitude of the charge on a cation equals the number of valence electrons *removed* from the original neutral species. The amount of negative charge on an anion represents the number of electrons *added*.

Consider the ammonium cation, NH_4^+. The positive charge tells us that one valence electron has been removed from the total number of valence electrons possessed by the five neutral atoms. To begin this Lewis structure, we therefore count a total of $5 + (4 \times 1) - 1 = 8$ valence electrons. Following the above steps, we eventually arrive at the Lewis structure in in Figure 2.2.10. We normally enclose Lewis structures for both monatomic and polyatomic ions in square brackets, as shown.

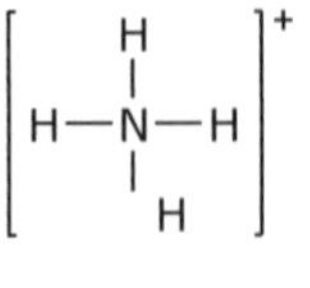

Figure 2.2.10 *Lewis structure for the ammonium cation, NH_4^+*

The Curious Case of Resonance

When a molecule or ion contains double bonds next to single bonds, there are often several different and equally correct Lewis structures that we can draw. Consider the case of the carbonate anion, CO_3^{2-}. This ion has a total of: $4 + (3 \times 6) + 2 = 24$ valence electrons. (Note the extra two electrons due to the charge.)

Following the steps learned earlier, we realize that we are short two electrons when completing the octets of all the atoms. We therefore incorporate one double bond into the skeleton. The final Lewis structure therefore becomes the one shown in Figure 2.2.11.

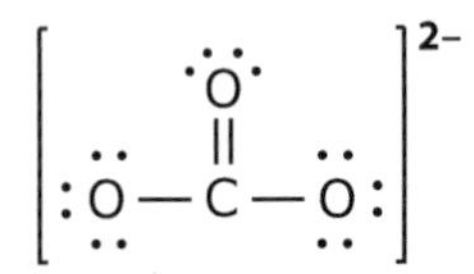

Figure 2.2.11 *Lewis structure for the carbonate anion, CO_3^{2-}*

If this represented the actual structure, we would expect that the two single carbon – oxygen bonds would prove to be longer and weaker than the double bond. Experimental data indicates, however, that all three bonds are equal in strength and length. They appear to be stronger than a single C – O bond, but weaker than a double bond. They are also slightly shorter than a single bond, but slightly longer than a double bond. It is as if the two electrons in the multiple bond have been shared equally or "averaged" between the central carbon and each of the three oxygen atoms.

Chemists call these electrons "delocalized" because they're not associated with any one pair of bonded atoms, but are rather "spread out" equally between all three pairs. Lewis structures cannot properly show delocalized electrons. They represent this phenomenon by depicting the double bond in each of the possible locations in a series of diagrams and connecting each diagram with a set of double arrows. The diagrams are called **resonance structures**. It must be emphasized, however, that the pair of electrons *does not* move around between pairs of atoms as the diagrams might suggest. The three diagrams in Figure 2.2.12 are simply the only way to depict delocalized bonding electrons using Lewis structures. The phenomenon of resonance is evident in an important organic compound called benzene.

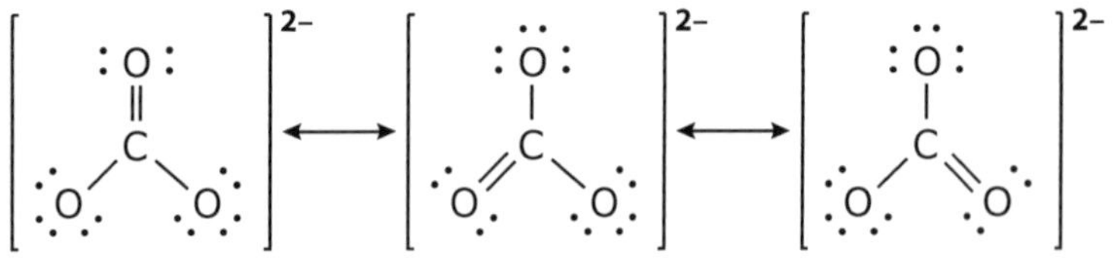

Figure 2.2.12 *Resonance structures for a carbonate ion*

Lewis Structures for Molecules with More than One Central Atom

Molecules and ions can be much more complicated than we have discussed above. Lewis structures are not often used to depict such species, but we can still employ the process when several central atoms exist in relatively simple molecules and ions. In these examples, you will be given the basic skeleton and can then proceed with the remaining steps to generate the correct Lewis structure.

Consider a simple organic acid called formic acid whose formula is CH_2O_2 (or HCOOH). Recall that carbon, oxygen, and hydrogen normally form four bonds, two bonds, and one bond respectively. In Figure 2.2.13, note that both a carbon atom and an oxygen atom are between other atoms in different locations in the structure.

You should now be able to complete the diagram following the remaining steps. The final Lewis structure you arrive at should be the one shown in Figure 2.2.14. You will encounter many such molecules when discussing organic chemistry.

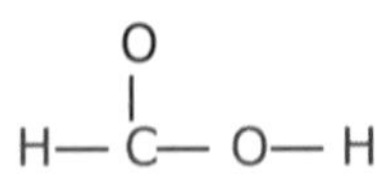

Figure 2.2.13 *Skeleton for formic acid, CH_2O_2 (or HCOOH)*

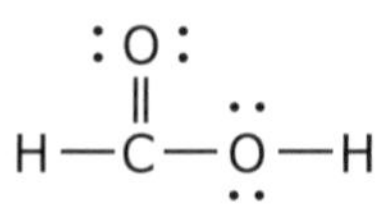

Figure 2.2.14 *Lewis structure for formic acid, CH_2O_2 (or HCOOH)*

2.2 Activity: Making the Leap to Three Dimensions

Question

How can we use Lewis structures to predict the three-dimensional shapes of molecules or polyatomic ions?

Materials

modelling clay
Popsicle® sticks or wooden splints

Procedure

1. Consider the Lewis structures discussed in this section: NCl_3, H_2O, CO_2, NH_4^+, XeF_4, and CO_3^{2-}. Review each as you fill in the following table. The first one is done for you.

1. Chemical Formula	2. Number of Atoms Bonded to Central Atom	3. Number of Lone Pairs on Central Atom	4. Sum of Columns 2 and 3
NCl_3	3	1	3 + 1 = 4
H_2O			
CO_2			
NH_4^+			
XeF_4			
CO_3^{2-}			

2. Obtain some modeling clay and wooden splints or Popsicle® sticks. Using the clay, make a small sphere about the size of a lemon. This will represent the central atom in each of the above species.

   In any chemical species, each pair of bonding or lone pair of electrons represents regions of negative charge. It follows, then, that when these are attached to a central atom in a molecule or polyatomic ion, they will attempt to minimize the repulsive forces between them. They accomplish this by assuming positions in three-dimensional space around the central atom such that they are as far away from each other as possible, while still remaining bonded to that central atom.

3. To represent this, consider each molecule and ion listed above. Look at the total number in column 4 for each species and select that number of sticks. Now insert them into the clay such that they are all as far away from each other as possible in three-dimensional space.

Continued

4. Sketch the shapes that you construct for each species in the appropriate space in the table below.

Chemical Formula	Sketch of 3-D Shape
NCl_3	
H_2O	
CO_2	
NH_4^+	
XeF_4	
CO_3^{2-}	

5. Are all of the shapes different? If not, which ones look similar? How do the numbers in column 4 compare for those shapes that might look similar?

2.2 Review Questions

1. Consider the following list of elements. Place each in the appropriate column in the table below depending on whether it obeys the octet rule, likely has an incomplete octet, or could potentially have an expanded octet in a Lewis structure.

   H, Be, B, C, N, O, F, Al, Si, P, S, Cl

Incomplete Valence Octet	Valence Octet	Expanded Valence Octet

2. Helium and neon are in the same chemical family but yet have different numbers of dots in their Lewis structures. What is the reason for this? Explain why neither element ever forms chemical compounds.

3. Consider the following pairs of elements in the table below. If each pair was part of a molecule or polyatomic ion, which of the two would most likely be the central atom and which would be the peripheral or surrounding atom? Place each element of each pair in the appropriate column in the table.

4. The molecule tetrafluoroethene is a building block of the synthetic material known as Teflon®. Tetrafluoroethene has the formula C_2F_4. Consider the following molecular skeletons for this molecule. Complete the Lewis structure for the most likely skeleton.

   F₂C—C(=F)F skeleton: F and F bonded to C, C—C, second C double-bonded to F and single-bonded to F

   F₂C=CF₂ skeleton: F and F bonded to C, C=C, second C bonded to F and F

   F₂C=F skeleton: F and F bonded to C, C=F, F bonded to C and F

5. Draw Lewis structures for each of the following molecules in the space provided.

   OF_2

   H_2S

Element Pair	Probable Central Atom	Probable Peripheral Atom
(a) phosphorus and chlorine		
(b) nitrogen and oxygen		
(c) carbon and sulfur		
(d) nitrogen and hydrogen		
(e) oxygen and fluorine		

PCl_3

CCl_2F_2

6. Draw Lewis structures for each of the polyatomic ions in the space provided.

OH^-

AlH_4^-

CN^-

7. Draw Lewis structures for each of the following. Each central atom in the molecules or ions has an expanded octet.

SF_6

PCl_5

ICl_4^-

$SeBr_4$

8. Draw Lewis structures for each of the following containing multiple bonds.

CS_2

SCO (C is central)

O_3 (Draw two resonance structures)

NO_3^- (Draw three resonance structures)

9. Convert the following molecular skeletons into complete Lewis structures.

H—C—C—H

H—O—O—H

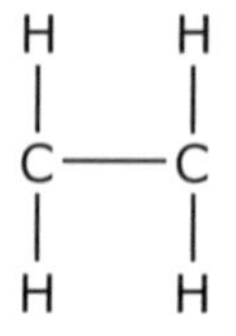

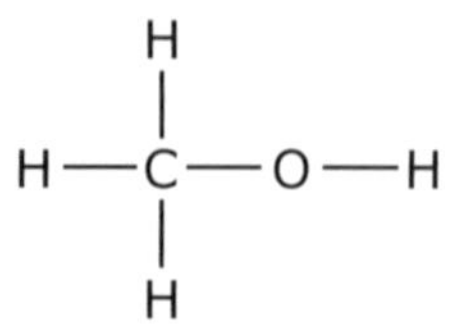

```
H   H
|   |
C———C
|   |
H   H
```

```
    H
    |
H———C———O———H
    |
    H
```

2.3 The Shape and Behaviour of Molecules

Warm Up

1. What does an element's electronegativity tell us?

   ____

2. Use your answer to question 1 to define the term "polar covalent bond."

   ____

3. If a substance contains polar *molecules*, how might that affect its melting and boiling points?

   ____

Converting Lewis Structures into Three Dimensions — VSEPR Theory

Drawing Lewis structures serves an important purpose beyond indicating connectivity of atoms in molecules and polyatomic ions. The two-dimensional collections of symbols, lines, and dots often allow us to deduce the three-dimensional shapes of the chemical species they represent. Determining the shapes of those chemical species is an essential part of understanding and predicting their physical and chemical behaviour.

The process of inferring a three-dimensional shape from a Lewis structure is based on a very simple premise: Valence electrons represent regions of negative charge that repel each other.

> Any group of valence electrons associated with a central atom will tend to orient themselves in three-dimensional space around that atom so as to minimize the repulsion between them. Examples of such groups of valence electrons include a lone pair, bonding pair, or multiple pairs involved in a double or triple bond.

In short, while remaining attached to the central atom, these groups of electrons will position themselves as far away from each other as possible. This is the fundamental principle behind the **valence shell electron pair repulsion (VSEPR) theory,** which chemists use whenever they convert Lewis structures into molecular shapes.

Let's imagine a central atom in three-dimensional space and apply the above principle to distribute two, three, four, five, and six electron groups around that centre. When we do, we discover that a different spatial arrangement results for each number of electron groups. Each arrangement minimizes the repulsive forces between the groups by occupying the maximum amount of space around the central atom.

We can show these five arrangements using balloons attached together to represent the electron groups. Just as the balloons will fill up all the available space around their centre of attachment, so too will electron groups fill up the available space around a central atom (Figure 2.3.1).

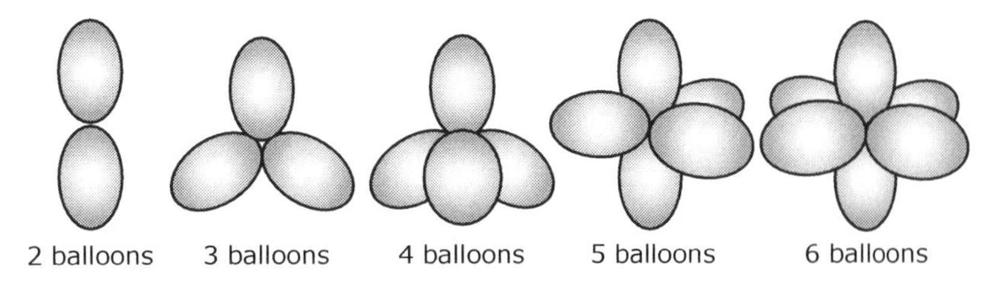

Figure 2.3.1 *Balloons in different arrangements around a central attachment*

If the electron groups are *bonding electrons*, then the peripheral atoms they bind to the central atom adopt that same arrangement and produce a *molecular shape*.

Several experimental tools exist that allow us to determine molecular geometry. X-ray crystallography as well as neutron and electron diffraction are employed for compounds in the solid phase. For molecules in the gaseous phase, gas electron diffraction is used.

Electron groups and their repulsive effects ultimately determine where and how the nuclei of the atoms in a molecule or polyatomic ion arrange themselves in three-dimensional space. And it's the resulting *shapes of those species* that we really care about.

We will consider each of the five electron group arrangements separately. Let's begin by assuming that each electron group is a bonding group connecting the central atom (with single or multiple bonds) to the peripheral atoms. We'll then expand our discussion to include lone-pair electron groups on the central atom. As a general notation, the central atom is "**A**," a peripheral or surrounding atom is "**X**," and a lone-pair of electrons on the central atom is "**E**."

Two-Bonding Electron Groups: AX_2

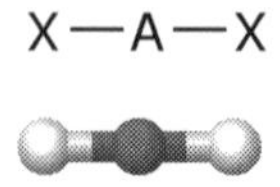

X—A—X

Figure 2.3.2 *The shape of two-bonding electron groups is linear.*

When two groups of bonding electrons connect the central atom to two peripheral atoms, the notation "AX_2" applies. The surrounding atoms are as far as possible from each other on opposite sides of the central atom. The shape is *linear* with the X–A–X bond angle being 180° (Figure 2.3.2).

The shape is the same whether the two-bonding groups are the shared electrons in two single bonds, two double bonds, or a single and a triple bond. For example, consider the following three molecules. Note that all are AX_2 molecules with the same linear shape and that any lone-pairs attached to the surrounding atoms do not affect their orientation around the central atom.

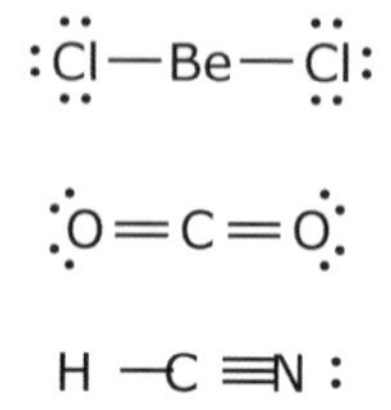

:Cl—Be—Cl:

:O=C=O:

H—C≡N:

Figure 2.3.3 *AX_2 molecules have the same linear shape whether the shared electrons form two single bonds, two double bonds, or a single and a triple bond.*

Three-Electron Groups: AX_3 and AX_2E

When three groups of electrons orient around a central atom, two shapes are possible. If all the electron groups are bonding, then an AX_3 arrangement gives rise to a *trigonal planar* (or flat triangle) molecule with X–A–X bond angles of 120°. The bonding electron group interactions are called "*bond-pair – bond-pair*" (BP-BP) interactions.

If one of the three electron groups is a lone-pair rather than a bonding pair, we use the notation **AX_2E**. The molecule that we see is *bent* or *angular* with the lone-pair occupying one of the three corners of the triangle. As lone-pair electrons are attracted to only one atomic nucleus, they are held less tightly than bonding electron groups. Their electron clouds therefore occupy more space and exert more repulsive force on bonding electron groups than those groups exert on each other. These more intense "*lone-pair – bond-pair*" (LP-BP) interactions force the bonded atoms closer together in an AX_2E molecule and so reduce the X–A–X bond angle to less than 120°.

Similar to lone-pairs, we would also expect that larger peripheral atoms would exert *more repulsive forces* than smaller ones, and thus affect bond angles in a molecule. In Table 2.3.1, a solid triangle represents an atom or lone electron pair projecting out of the page, while a dashed line means the atom or lone-pair goes into the page.

Table 2.3.1 *Shapes of Three-Electron Groups: AX_3 and AX_2E*

AX_mE_n Notation	Molecular Shape	Sample Lewis Structure
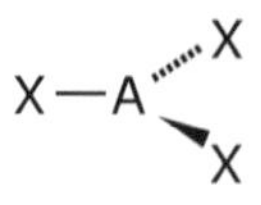 AX_3	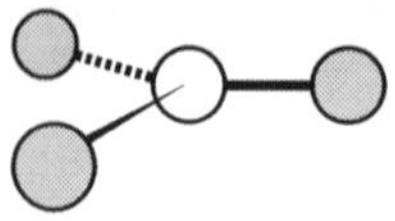 trigonal planar	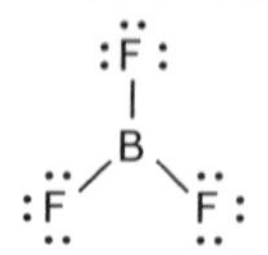 boron trifluoride
 AX_2E	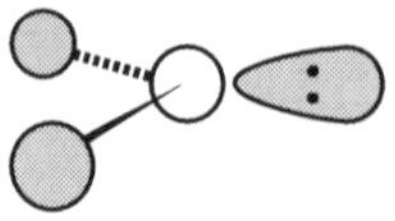 bent or angular	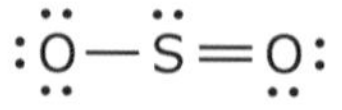 :O—S=O: sulfur dioxide (1of 2 resonance structures)

Four-Electron Groups: AX_4, AX_3E, and AX_2E_2

Four electron groups will occupy the four corners of a regular tetrahedron and may result in three different molecular shapes. If all the electron groups are bonding, then the molecule is labeled as $\mathbf{AX_4}$ and adopts a tetrahedral (four-sided or four-faced) shape with each of the X–A–X bond angles at 109.5°. An example of this is methane gas, CH_4.

If one of the four electron groups is non-bonding, the molecule is considered $\mathbf{AX_3E}$ and the lone-pair occupies one of the four corners of the tetrahedron. The molecule we see is called a trigonal pyramid. Once again, the more intense LP-BP interactions will push the bonded atoms closer together than they would be in an AX_4 molecule. Evidence of this is seen in an AX_3E molecule such as ammonia in which the H–N–H bond angles are only 107° rather than 109.5°.

When two of the four groups of electrons are lone-pairs, the designation $\mathbf{AX_2E_2}$ applies. Two of the four corners will be occupied by the two bonded atoms and the remaining two corners by the lone-pairs. The molecule will be an angular shape similar to AX_2E, although the X–A–X bond angle will be smaller. In such an arrangement, not only will each of the two lone-pairs force the bonded atoms closer together via LP-BP interactions, but they will also exert a repulsive force on each other called a *lone-pair – lone-pair* (LP-LP) interaction. This is the most intense of the electron group repulsive interactions. The combined result of the additional repulsive forces is an even smaller X–A–X bond angle. In water, for example, the H–O–H bond angle is found to be only 104.5°. Table 2.3.2 below shows the molecular shapes of four-electron groups.

Table 2.3.2 *Shapes of Four-Electron Groups: AX_4, AX_3E, and AX_2E_2*

AX_mE_n Notation	Molecular Shape	Sample Lewis Structure
AX_4	tetrahedral	methane
AX_3E	trigonal pyramidal	ammonia
AX_2E_2	bent or angular	water

Five-Electron Groups: AX_5, AX_4E, AX_3E_2, and AX_2E_3

If more than four electron groups surround a central atom, that atom will have an expanded octet so it must belong to period 3 or higher in the periodic table. Expanded octets are only possible if d orbitals are available and none exist below the third energy level.

When five electron groups are present, two distinct sets of positions are occupied by those groups. One set of three positions lies in a trigonal plane, and the electron groups are referred to as *equatorial groups*. A second set of two positions places each group of electrons above and below the trigonal plane. These are called *axial groups*. The equatorial electron groups are separated by 120° bond angles, and the axial and equatorial groups are separated by 90°. Once again, LP-BP and LP-LP interactions play a role in reducing X–A–X bond angles as the number of lone-pairs attached to the central atom increases. Table 2.3.3 shows the molecular shapes of five-electron group systems.

Table 2.3.3 *Shapes of Five-Electron Groups: AX_5, AX_4E, AX_3E_2, and AX_2E_3*

AX_mE_n Notation	Molecular Shape	Sample Lewis Structure
AX_5	trigonal bipyramidal	phosphorus pentachloride
AX_4E	seesaw	sulfur tetrafluoride
AX_3E_2	T-Shaped	chlorine trifluoride
AX_2E_3	linear	xenon difluoride

Six-Electron Groups: AX_6, AX_5E, and AX_4E_2

The final major electron group arrangement has six electron groups around the central atom. Unlike the five-electron group system, all six vertices are equivalent and point towards the corners of an octahedron as shown in Table 2.3.4.

If all of the electron groups are bonding, then the molecule is labeled as $\mathbf{AX_6}$. The shape adopted by the molecule is octahedral (eight-faced) and all of the X–A–X bond angles are 90°.

When one of the six-electron groups is a non-bonding pair, it doesn't matter which of the six locations that lone-pair occupies around the central atom because all locations are identical. The molecule is classified as $\mathbf{AX_5E}$ and the molecular shape is square pyramidal. The lone pair is directed downward at the bottom centre of the four-based pyramid as Table 2.3.4 shows.

If two of the six-electron groups are lone-pairs, there are two orientations available in an octahedral shape. They could lie adjacent to each other with a separation of 90°, or lie opposite each other separated by 180°. As the diagram shows below, the two lone-pairs will always be as far away from each other as possible and separated by 180°. This minimizes the significant LP-LP repulsive interaction between them.

Table 2.3.4 *Shapes of Six-Electron Groups: AX_6, AX_5E, and AX_4E_2*

AX_mE_n Notation	Molecular Shape	Sample Lewis Structure
 AX_6	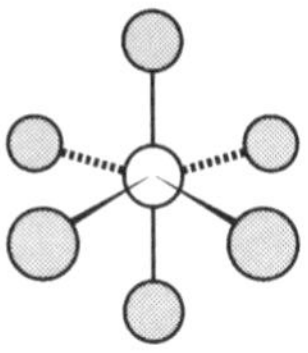 octahedral	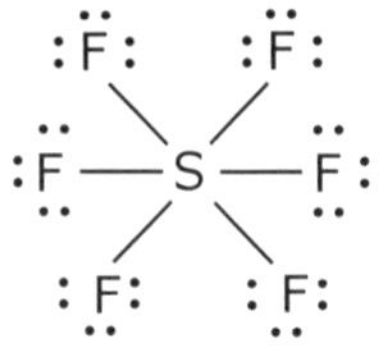 sulfur hexafluoride
 AX_5E	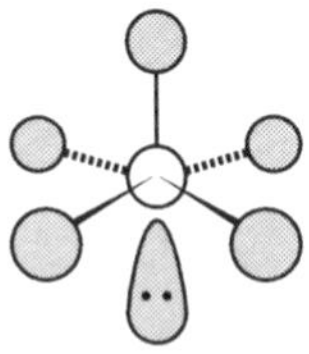 square pyramidal	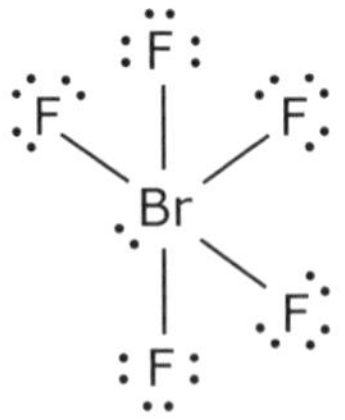 bromine pentafluoride
 AX_4E_2	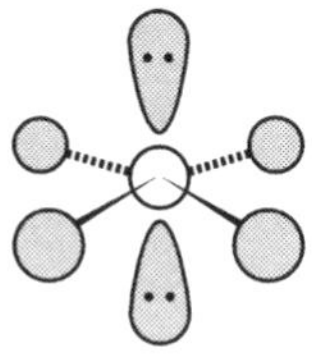 square planar	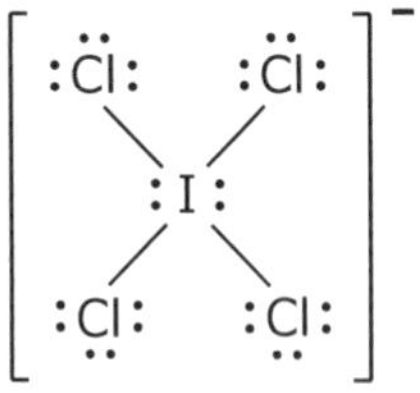 tetrachloroiodate ion

Quick Check

1. What is the fundamental principle associated with VSEPR Theory?

   ____

2. Consider the electron group interactions: LP-BP, BP-BP, and LP-LP. Arrange these in order from least intense to most intense.

   ____

3. Although methane, ammonia, and water each have four electron groups associated with the central atom, the bond angles between the atoms in each molecule are 109.5°, 107°, and 104.5° respectively. Explain why.

   ____

Molecular Formulas to Molecular Shapes

We are now in a position to combine the information from this and the previous section to predict molecular shapes starting with a molecular formula. The steps will guide you through this process:

Step 1: Beginning with the formula, determine the Lewis structure.

Step 2: Consider the central atom in the completed Lewis structure. Note the number of bonded atoms and lone pairs associated with that atom.

Step 3: Assign an AX_mE_n notation to the molecule or polyatomic ion. (Note any bond angles affected by the presence of one or more lone pairs.)

Step 4: Refer to the appropriate electron group arrangement category given in the tables above to determine the shape of the molecule.

(You're done!)

Sample Problem – Deducing a Molecular Shape

Determine the shape of the molecule tellurium tetrachloride, $TeCl_4$

What to Think about	How to Do It
1. Refer to the steps listed in section 2.1 to determine the Lewis structure for the molecule.	
2. Tellurium has the lower electronegativity and so is the central atom. All of the chlorine atoms will therefore obey the octet rule and form only one bond. Note that tellurium is a member of the 5th period in the periodic table and is therefore capable of having an expanded octet.	:Cl: — Te(:) — Cl: with Cl above and below (Lewis structure of $TeCl_4$)
3. There are five electron groups around the central atom. Four are bonding groups and one is a lone-pair of electrons. The molecule is therefore classified as AX_4E. An AX_4E molecule will have a "seesaw" shape.	

Practice Problems

1. Complete the following table for each of the chemical species.

Lewis Structure	AX_mE_n Notation	Molecular Shape (Name and Diagram)
(a) SOF_4 Lewis structure: O double-bonded to S; four F single-bonded to S		
(b) XeF_4 Lewis structure: four F single-bonded to Xe; two lone pairs on Xe		

2. Complete the following table for each of the chemical species.

Chemical Formula	Lewis Structure	AX_mE_n Notation	Molecular Shape (Name and Diagram)
(a) CCl_4			
(b) PF_3			
(c) SCl_2			

From Polar Bonds to Polar Molecules

Below is a table of electronegativity values.

Increasing EN →

H 2.1																	He
Li 1.0	Be 1.5											B 2.0	C 2.5	N 3.0	O 3.5	F 4.0	Ne
Na 0.9	Mg 1.2											Al 1.5	Si 1.8	P 2.1	S 2.5	Cl 3.0	Ar
K 0.8	Ca 1.0	Sc 1.3	Ti 1.5	V 1.6	Cr 1.6	Mn 1.5	Fe 1.8	Co 1.8	Ni 1.8	Cu 1.9	Zn 1.6	Ga 1.6	Ge 1.8	As 2.0	Se 2.4	Br 2.8	Kr
Rb 0.8	Sr 1.0	Y 1.3	Zr 1.4	Nb 1.6	Mo 1.8	Tc	Ru 2.2	Rh 2.2	Pd 2.2	Ag 1.9	Cd 1.7	In 1.7	Sn 1.8	Sb 1.9	Te 2.1	I 2.5	Xe
Cs 0.7	Ba 0.9	La 1.1	Hf 1.3	Ta 1.5	W 1.7	Re 1.9	Os 2.2	Ir 2.2	Pt 2.2	Au 2.4	Hg 1.9	Tl 1.8	Pb 1.8	Bi 1.9	Po 2.0	At 2.2	Rn
Fr 0.7	Ra 0.9	Ac 1.1															

Increasing EN ↑

Ce 1.1	Pr 1,1	Nd 1.2	Pm	Sm 1.2	Eu 1.2	Gd 1.1	Tb 1.2	Dy 1.2	Ho 1.2	Er 1.2	Tm 1.2	Yb 1.1	Lu 1.2
Th 1.3	Pa 1.5	U 1.7											

Figure 2.3.4 *Periodic table showing electronegativity values*

As stated at the beginning of this section, an essential part of understanding and predicting the chemical and physical properties of substances is determining the shapes of their molecules. Among the most *significant consequences* of molecular shape is the *polarity of molecules.*

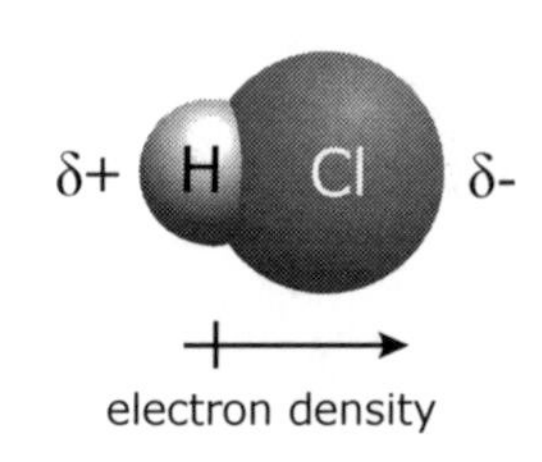

Figure 2.3.5 *HCl is a diatomic molecule containing a polar bond.*

Molecular polarity not only affects physical properties such as melting point, boiling point, and solubility, but also influences a substance's chemical reactivity in both synthetic and biological processes.

Recall that a chemical bond is considered to be polar if electron-sharing in the bond is unequal enough due to the electronegativity differences of the atoms involved. If a diatomic molecule contains a polar bond, then the *molecule itself* must also be polar, as in a compound such as HCl (Figure 2.3.5).

However, if a molecule contains *more than two atoms*, the shape of the molecule as well as the polarity of its bonds will play a role in determining if the entire molecule will be polar. Stated another way, if the bonds within the molecule are polar, the molecule itself may or may not be, depending on its shape. Let's consider an example of each.

In carbon dioxide, each of the two C==O double bonds is quite polar because the two atoms have a ΔEN = 1.0. However, because the molecule itself is AX_2 and therefore linear, each of those identical bond dipoles is pointing in a direction exactly opposite to the other because of the 180° O – C – O bond angle. This means that the molecular shape is such that the bond dipoles *effectively cancel each other out* resulting in a non-polar molecule. You can compare this to two evenly matched tug-of-war teams pulling in opposite directions on a rope — neither team wins because they are equally strong.

In water, just as in CO_2, a central atom is bonded between two identical peripheral atoms and each of those two bonds has a significant and identical dipole. However, because H_2O qualifies as an AX_2E_2 molecule, it is bent or V-shaped. This means that the molecular shape is such that the bond dipoles point in the same general direction and so reinforce each other. This results in a polar molecule.

Chemists can detect and measure a molecule's polarity in an electric field. They assign a magnitude to that polarity expressed as a "dipole moment." Water is very polar and has a significant dipole moment, but the dipole moment of non-polar carbon dioxide is zero. As Figure 2.3.6 shows, the water molecule has a net dipole, while the carbon dioxide molecule does not. The importance of the polarity of water molecules cannot be overstated as we will soon see.

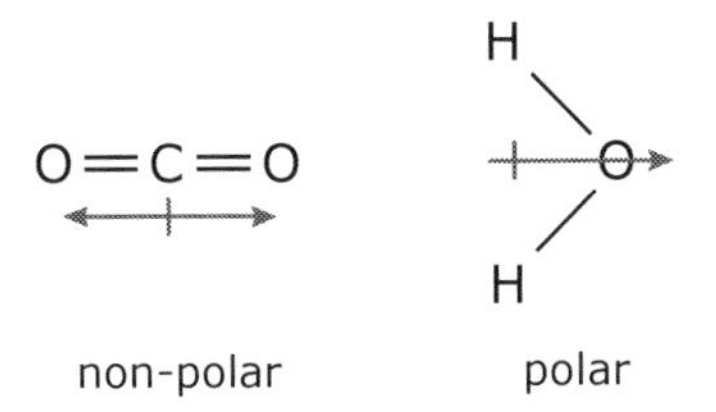

Figure 2.3.6 *The V-shape of a water molecule results in a significant dipole moment.*

In the above example, two *different molecular shapes* were the reason that bond dipoles in one molecule cancelled out, but didn't cancel in another molecule. There is also a possibility that two molecules having the *same shape* and containing polar bonds could be either polar or non-polar. We can use two AX_4 molecules to demonstrate this.

In Figure 2.3.7, carbon tetrachloride on the left is a symmetric molecule with four chlorines situated at the corners of a tetrahedron. Each C – Cl bond is polar in the direction of chlorine because carbon and chlorine have electronegativities of 2.5 and 3.0 respectively. The four bond dipoles, however, cancel out as they point in opposite directions in the symmetric molecule and so the molecule itself is non-polar. Carbon tetrachloride is a liquid used as a solvent for other non-polar substances. As you will soon see, one non-polar substance will usually mix well with another.

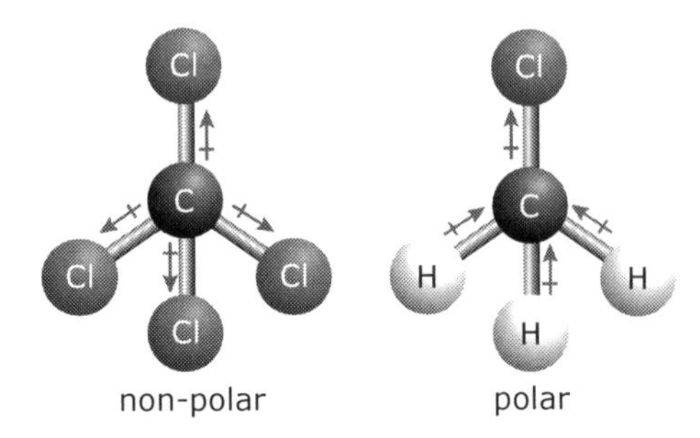

Figure 2.3.7 *Two molecules having the same shape can have different polarities. Carbon tetrachloride, on the left, is non-polar; chloromethane, on the right, is polar.*

The molecule on the right in Figure 2.3.7 is called chloromethane. All of its bond dipoles point in the same general direction. Each C – H bond is polar towards the carbon due to carbon's higher EN value (2.5 vs. 2.1), and the C – Cl bond polarity points in a similar direction towards chlorine. Now, as was the case with water above, the bond dipoles reinforce each other and so the entire molecule is polar.

In this example, molecular composition rather than molecular shape determined whether a molecule was polar or non-polar. In all cases, however, the key question is the same.

Does the molecule contain polar bonds and, if so, do the bond dipoles cancel each other or not?

If bond dipoles exist but cancel each other, then the molecule is non-polar. If bond dipoles don't cancel or if they reinforce each other, then the molecule is polar. Answering this question often involves attempting to visualize and even manipulate a three-dimensional shape based on a diagram drawn on a flat page. Although that might seem difficult at first, it will become easier with practice. Remembering the simple guidelines below will also help.

Guidelines for Determining If a Molecule Is Non-polar or Polar

1. When the peripheral atoms in a molecule are identical and arranged symmetrically around a central atom, any bond dipoles that exist will cancel out and the molecule will be non-polar.
2. When the molecule is asymmetric (not symmetric) either due to its shape or its composition, any bond dipoles that exist will usually not cancel out and the molecule will be polar.

If you review all the shapes listed in the tables given earlier, you will notice that several shapes have the peripheral atoms arranged *symmetrically* around the central atom. "Symmetrical" means balanced or evenly arranged.

In most cases, symmetrical molecules are AX_m molecules in which no lone pairs exist on the central atom. All such molecules containing identical peripheral atoms will be non-polar, regardless of the bond dipoles that exist.

Can you discover any shapes where lone pairs *do exist* on the central atoms that include symmetrically arranged peripheral atoms? If so, then those molecules will also prove to be non-polar as long as the peripheral atoms are all the same.

Sample Problem

Consider the Lewis structure shown here for the compound chlorine trifluoride:
Determine the shape of the molecule and if the molecule is polar.

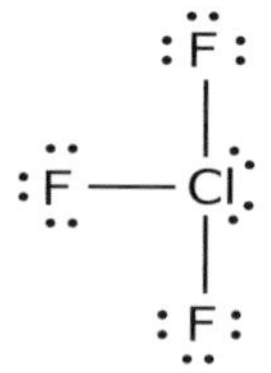

What to Think about

1. To determine if the bonds are polar, find the ΔEN from the electronegativity table.
   The bonds are therefore polar in the direction of fluorine.
2. To determine if the molecule is polar, assign an AX_mE_n label and find the molecular shape.
   The molecule has an AX_3E_2 designation and so adopts a "T-shaped" structure.
3. Considering the molecular shape, decide if the molecule is symmetric or asymmetric and therefore either polar or non-polar.
   The bond dipoles therefore do not cancel and so the molecule is polar.

How to Do It

$\Delta EN = 4.0 - 3.0 = 1.0$

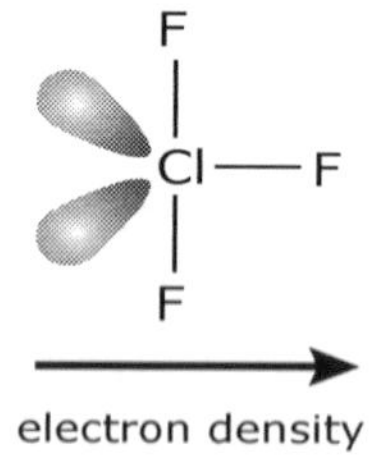

electron density

Practice Problems

1. Complete the following table by listing the AX_mE_n notations and their shapes in the appropriate columns for all the symmetric and asymmetric molecules that you can find. Assume that all the peripheral atoms in the molecules are the same. The first entries are done for you.

Symmetric Molecules		*Asymmetric* Molecules	
AX_mE_n Notation	Shape of Molecule	AX_mE_n Notation	Shape of Molecule
AX_2	linear	AX_2E	bent or angular

2. Complete the following table.

Lewis Structure	AX_mE_n Notation	Molecular Shape (Name and Diagram)	Polar Molecule? (Yes / No)
(a) H—C(—H)=Ö:			
(b) H—N̈(—H)—H			
(c) PCl_5: P bonded to five :C̈l: atoms			

Intermolecular Forces

We have seen that opposite charges are ultimately responsible for all chemical bonds. Electron-deficient positive ions are attracted to electron-abundant negative ions in ionic bonds. Pairs of negative electrons are attracted to adjacent positive nuclei in covalent bonds.

The chemical bonds within molecules are called **intramolecular** forces. ("Intra" means "within.") Attractive forces between molecules and between ions and molecules are called **intermolecular forces.**

Intermolecular forces are as dependent on electrostatic attraction as intramolecular forces are. However, because they typically involve smaller charges and/or greater distances between the chemical species, they aren't as strong as chemical bonds. Yet these forces are so important that without them, life itself could never exist on this tiny "blue marble" in space we call Earth.

Our final discussion of this chapter will focus on the various types of intermolecular forces that exist. We will begin with the forces that act between neutral molecules, and then consider a force that acts between molecules and ions. Let's start where our previous discussion ended by revisiting polar molecules.

Dipole-Dipole Forces — Attractions Between Polar Molecules

Within any substance containing polar molecules, each molecule has a positive and a negative pole — a **molecular dipole**. Because of these partial charges, the molecules in the liquid and solid phases will naturally orient themselves so that the positive pole of one molecule will be next to and attract the negative pole of an adjacent molecule. This force of attraction is called a **dipole-dipole force**. This network of dipole-dipole forces will result in higher melting and boiling points because more energy will be required to overcome the attractions between the molecules.

The more polar those molecules are, the stronger the dipole-dipole forces. Figure 2.3.8 shows two depictions of polar HCl molecules with the dipole-dipole force acting between them.

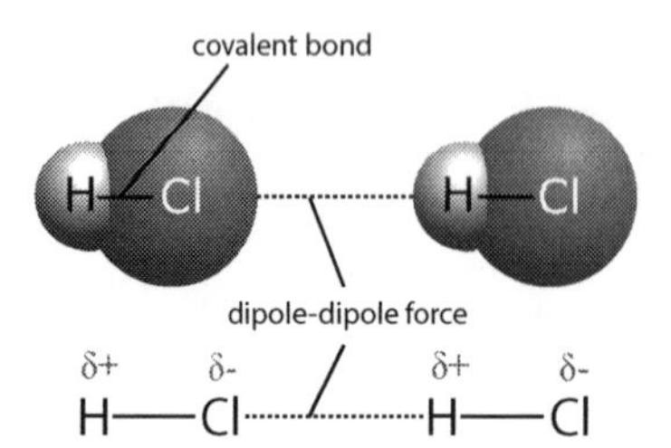

Figure 2.3.8 *One way to show dipole-dipole forces is to draw the actual molecule shapes (top diagram). Another way is to use the element symbols only (bottom diagram.*

Hydrogen Bonds — Special Dipole-Dipole Forces

A much stronger example of a dipole-dipole force exists between polar molecules that contain a hydrogen atom bonded to either nitrogen, oxygen, or fluorine. The atoms of these 2nd period elements are each small, highly electronegative, and have lone electron pairs. All of these properties are significant.

The H – **N**, H – **O**, and H – **F** bonds in each of these molecules will be *very polar* due to hydrogen's low electronegativity resulting in a large ΔEN. This means that a significant amount of electron density will be removed from hydrogen, leaving it with a large partial positive charge. This will also leave its nucleus almost unshielded because hydrogen has no core electrons. The other end of the molecule will gain that electron density and thus acquire a large partial negative charge.

The partially positive hydrogen in one molecule will then be attracted to the lone electron pair of the partially negative atom of another molecule. That attractive force will be particularly strong not only because of the extremely polar bonds within the molecules, but also because *all of the atoms involved are small.* This allows the tiny electropositive hydrogen to get very close to the lone pairs on the partially negative nitrogen, oxygen, or fluorine atoms of the other molecules. This intense intermolecular force is known as a **hydrogen bond**.

It is not an exaggeration to state that hydrogen bonds make life on Earth possible. For example, consider that most of our Earth and most of our bodies are composed of water. Water molecules have a relatively low mass and the vast majority of substances composed of such molecules have very low boiling points, even if those molecules are polar. Look at Figure 2.3.9 showing the boiling points of the binary (two element) hydrides of groups 14 to 17 of the periodic table.

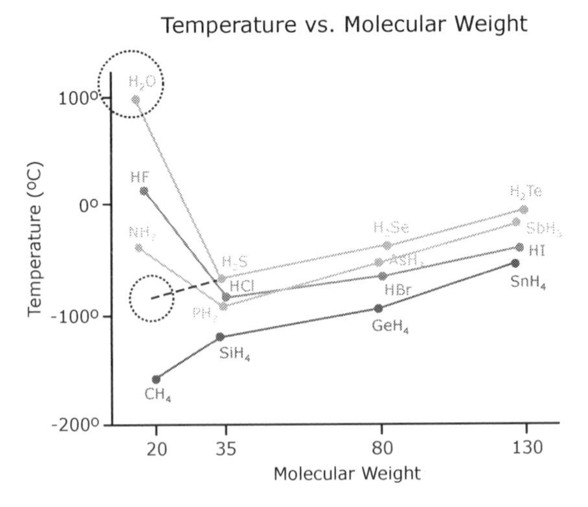

Figure 2.3.9 *Boiling points of binary hydrides of groups 14 to 17*

The group 14 hydrides are all symmetric AX_4 molecules and non-polar, so we would expect those substances (SnH_4, GeH_4, SiH_4, and CH_4) to have low boiling points, and they do. Note that the boiling points of these compounds decrease with decreasing molar mass. The binary hydrides of the remaining groups, however, are asymmetric polar molecules. Their dipole-dipole forces contribute to higher boiling points than seen in group 14.

Something very interesting occurs, however, with the lightest hydrides in groups 15, 16, and 17. Look at how the boiling points change for these substances as we move up each group. Consider the group 16 binary hydrides for example: H_2Te, H_2Se, H_2S, and finally H_2O (water). As the mass of each polar AX_2E_2 molecule decreases, the boiling point drops, but not consistently. After H_2S, if the trend were consistent, we would expect water to have a boiling point of approximately −90°C (see dashed line in Figure 2.3.9). The fact that the actual boiling point is almost 200°C higher than that is clear evidence of the strength of the hydrogen bonds in water (Figure 2.3.10a). Life as we know it would be very unlikely if water became a gas at −90°C! Even the fact that ice floats is due to hydrogen bonding. That characteristic of water is of great importance to aquatic life during cold temperatures.

The significance of hydrogen bonds is further demonstrated by the fact that the three-dimensional structure of many proteins and even the base-pairing in the double helix of DNA molecules depend on the existence of these essential forces. These are hydrogen bonds involving an oxygen or nitrogen atom (Figure 2.3.10b).

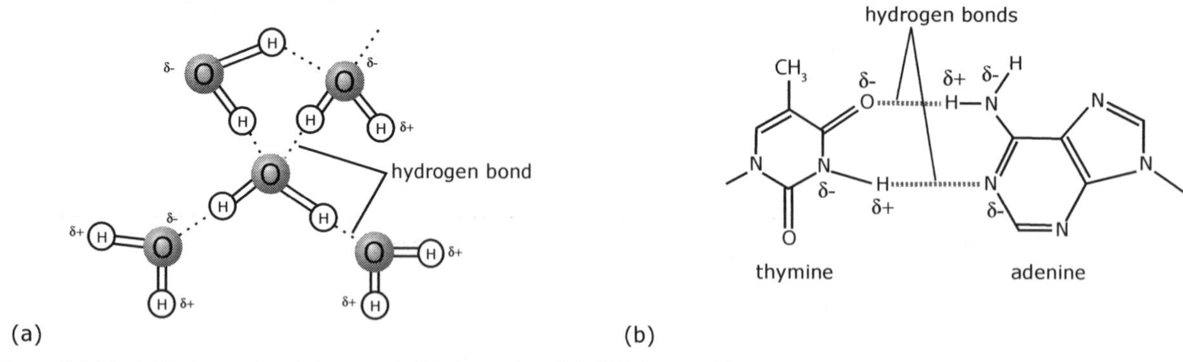

Figure 2.3.10 *(a) Hydrogen bonds in water; (b) Hydrogen bonds in DNA base-pairing*

Dispersion (London) Forces — A Growing Attraction

For a molecular substance to exist as a liquid or solid, the molecules must be close together. This means some kind of intermolecular attractive force must exist between those molecules.

So far, we have discussed two of these intermolecular forces. Dipole-dipole forces and hydrogen bonds act to cause polar molecules to "stick" together and maintain a molecular substance in the liquid or solid state of matter.

However, we might expect that substances composed of non-polar molecules might never exist as liquids or solids since they have no particular reason to attract each other. That is definitely not the case. Many molecular substances composed of non-polar molecules exist as liquids or even solids at room temperatures. Those that don't can usually be condensed or solidified under the right conditions. The obvious question would be: What intermolecular force would cause non-polar molecules to attract each other?

The explanation of this force relies on the quantum mechanical description of the atom and the force itself is named for the physicist, Fritz London, who used quantum mechanics to explain the basis of the attraction. We'll use a non-polar molecule as an example.

Consider a sample of chlorine gas, Cl_2. As the $\Delta EN = 0$, the molecules are non-polar and the electron density in the negative cloud surrounding this diatomic molecule is evenly distributed. This means that *on average*, the electrons will spend no more of their time nearer one chlorine nucleus than the other, and so the probability distribution is even throughout the orbital cloud.

However, at any instant, there is a *possibility* that there may be more electron density on one side of the molecule than the other, resulting in an instantaneous molecular dipole. This dipole will have little effect on any other Cl_2 molecules that are far away. But if those molecules are in close proximity, even a short-lived dipole in one molecule will distort or polarize the electron cloud of a neighbouring molecule. This happens because the negative pole of the instantaneous dipole will repel electron density in the nearby electron cloud to the opposite side of that molecule. As well, the positive pole will pull electron density to the near side of another neighbouring molecule. Each induced dipole results in an intermolecular attraction between the newly polarized molecules and induces more dipoles in surrounding molecules. As a result, the dipoles *disperse* throughout the sample, causing the molecules to attract each other. These intermolecular forces of attraction are called **dispersion forces** or **London dispersion forces**.

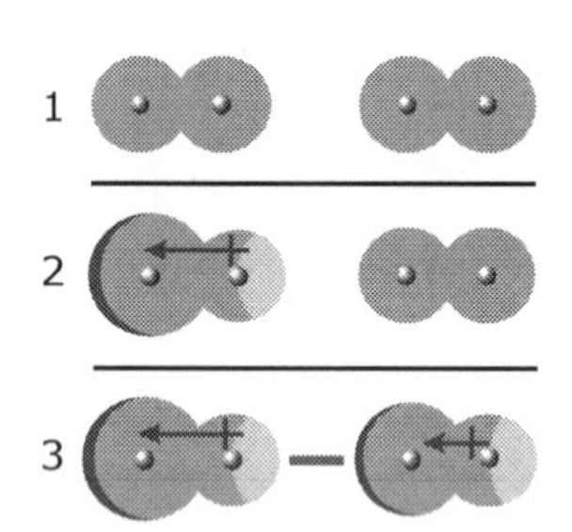

Figure 2.3.11 *An instantaneous dipole in the non-polar molecule on the left (2 induces a dipole in its neighbouring molecule on the right (3.*

Figure 2.3.11 shows an instantaneous dipole in the non-polar molecule on the left inducing a dipole in the neighbouring molecule on the right. The dispersion force then exists between the two molecules.

Although London forces are the *only* forces acting between non-polar molecules, they exist between the particles of *all* substances. Except in the case of strong hydrogen bonds, they may be the dominant intermolecular force even for polar molecules.

The strength of dispersion forces will increase as the size of the molecules involved increases. This is because large electron clouds are more loosely held than smaller clouds. Thus they are more easily deformed or polarized by a nearby dipole than compact tightly held clouds are.

Even molecular shape can play a role in dispersion forces. Molecules with more surface area have electron clouds that are spread out and so are more easily distorted by neighboring dipoles.

Consider the melting and boiling points of diatomic halogens of group 17. The higher temperatures required for these phase changes as we descend the group is evidence of the increasing strength of the London forces between the molecules.

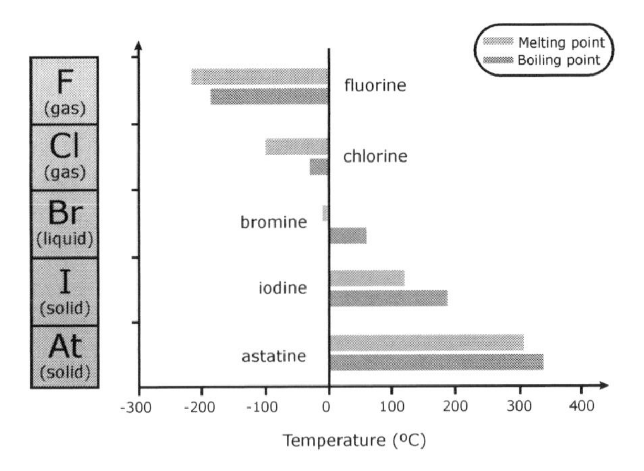

Figure 2.3.12 *Melting and boiling points of diatomic halogens of group 17*

Ion-Dipole Forces — Surround and Separate

We will conclude our discussion of intermolecular forces by focusing on an important interaction that occurs when an ionic compound dissolves in water.

The ionic bonds holding a crystal lattice together are strong. However, when the surface of that lattice is in contact with water, each ion on that surface will attract the oppositely charged end of polar water molecules near them. That attraction between an ion and a polar molecule is called an **ion-dipole force.** These attractive forces soon overcome those between the ions themselves, so the crystal structure begins to break down. As the ions move away from the lattice surface, they immediately become surrounded or enclosed in what chemists call a **hydration shell.**

At the centre of one type of hydration shell, the negative oxygen ends of water molecules orient themselves next to and surround a cation. At the centre of another shell, an anion is engulfed by water molecules oriented with their positive hydrogens next to the ion's negative charge. Figure 2.3.13 shows the ion-dipole forces acting between water and Na^+ and Cl^- ions in an aqueous solution. Ion-dipole forces are the primary force responsible for the solubility of ionic compounds in water and aqueous solutions of some ionic compounds are almost as necessary for life as water itself.

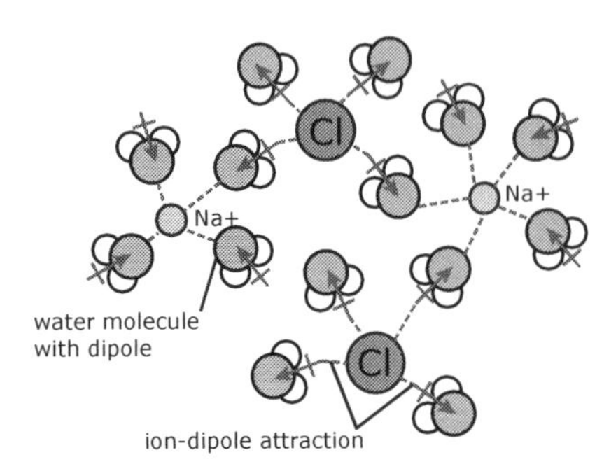

Figure 2.3.13 *Ion-dipole forces between water molecules and Na^+ and Cl^- ions in an aqueous solution*

Valence Bond Theory — The Hybridization of Atomic Orbitals and the Concept of Formal Charge

G.N. Lewis's dot structures provide useful models of the arrangement of atoms in covalent molecules. By evaluating the total number of valence electrons in a molecule and the formal charge on the atoms, Lewis structures provide a way to represent whether covalent molecules contain single or multiple bonds. The repulsion that occurs between bonding and/or non-bonding pairs of electrons can be used to predict molecular shape. This is the VSEPR theory. Consideration of the electronegativity of atoms within a molecule's Lewis structure provides a way to deduce whether a molecular dipole exists. The strength of the intermolecular forces (IMFs) in molecules is determined by a combination of London dispersion forces and dipole forces. Intermolecular forces influence all of the physical and chemical characteristics of these molecules.

There are some limitations and over simplifications associated with the Lewis structure model of covalent molecules. For example, we know that electrons are not accurately represented as pairs of dots in a region of space between two atoms that produce a bond. The quantum mechanical model explains that electrons actually exhibit particle-wave duality in atoms and that they are located in orbitals.

Valence bond theory describes the location of bonding and non-bonding, lone electrons in quantum-mechanical orbitals, created by overlap of the standard s, p, d, and f orbitals. **Hybridization** is a mathematical process in which these standard atomic orbitals are combined to form new atomic orbitals called **hybrid orbitals**. Hybrid orbitals are located on individual atoms, but their shapes and energies differ from those of standard atomic orbitals. Hybrid orbitals are more stable than standard atomic orbitals. They *minimize* the energy of the molecule by *maximizing* the orbital overlap in a bond. The mathematical equations involved in hybridization are very complex; however, the following statements help describe it.

- The sum of the number of standard atomic orbitals is equal to the number of hybrid orbitals formed.
- The combinations of standard atomic orbitals determine the number and energies of the hybrid orbitals formed.
- The type of hybridization that occurs is the one with the lowest overall potential energy.
- We can use the electron geometry determined by the VSEPR theory to predict the type of hybridization.

sp^3 Hybridization

This is the most common type of hybridization as it is found in molecules whose central atom is surrounded by a stable octet. Methane, CH_4 is a classic example of sp^3 hybridization. Each hydrogen has one valence electron existing in a 1s orbital, while carbon has four valence electrons, two existing in a 2s orbital, and two in two lobes of a 2p orbital. Carbon's orbital diagram would convert as shown in Figure 2.3.14 (notice the 1s electrons are not affected).

C $1s^2 2s^2 2p^2$

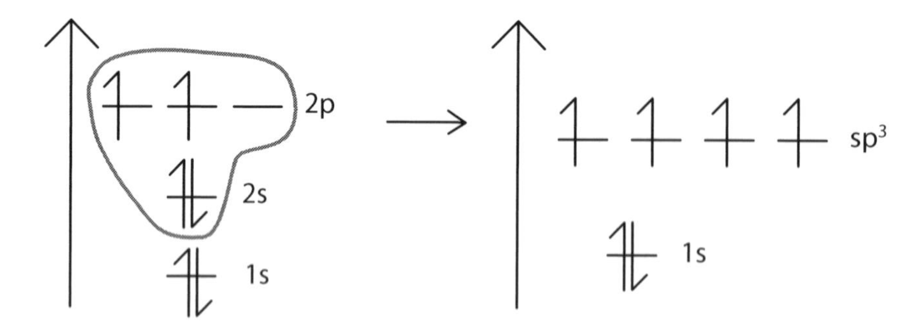

Figure 2.3.14 *Conversion of carbon's orbital diagram*

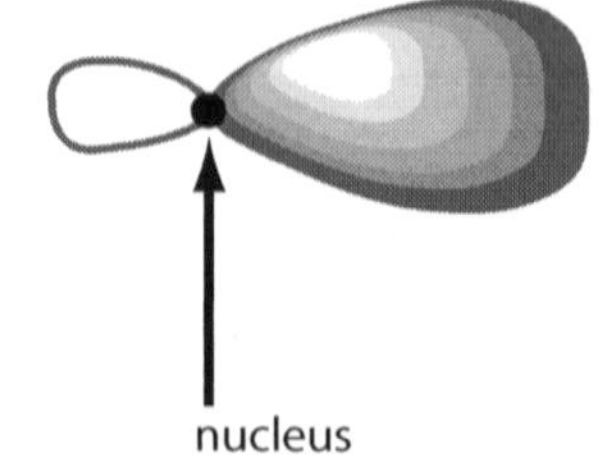

Figure 2.3.15 *An sp³ hybrid orbital*

The s and p orbitals combine to form four *identical* bonding orbitals, designated sp^3. Each of these can share their electron with one hydrogen atom. This is called sp^3 hybridization. *One* spherical s orbital and *three* figure-8-shaped p orbitals (one p_x, one p_y and one p_z) combine to form *four* identical sp^3 hybrid orbitals. An sp^3 hybrid orbital resembles a p orbital with an enlarged end (Figure 2.3.15).

There are *four* of these that overlap about a central point to make a methane molecule, CH_4 (or any AX_4 species). This is typical of a *tetrahedral* arrangement with all bond angles approximately 109.5° (Figure 2.3.16).

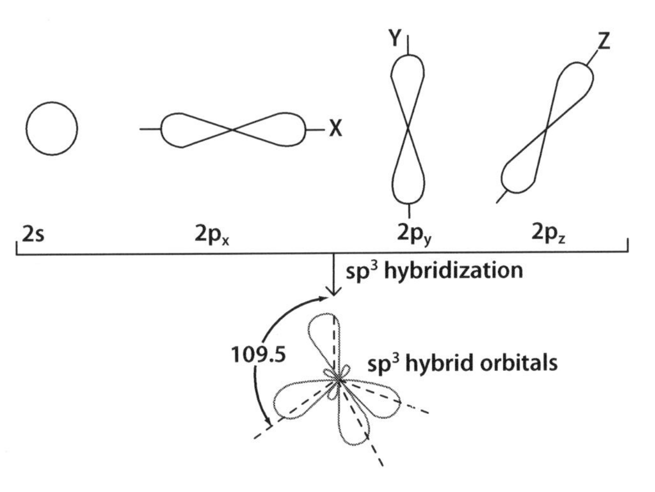

Figure 2.3.16 *A methane molecule*

- Hybridized orbitals can hold lone pairs or bonding pairs.
- The region in space occupied by a pair of bonding or lone electrons, regions of high electron density, is a "domain".
- Lone electrons exert greater repulsive forces than bonding electrons.

Sample Problem — Deducing Molecular Shape and Hybridization

Determine the shape and the hybridization for a molecule of water.

What to Think About	How To Do It
1. Determine the Lewis structure for the molecule.	$H-\ddot{O}-H$ (lone pairs on O)
2. Determine the number of electron "domains" around the central oxygen atom.	The four electron domains are arranged in a tetrahedron. Two of the domains contain lone pairs of electrons. **Four sp^3 hybrid orbitals are** oriented in a tetrahedral array. Two of the sp^3 orbitals are occupied by bonding electron pairs and two are occupied by non-bonding electron pairs leading to an **angular** or **bent** (**V-shaped**) arrangement.
3. Four electron domains will be most likely to exist as four sp^3 hybrid orbitals.	Due to the large interelectron repulsion of the lone-paired electrons, the usual 109.5° bond angle found in a tetrahedron will be reduced and closer to 104.5° between the hydrogen atoms. 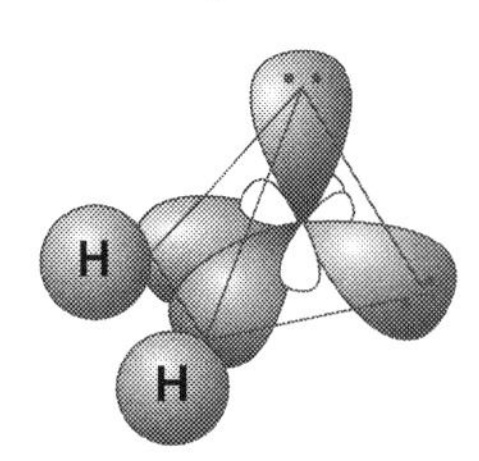

sp^3d and sp^3d^2 Hybridization

Elements in the third row of the periodic table (or below) are able to form bonding arrangements involving *expanded octets*. In third period elements such as phosphorus, sulfur, and chlorine, the 3d orbitals are so close in energy to the 3s and 3p orbitals that the hybridization of one s, three p, and one d orbital results in a *trigonal bipyramid* geometry. Sp^3d hybridization is particularly common for molecules whose central atoms have five valence electrons.

Elements with six, seven, or eight valence electrons can accommodate an expanded octet to produce up to six bonds. The formation of sp^3d^2 hybrid orbitals in an *octahedral* (or *square bipyramid*) array can be accomplished by the hybridizing of one s, three p, and two d orbitals. (See Figure 2.3.17)

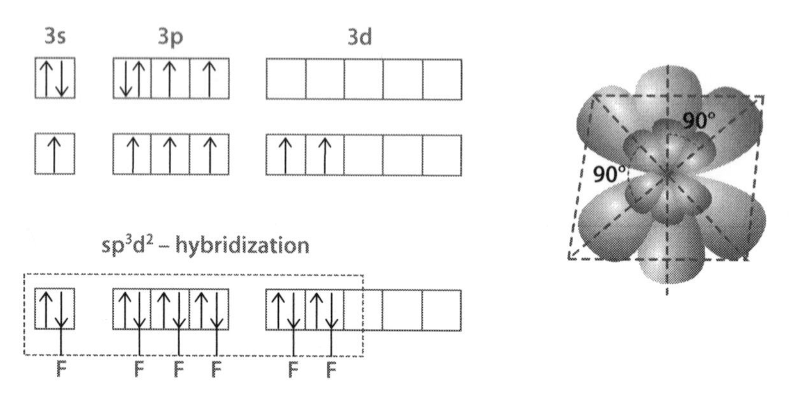

Figure 2.3.17 *As shown, sp^3d^2 hybridization creates six degenerate orbitals in an octahedral array. Six single bonds all 90° apart extend from a central atom as in sulfur hexafluoride, SF_6, for example.*

Note: While the use of electron geometry to predict hybridization is largely successful, there are cases where it fails. H_2S for example is predicted to have tetrahedral *electron* geometry and a bent shape with about a bond angle of about 104°. In fact, the bond angle is closer to 90°, indicating that this molecule is largely unhybridized. Recently, complex computer-based calculations indicate that the sp^3d and sp^3d^2 hybrids are the most difficult to accurately predict. For this reason, these two types of hybridization are not being assessed on the AP Chemistry examination at the moment.

Sigma (σ) and Pi (π) Bonding

A sigma (σ) bond occurs when two atomic orbitals combine to form a covalent bond that lies along an axis connecting the nuclei of the two atoms. The simplest example of a sigma bond would be the overlap of two 1s orbitals in the formation of diatomic hydrogen, H_2. Sigma bonds are also formed by the overlap of two hybridized orbitals. In double bond formation, there is overlap between two hybridized orbitals, called a sigma bond overlap, and the overlap of two unhybridized p orbitals, which is called a pi (π) bond overlap. A double bond consists of one sigma and one pi bond overlap.

A pi bond occurs due to p_y or p_z orbital overlap in a sausage-shaped region above and below (in the case of p_y overlap) or in front and behind (in the case of p_z overlap) the nuclei of bonded atoms (Figure 2.3.18).

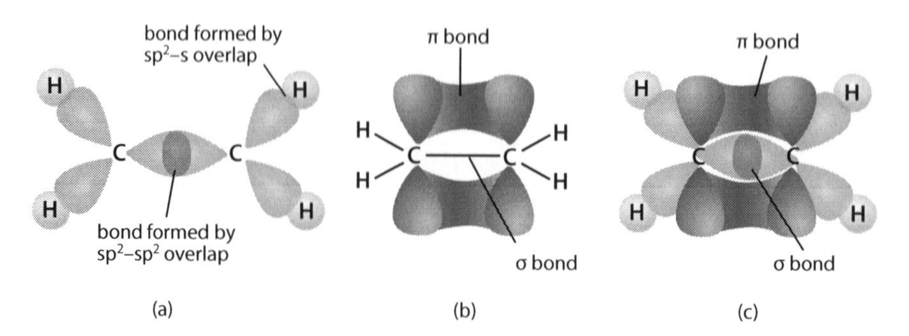

Figure 2.3.18 *(a) shows overlap of p_x hybridized orbitals along an axis between the carbon atoms to form a σ bond; (b)shows overlap of p_y orbitals above and below an axis between the carbon atoms to form a π bond; (c) shows double-bonded C_2H_4 with one σ and one π bond between the two carbon atoms in the molecule.*

sp and sp^2 Hybridization

Double and triple bonds are commonly associated with carbon atoms and always consist of one sigma (σ) and one or two pi (π) bonds. In terms of hybridization, the entire region of orbital overlap is considered one hybrid orbital, even though it may be a double or triple bond. For this reason, multiple bonds are often associated with sp or sp^2 hybridization.

> In the determination of molecular shape and/or hybridization, it is important to think of a double or triple covalent bond as occupying one domain only.

Other examples of compounds that exhibit sp and sp^2 hybridization are those with beryllium or boron as these may form stable compounds with less than an octet of electrons around their central atoms.

Sample Problem — Deducing Molecular Shape, Hybridization, and Presence of Sigma (σ) and Pi (π) Bonds

Determine the shape and hybridization for a molecule of methanal, CH_2O. Determine the number of sigma and pi bonds in the molecule. The common name for methanal is formaldehyde.

What To Think About	How To Do It
1. Refer to the steps listed in Section 2.1 to determine the Lewis structure for the molecule.	H and H single-bonded to C; C = O with two lone pairs on O
2. Determine the number of electron "domains" existing around the central atom (the double bond is one domain).	There are a total of 12 valence electrons with carbon occupying the central position in the molecule. This means a double bond is needed between the carbon and the oxygen atoms.
3. The total number of orbitals is conserved.	There are **three** electron domains. This indicates three hybrid orbitals. The orbitals should be **sp^2 hybridized**.
4. Maximize the inter-domain distance to predict the shape of the molecule and the bond angles.	The molecule should have 120.5° bond angles and should be **trigonal planar**.
5. All single bonds are σ and all multiple bonds consist of first σ and then π bonds.	There should be 3 σ bonds (between C and each H and C and O) and 1 π bond (between C and O).

Practice Problems—Deducing Molecular Shape, Hybridization, and Presence of Sigma (σ) and Pi (π) Bonds

1. Draw Lewis structures for each of the following species.

   a) CH_4 b) H_3O^+ c) OF_2 d) HCN e) SF_6 f) SOF_4

2. State the shape and the central atom hybridization for each of the structures.

3. Label each molecule as polar or non-polar.

Table 2.3.5 *Summary Table Including Hybridization, Bond Type, and Shape*

Hybridization	# Of Bonds	# Lone Pairs	Molecular Shape	Bond Angle	Example
sp	2	0	Linear	180°	CO_2
sp^2	3	0	Trigonal planar	120°	SO_3
sp^2	2	1	Angular	< 120°	SO_2
sp^3	4	0	Tetrahedral	109.5°	CH_4
sp^3	3	1	Trigonal pyramidal	< 109.5°	NH_3
sp^3	2	2	Bent (angular)	< 109.5°	H_2O
sp^3d	5	0	Trigonal bipyramidal	120°, 90°	PCl_5
sp^3d	4	1	Seesaw or irregular tetrahedron	< 120°, < 90°	SF_4
sp^3d	3	2	T-shaped	< 90°	CF_3
sp^3d	2	3	Linear	180°	XeF_2
sp^3d^2	6	0	Octahedron	90°	SF_8
sp^3d^2	5	1	Square pyramidal	< 90°	IF_5
sp^3d^2	4	2	Square planar	90°	XeF_4

Formal Charge

Formal charge is an entirely fictitious charge that is used to defend the most probable Lewis structure of a molecule when several different Lewis structure arrangements are possible. The formal charge on an atom in a molecule is the charge each atom would have *if all bonding electrons were shared equally between the bonded atoms.* There are a couple of ways to calculate the formal charge of each atom.

formal charge of an atom = the number of valence electrons [the number of lone electrons + the number of bonding electron pairs]

This method for calculating formal charge can be simplified if the Lewis structure is drawn using lines for each bonding pair of electrons. In that case:

formal charge = valence electrons – (dots + lines)

While not particularly scientific sounding, this is a very easy way to calculate formal charge. Formal charges are generally shown next to each atom in a structure with a *circle* drawn around the charge.

It is important to remember that formal charges are *not* actual charges. They do *not* produce electronegativity or polarity in a molecule. They simply assist us in determining which is the most likely structure from among a selection of Lewis structures. The following general rules apply to formal charges.

1. The *sum* of all formal charges in a *neutral molecule* is equal to *zero*.
2. The *sum* of all formal charges in an *ion* is equal to the *ion's charge*.
3. *Small* or *zero* formal charges on atoms are preferred.*
4. For structures with atoms with a non-zero formal charge, the preferred structure will be the one with a negative charge on the more electronegative element.

* *Statement 3 has been questioned by bonding theorists lately — in fact a structure that satisfies the octet rule may be more likely than one in which formal charges are minimized. For the AP exam, it is a good idea for a student to indicate awareness that the predictive power of formal charge is limited.*

Sample Problem — Deduction of a Preferred Structure Using Formal Charge

Hydrocyanic acid is produced by bubbling gaseous hydrogen cyanide through water to produce an aqueous solution. Draw two possible structures for the molecule with a triple bond between the C and the N and assign formal charges to all atoms. Which structure is preferred based on minimizing formal charge?

What to Think About	How to Do It
1. Refer to the steps listed in Section 6.5 to determine the Lewis structure for the molecule. 2. If there is more than one possible resonance structure or isomer, repeat the steps and produce any alternate structures. Note: there are several resonance structures possible, but the question limits us to the two involving a triple C-N bond.	There are a total of 10 valence electrons. The structure may be drawn with the carbon in the centre or the nitrogen. Either way, the C-N bond must be triple (as indicated in the question) and the H bond single. Possible structures include: $H-C\equiv N:$ and $H-N\equiv C:$
3. Calculate formal charges using the formula: valence electrons – (dots + dashes) for each atom in the first structure.	H: $1 - (0 + 1) = 0$ C: $4 - (0 + 4) = 0$ N: $5 - (2 + 3) = 0$
4. Repeat for the second structure.	H: $1 - (0 + 1) = 0$ N: $5 - (0 + 4) = +1$ C: $4 - (2 + 3) = -1$
5. Place the "charges" on the appropriate atoms in a circle.	(0) (0) (0) $H-C\equiv\ddot{N}$ and (0) (+1) (−1) $H-N\equiv\ddot{C}$
6. Predict the preferred structure.	The first structure (with the central carbon) is preferred.

Practice Problems—Assigning and Using Formal Charges

1. Assign formal charges to each atom in each of the following two structures for CO_2. Predict which structure is favoured.

   (a) $\ddot{\underset{..}{O}}=C=\ddot{\underset{..}{O}}$ (b) $:\ddot{\underset{..}{O}}-C\equiv O:$

2. Assign formal charges to each atom in each of the following six structures for SCO. Predict which structure is favoured. Which is least likely to form?

   (a) $:\ddot{\underset{..}{O}}=C=\ddot{S}:$

   (b) $:\ddot{\underset{..}{O}}-C\equiv S:$

   (c) $:O\equiv C-\ddot{\underset{..}{S}}:$

   (d) $:\ddot{C}=O=\ddot{S}:$

   (e) $:\ddot{\underset{..}{C}}-O\equiv S:$

   (f) $:C\equiv O-\ddot{\underset{..}{S}}:$

3. Draw two structures for SO_3, one with an expanded octet and one without. You do not need to show resonance structures for the non-expanded form. Use formal charges to predict which structure is favoured. Check the Internet to see whether you can find any information indicating that the other structure might, in fact, be favoured.

2.3 Activity: Modeling the AX_mE_n Molecules

Question

How can building the various AX_mE_n shapes help us to determine molecular polarities?

Build each of the shapes listed in the table below, but before you take each apart, look at each structure and ask yourself the following question: If each of the bonds in these molecules were polar and all of the peripheral atoms were the same, would the *molecule* be polar or non-polar?

Complete the following table below as you construct each shape:

AX_mE_n Notation	Sample Molecule	Name of Shape	Polar Molecule? Yes/No
AX_2	CO_2		
AX_3	BF_3		
AX_2E	SO_2		
AX_4	CH_4		
AX_3E	NH_3		
AX_2E_2	H_2O		
AX_5	PCl_5		
AX_4E	SF_4		
AX_3E_2	BrF_3		
AX_2E_3	XeF_2		
AX_6	SF_6		
AX_5E	BrF_5		
AX_4E_2	XeF_4		

Results and Discussion

1. Note that an electronegativity value is not listed for xenon in the table shown earlier in this section. In spite of this, you are still able to determine if the two molecules above containing Xe as the central atom are polar or not. Why?

2.3 Review Questions

1. (a) What do the letters: V S E P and R in the term "VSEPR theory" stand for?

   (b) What does the theory allow us to do?

2. Why do non-bonding or lone-pair electrons attached to a central atom occupy more space than bonding electron pairs?

3. Consider the following Lewis structures. Would you expect these molecules to have the same shape or a different shape? Explain.

:F̤̈—B—F̤̈:
|
:F̤:

H
|
H—C=Ö:

4. For each pair of columns, draw lines to connect the AX_mE_n notation on the left to the correct shape listed on the right. (The first one is done for you.)

AX_mE_n Notation	Molecular Shape	AX_mE_n Notation	Molecular Shape
AX_3	angular	AX_4E	T-shaped
AX_2E_3	trigonal bipyramidal	AX_2E	octahedral
AX_4	trigonal pyramidal	AX_3E_2	square pyramidal
AX_3E	trigonal planar	AX_6	square planar
AX_2E_2	tetrahedral	AX_5E	angular
AX_5	linear	AX_4E_2	seesaw

5. Consider the Lewis structures for methane and ammonia.
   (a) Which molecule will have the smaller X–A–X bond angle and why?

H
|
H—C—H
|
H

H—N̈—H
|
H

   (b) Identify the main intermolecular force acting between the molecules of methane and between the molecules of ammonia in pure samples of each compound.

6. Assume that all of the peripheral atoms are the same for each AX_mE_n category listed below and complete the following table. (Note that two different bond angles exist in an AX_5 molecule.)

AX_mE_n Category	**AX_2**	**AX_3**	**AX_4**	**AX_5**		**AX_2E_3**	**AX_6**	**AX_4E_2**
X–A–X Bond Angle								

7. Consider the following group 17 binary hydrides: HI, HBr, HCl, and HF. Which should have the highest boiling point and why?

8. The industrial production of ammonia, NH_3, from H_2 and N_2 is called the Haber process, named for Fritz Haber, the German chemist who developed it just before World War I. During the process, in a gaseous mixture of all three substances, NH_3 must be separated from H_2 and N_2. This is done by cooling the gaseous mixture so as to condense only the NH_3. This leaves the elemental nitrogen and hydrogen as gases to be recycled and produce more ammonia. Why does only the ammonia liquefy upon cooling, but not the H_2 or N_2?

9. Identify two examples of how hydrogen bonding between molecules makes life on Earth possible.

10. Iodine is a non-polar diatomic molecule, yet its molecules have enough attraction for each other that the element exists as a solid at room temperature. Identify the attractive force and explain why it is strong enough to keep the molecules of I_2 attached to each other even at room temperature.

11. Ionic compounds such as NaCl have very high melting points because a great deal of energy is required to overcome the many attractive forces between the oppositely charged ions in an ionic crystal lattice. NaCl melts at 801°C, yet its ions will readily separate from each other at room temperature when the solid is added to water. Explain this by discussing the predominant force that allows an ionic compound to dissolve in water.

12. Complete the following table:

Lewis Structure	AX_mE_n Notation	Shape of Molecule (Name and Diagram)	Type of Intermolecular Force Acting Between Molecules
(a) dichloromethane			
(b) phosgene			
(c) sulfur hexafluoride			
(d) iodine pentafluoride			

13. (a) Draw Lewis structures for each of the species below in the space provided.

(b) State the shape and the central atom hybridization for each.

(c) Consider the polarity of the bonds in each molecule and then determine whether there is a molecular dipole.

(d) Indicate the number of sigma and/or pi bonds in each molecule or ion.

(e) Assign formal charges to each atom in each of the species.

SCl_2

TeF_5^-

XeF_4

CO_3^{-2}

IOF_5

IF_4^+

2.4 Intermolecular Forces and Separation Techniques for Mixtures

Non-Mechanical Means of Separation

Chromatography

Chromatography is one of the most widely used techniques in scientific research today. The processes involved in the separation are generally mild ones. Chromatography has been successfully employed to separate some of the most fragile and elusive substances. Researchers have been able to devise a chromatographic method for separating all but a few mixtures.

Chromatography separates the substances in a solution by having a flowing liquid or gas carry them at different rates through a *stationary phase*. The flowing liquid or gas is called the *mobile phase*. Each substance travels through the stationary phase at its own characteristic rate, according to its relative affinities for the two phases. A substance that adheres strongly to the stationary phase but isn't very soluble in the mobile phase travels slowly through the chromatogram. Conversely, a substance that adheres weakly to the stationary phase but is very soluble in the mobile phase travels quickly through the chromatogram.

There are many forms of chromatography. These include gas chromatography, column chromatography, thin layer chromatography, and paper chromatography. In thin layer chromatography (TLC), the stationary phase is a thin layer of silica gel dried onto a glass plate. In paper chromatography, the stationary phase is a strip or sheet of paper. The mobile phase in both forms of chromatography could be water, an organic solvent such as alcohol, or a mixture of solvents. A drop of the solution to be separated is placed near the bottom of the sheet or plate and allowed to dry. Another drop of the solution is then placed on top of the first and also allowed to dry.

This process is repeated many times until there is a sufficient amount of each solute to produce a clear chromatogram. The bottom of the chromatogram is lowered into a pool of the solvent. **Capillary action** is the tendency of a liquid to rise in narrow tubes or to be drawn into small openings. Capillary action results from the adhesive forces between the solvent molecules and those of the wicking material in combination with the cohesive forces between the solvent molecules themselves. Capillary action causes the solvent to rise up the stationary medium, between the paper fibres or the grains of the gel, past the deposit of solutes, and up the remainder of the paper or glass plate.

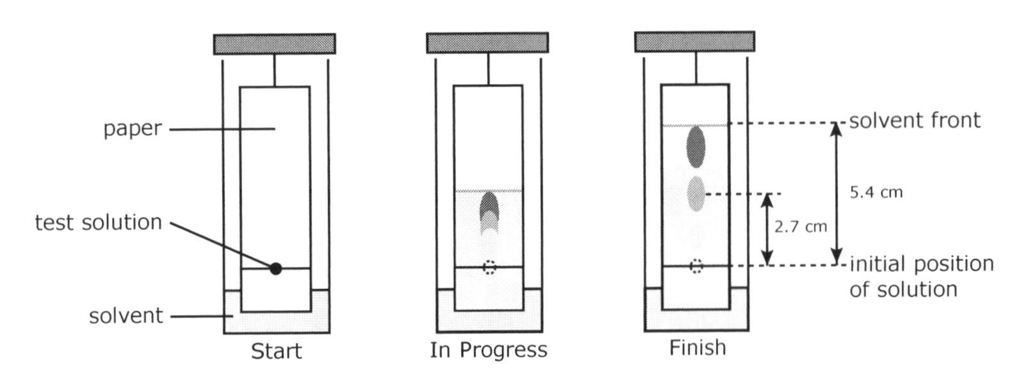

Figure 2.4.1 *Thin layer or paper chromatography*

A substance's $\boldsymbol{R_f}$ (retention factor) for any particular system is defined as its flow speed relative to that of the mobile phase. Here is an example calculation:

$$R_f = \frac{\text{distance the substance flows}}{\text{distance the solvent flows}} \quad \text{(in a given time period)}$$

$$= \frac{2.7 \text{ cm}}{5.4 \text{ cm}} = 0.50$$

A substance's R_f may help identify it or at least support its identification by more definitive means.

"Developing a chromatogram" is the spraying of chemicals on a chromatogram to form colored complexes with the separated substances so they reveal their location. *Elution* is the process of rinsing the separated substances off the chromatogram. Their recovery is usually necessary so that they can be identified through further analysis. Chemists commonly run at least two chromatograms under identical conditions. One is developed to determine the location of the separated substances. The substances are then eluted from the same locations on the undeveloped chromatogram.

In column chromatography, the stationary phase is a glass tube packed with specially treated resin beads. The mobile phase is sometimes just the solution itself but another solvent may be needed to wash the solutes through. Column chromatography is an "open-ended" form of chromatography in which the separated substances flow out the bottom end of the column at different times. Periodic chemical tests or constant electronic monitoring indicates the presence of substances as they leave the column. For column chromatography, the substances' R_f values are calculated as:

$$R_f = \frac{\text{substance time}}{\text{solvent time}} \quad \text{(to travel through the column)}$$

Electrophoresis is similar to chromatography except that the stationary phase is a gel-coated slide or gel-filled dish with oppositely charged electrodes at either end. Species are separated according to their charge or polarity, mass, and size. Other separation methods that involve solubility include solvent extraction and recrystallization. In solvent extraction, one or more compounds are soluble in a particular solvent while the others are not. In recrystallization, trace amounts of impurities stay in solution as the solution is cooled

Distillation

Distillation is any process that separates a mixture of substances by using their different vapor pressures or boiling points. Distillations require a heating device, a flask containing the original mixture, a condenser to cool and condense the vapors, and something to collect the condensed substances as they leave the condenser one after the other (Figure 2.4.2). Distilled water is produced by boiling tap water, cooling its vapors, and then collecting the condensate or **distillate**. The impurities that were dissolved in the water remain as **residue** in the original flask.

Such *simple distillations* are suitable for separating dissolved solids from a solvent but there is a fundamental problem using this technique to separate two liquids. Liquids can evaporate long before boiling occurs as evidenced by the puddles on our street that come and go without ever boiling. Because of this, the initial distillate is still a mixture although it is now richer in the liquid with the lower boiling point. If you took this distillate and repeated the distillation process, the next distillate would be richer still in this liquid. If you repeated this process many times, each time the distillate would become increasingly richer in the substance with the lower boiling point but this would be a tedious process. A mixture that cannot be completely separated by simple distillation is called an azeotropic mixture.

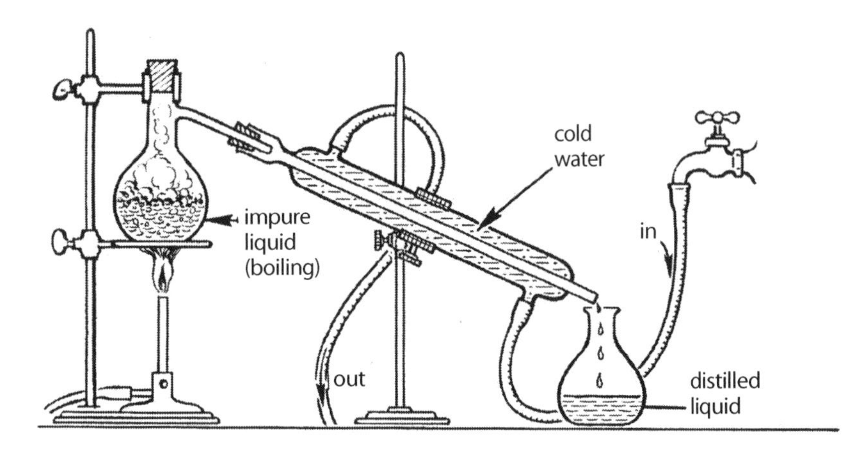

Figure 2.4.2 *Laboratory distillation apparatus*

Scientists have therefore devised a method called **fractional distillation** in which the simple distillation (vaporizing and condensing) is repeated many times within the one device. After evaporating, the vapor enters a *fractionating column*. This may be a tube packed with glass fibres, a tube containing overlapping glass lips or plates, or simply coiled tubing as popularized by backwoods stills. The idea is to provide surfaces on which the vapors can condense. As the hot vapors from below reheat the distillate, some compounds revaporize and travel farther up the column. At the same time, others with higher boiling points drip back in the opposite direction. This process is called *reflux*. The plates become progressively cooler as you move up the column. Each time the process is repeated, the distillate becomes richer in the liquid with the lower boiling point. The component liquids thus proceed at different rates up the fractionating column so as you move higher up, the mixture becomes increasing richer in the liquid with the lower boiling point. If the column is long enough, the liquid components may separate completely and enter the condenser one after the other. There are of course several variations on this same technique.

Distillation is an important laboratory and industrial process (Figure 2.4.3). Oil refineries employ distillation to separate the hundreds of different hydrocarbons in crude oil into smaller groups of hydrocarbons with similar boiling points. When distilling a single batch, as described and illustrated above, the temperatures within the column continuously change as the chemicals travel through the column much like solutes travelling up a piece of chromatography paper. By contrast, oil refineries continuously feed the vaporized crude oil mixture into large steel fractionating towers that electronically monitor and maintain a steady range of temperatures from 400°C at the bottom to 40°C at the top. Each compound rises until it reaches a section of the column that is cool enough for it to condense and be withdrawn from the column. For example, the gasoline fraction (meaning the fraction containing gasoline, itself a mixture) exits near the top of the tower at the 40°C to 110°C level.

Figure 2.4.3 *Industrial distillation*

Froth Flotation

Mining is a key contributor to the country's economy. Precious metals such as gold and silver are very stable or unreactive and are found in nature in their "native" or elemental form. This property is central to their value in jewellery. Other metal atoms such as copper are mostly found in nature in ionic compounds. Naturally occurring compounds are called **minerals**.

Rock containing a desired mineral is called **ore**. The first stage of mining is to extract the ore via blasting or drilling, depending on the kind of mine. The second stage is to mill or crush the ore into a fine powder. The third stage is to separate the target mineral(s) from the rest of the ore, called gangue. Copper compounds are separated by a technique called **froth flotation**. The powdered rock is mixed with water and then a small amount of pine oil is added that adheres to the mineral grains but not to the gangue. Oil and water don't mix so the grains are rendered **hydrophobic** or water repelling. Air is bubbled through the mixture and the hydrophobic grains of mineral escape the water by attaching to the air bubbles, which float them to the surface. The target mineral is then skimmed off, washed, dried, and shipped to a refinery where it is decomposed to recover the metal. Froth flotation is also used in wastewater treatment and paper recycling.

Quick Check

1. What is chromatography?

____

____

2. What is distillation?

____

____

3. Name three areas that use froth flotation.

______________________________ ______________________________

____

2.4 Activity: Separating Stuff

Question

Can you separate a variety of objects using methods that don't rely on their appearance?

Background

Chemists separate the substances in a mixture by picking on properties that clearly distinguish the substances from one another.

Procedure

1. Design and perform a procedure to separate a mixture of marbles, paper clips, pennies and small wooden discs.
2. Record your results in the table below.

	Procedure	Items Separated from Mixture
1.		
2.		
3.		

Results and Discussion

1. What property of each item allowed you to separate it from the mixture?

2. Was the order of the procedures important in your separation scheme?

3. Discuss any complications that arose during your procedures.

4. Compare your methods with those of other groups.

2.4 Review Questions

1. Briefly describe the role of a furnace filter.

2. Briefly describe how chromatography separates the substances in a mixture.

3 What does the phrase "developing a chromatogram" refer to?

4. What is elution and what is its usual purpose?

5. Why should you mark the starting position of the deposited solution on the chromatography paper with pencil rather than pen?

6. What is the R_f of the compound shown in the diagram ?

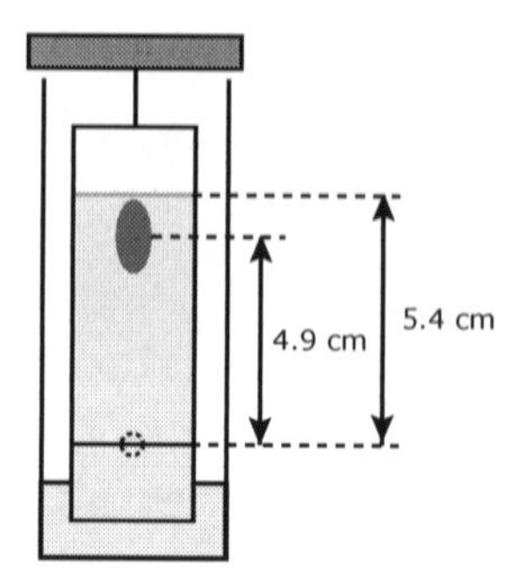

7. What is the basic problem with simple distillation?

8. Identify two factors that affect how completely the components of a solution are separated by fractional distillation.

9. Air is approximately 78% nitrogen (boiling point: –196°C) and 21% oxygen (boiling point: –183°C). Briefly describe how you would separate nitrogen and oxygen from air.

10. Which process requires more energy: chromatography or distillation? Explain.

11. Both density separations and froth flotations involve some materials floating and others sinking, yet density separations are considered a mechanical means of separation while froth flotations are not. What is the main difference between these two techniques?

2.5 Applying Quantum Mechanics to Electrons in Atoms

Warm Up

1. What part of Bohr's theory remains as part of the quantum mechanical view of the atom?

   ____

2. Quantum mechanics replaces the concept of an electron orbit with an orbital. What is an electron orbital?

   ____

3. The laws of probability are a necessary part of describing electron behaviour. Why?

   ____

Starting with Hydrogen — One on One

In this section, we will apply the quantum mechanical model of the atom to describing electrons in the atoms of the elements. We will begin with hydrogen and then use that information to expand our discussion to include multi-electron atoms.

An analogy of a guitar string can help to explain the requirement of standing waves for the allowed energy states of electrons in atoms. If we solve Schrdinger's wave equation for the allowed energy states for hydrogen, we see that each energy state results in different numbers and types of orbitals. The equation shows us that the higher the energy, the greater the number and types of orbitals present.

Quantum Numbers

In an atom, these three-dimensional electron waves or orbitals are more complicated than a standing wave on a guitar string. To describe them, quantum mechanics employs the use of special numbers called **quantum numbers** Each quantum number specifies something different about the orbitals and electrons. We will discuss these numbers as we investigate the orbitals associated with each of allowed energy states for hydrogen.

The Principal Quantum Number (*n*)

The first quantum number is called the **principal quantum number** (n). It indicates the relative size of the atomic orbital.

We have already been introduced to this number because it also represents the allowed energy states for the electron. We know that the value of n can be a positive integer (1, 2, 3, and so on).

When hydrogen's electron is in the lowest allowed energy state or ground state, then $n = 1$. Schrödinger's equation shows us where an electron possessing that amount of energy will most likely be found. When we represent this pictorially, we see an electron "probability density diagram" resembling a spherical cloud. The cloud is what you might see if you could take many snapshots of the hydrogen electron around the nucleus and then superimpose all of them onto one picture. At the centre of this cloud is the hydrogen nucleus. The cloud's density is not uniform throughout, but is greater near the nucleus and decreases as we move away. This tells us that the probability of locating the electron is higher closer to the nucleus and lower further away from the nucleus.

As we move out from the nucleus, we find that hydrogen's electron in its ground state is likely to spend most of its time a slight distance from the nucleus, rather than at the nucleus itself. This is called the "radial probability." It's interesting to note that the electron's distance from the nucleus to the region of highest probability corresponds exactly to the orbit for this electron that Bohr calculated. Remember, however, that Bohr assumed the electron followed a circular path and would always be found at that distance from the nucleus. Quantum mechanics describes this as the most probable distance from the nucleus for the electron.

When we enclose the cloud in a volume representing about a 90% probability of finding the electron, we call this the 1s orbital. The number "1" represents the principal quantum number, telling us the size of the orbital, and the letter "s" refers to the type or "shape" of the orbital. Figure 2.5.1(a) shows an artistic representation of what a spherical 1s orbital might look like if viewed from the outside. Figure 2.5.1(b) is a cross-sectional view showing radial probability (indicated by greater dot density a slight distance from nucleus).

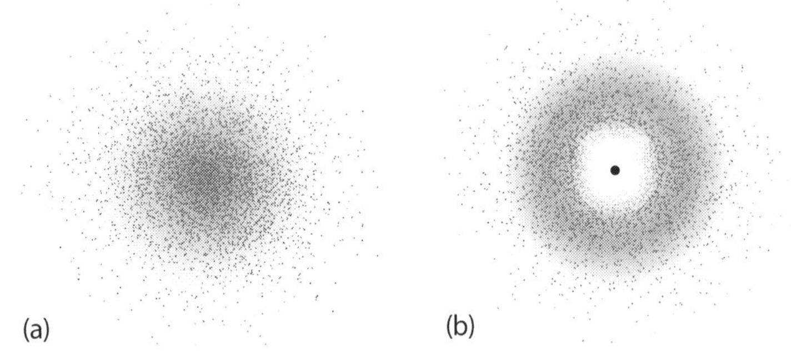

Figure 2.5.1 *(a) A view of a spherical 1s orbital from the outside; (b) A cross-sectional view of a spherical 1s orbital*

The Second Quantum Number (ℓ)

The second quantum number is called the **angular momentum quantum number** (ℓ). It is related to the shape of an atomic orbital.

The different values of ℓ at each energy level represent the number of orbital shapes or sublevels that exist in that energy level. That number equals the energy level itself. So for $n = 1$, there is only one orbital type or shape, namely the s orbital.

Each new energy level has one new orbital shape in addition to those existing in the previous level. So if hydrogen's electron is "excited" and absorbs enough energy to reach the second allowed energy state, then $n = 2$ and two orbital shapes or sublevels exist. There is an s orbital with a shape identical to the 1s, except larger, called the 2s orbital. This means that the electron with this greater amount of energy will spend more of its time farther from the nucleus. There is also a new shape: a p orbital. As $n = 2$, we call it a 2p orbital and it resembles a dumbbell or long balloon pinched in the middle (where the nucleus is located).

The Third Quantum Number (m_ℓ)

The third quantum number, called the **magnetic quantum number** (m_ℓ) tells us the orientation in space of a given atomic orbital.

The number of possible different orientations in space for any orbital shape also represents the number of individual orbitals of that particular shape or sublevel.

Only a single s orbital exists in any given energy level because a spherical cloud can only have one orientation in 3D space. However, this new p sublevel includes three separate orbitals, each with a different spatial orientation. If we consider a 3D set of Cartesian coordinates, one is oriented along an imaginary *x*-axis (with the nucleus at the origin) called a $2p_x$ orbital. The other two are oriented along the *y*- and *z*-axes and are called the $2p_y$ and $2p_z$ orbitals respectively. Each of these 2p orbitals is identical in energy to the others. For hydrogen, they are also identical in energy to the 2s orbital. Chemists call orbitals of equal energy "degenerate" orbitals.

In Figure 2.5.2, note that the lobes of each p orbital in the first three diagrams disappear at the origin where the nucleus is located. This means that the amplitude of the electron wave at the nucleus is zero. A wave amplitude of zero is called a node, and it tells us that there is a zero probability of locating the electron here. In the far left diagram in Figure 2.5.2, all three 2p orbitals are shown together. Once again, the nucleus is at the centre or origin.

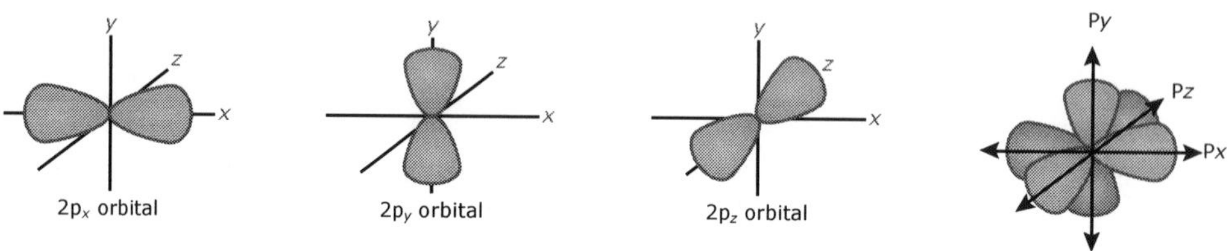

Figure 2.5.2 *The p orbitals are each shown individually in the first three diagrams. The last diagram shows them all together.*

We noted earlier that the number of different sublevels in any energy level equals the value of *n*. We also see here that a total of four orbitals exists in the second energy level. So the value n^2 tells us the number of orbitals existing in the nth energy level. In this case, there are $2^2 = 4$ orbitals: one 2s and three 2p orbitals.

The three quantum numbers, taken together, will always specify a particular atomic orbital because they tell us all we need to know about that orbital: its size, shape, and orientation in space.

If hydrogen's electron absorbs enough energy to reach the third allowed energy state, then $n = 3$ and three different orbital shapes or sublevels exist. As expected, we see one spherical 3s orbital and three dumbbell-shaped 3p orbitals. But we also discover a third sublevel whose orbitals have a more complicated shape. This is called the 3d sublevel and it contains five different orbitals, each with a different spatial orientation. Orbitals in a given sublevel are equal in energy to each other, and in hydrogen's case, are also equal in energy to all of the other orbitals in the energy level. This means that in a given energy level, hydrogen's electron has an equal likelihood of occupying any of them.

Although the d orbitals are shown in Figure 2.5.3, you may not be required to remember either their shapes or their names. You should, however, know that there are five of them.

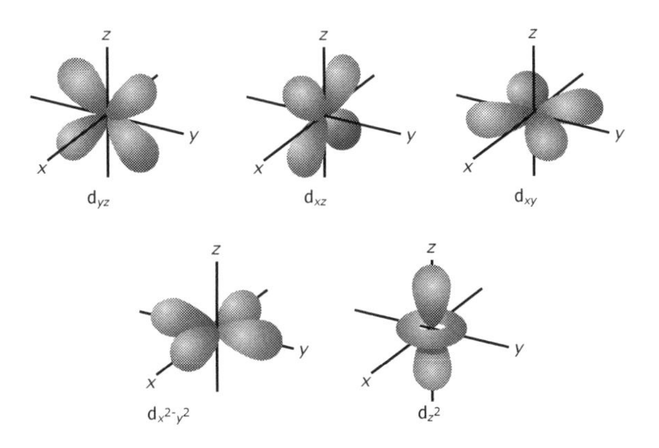

Figure 2.5.3 *The d orbitals*

Notice that as $n = 3$, there are three sublevels: 3s, 3p, and 3d. Also, there are a total of nine orbitals: one 3s orbital, three 3p orbitals, and five 3d orbitals corresponding to 3^2.

Finally, let's elevate hydrogen's electron to the fourth energy level, where $n = 4$. A higher energy level means that the electron will spend more of its time farther from the nucleus than when it possesses energy equal to $n = 1, 2,$ or 3. Therefore, the orbitals or "charge clouds" are larger.

In the fourth energy level, we see the expected 4s, three 4p, and five 4d orbitals. As well, because $n = 4$, we also see a fourth shape called the 4f sublevel. Each higher energy level introduces another sublevel with a greater number (by two) of more complicated orbitals than the previous ones, and so there are seven 4f orbitals, each with a more complicated shape than the d orbitals. You should remember the number of f orbitals as well. The fourth energy level results in $4^2 = 16$ orbitals: one 4s, three 4p, five 4d, and seven 4f orbitals, all of which are equal in energy in the case of hydrogen.

Let's summarize what we have learned about energy levels and orbitals using a table and a diagram. Table 2.5.1 shows the sublevels and orbitals for the first four energy levels. Figure 2.5.4 is the energy diagram for hydrogen showing the sublevels and orbitals present from $n = 1$ through $n = 4$. Each circle represents an orbital. Note that all the sublevels are of equal energy in each allowed energy state.

Table 2.5.1 *Sublevels and orbitals for the first four energy levels*

Principal Quantum Number or Energy Level (n)	Number of Orbital Shapes or Sublevels per Energy Level (n)	Total Number of Orbitals per Energy Level (n^2)
1	**1** – 1s sublevel	**1** – the 1s orbital
2	**2** – 2s sublevel 2p sublevel	**4** – one 2s orbital three 2p orbitals
3	**3** – 3s sublevel 3p sublevel 3d sublevel	**9** – one 3s orbital three 3p orbitals five 3d orbitals
4	**4** – 4s sublevel 4p sublevel 4d sublevel 4f sublevel	**16** – one 4s orbital three 4p orbitals five 4d orbitals seven 4f orbitals

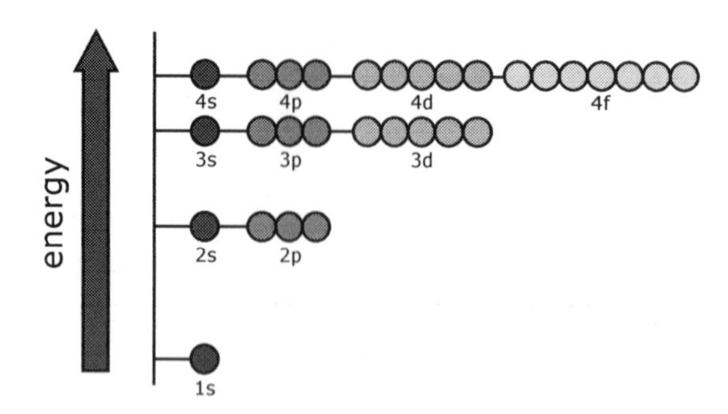

Figure 2.5.4 *Energy diagram for hydrogen. Each circle represents an orbital*

Quick Check

1. State what each of the three quantum numbers described above tells us about atomic orbitals.

____

____

2. (a) What is the difference between a 1s and a 2s orbital?

____

(b) What is the difference between a $2p_x$ orbital and a $2p_y$ orbital?

____

3. How many different orbitals are available to an excited hydrogen electron in the fourth energy level?

____

The Orbitals of Multi-Electron Atoms

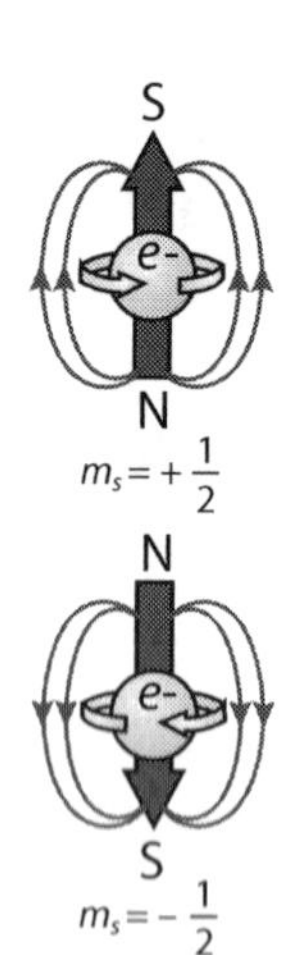

Figure 2.5.5 *The spin quantum number (m_s) identifies which possible spin an electron has.*

Hydrogen is the simplest atom with one proton in the nucleus surrounded by one electron in a 1s orbital in its ground state. There are no electron-electron interactions, and in any excited state, all of the atomic orbitals available to that single electron are of equal energy.

We might expect a different situation, however, for multi-electron atoms. Electrons are charged particle-waves. It seems reasonable to conclude that they will affect each other when two or more of them occupy the same region of space around an atom's nucleus — and they do.

To describe those electrons in multi-electron atoms, we must introduce several additional considerations.

Experiments have shown that the single electron in hydrogen generates a tiny magnetic field as if the electron were a spinning charge. Also, in any sample of hydrogen, analyzing the many atoms present shows two opposing magnetic fields. This tells us that in half of the atoms, the electrons seem to spin in one direction and, in the remainder of the atoms, in the other direction. An electron's spin is as fundamental a part of its nature as its charge.

The fourth quantum number is called the **spin quantum number** (m_s). It tells us the two possible electron spins, either +½ or –½.

The Pauli Exclusion Principle

We already know that we can identify any orbital in an atom by the use of the first three quantum numbers, but we must use all four quantum numbers mentioned to specify any electron in an atom.

This is based on the fact that any atomic orbital can hold a maximum of two electrons. When two electrons are in the same orbital, their spins must be opposite. Originally proposed in 1925 by the Austrian physicist Wolfgang Pauli, this can be viewed as the first rule governing electrons in multi-electron atoms.

1. The **Pauli exclusion principle**: No two electrons in the same atom can be described by the same set of four quantum numbers.

If two electrons are in the same atomic orbital, they therefore have the same first three quantum numbers. Because they then must have opposite spins, their fourth quantum numbers are different.

We noted earlier that the total number of orbitals existing in any level n equals n^2.

If two electrons can occupy each orbital, the maximum number of electrons that can exist in any energy level n is given by $2n^2$.

A further consideration for multi-electron atoms is the effect of electron-electron repulsions on the relative energies of the sublevels in a given energy level. For hydrogen, where no repulsive forces exist, all of the sublevels in any energy level have identical energies. This is not the case for atoms of other elements. Although the same types of orbitals exist in multi-electron atoms, their relative energies are different. Repulsive forces cause a sublevel with a greater number of orbitals to have a greater energy. Therefore the order of sublevel energies is:

$s < p < d < f$.

Consider Figure 2.5.6. Compare this energy diagram for a multi-electron atom with Figure 2.5.4 for hydrogen. Note that in several cases energies get closer together as n increases. In these cases, repulsive forces are such that some sublevels containing smaller orbitals actually have higher energies than some larger orbitals. For example, observe the relative energy of the 3d compared to the 4s sublevel.

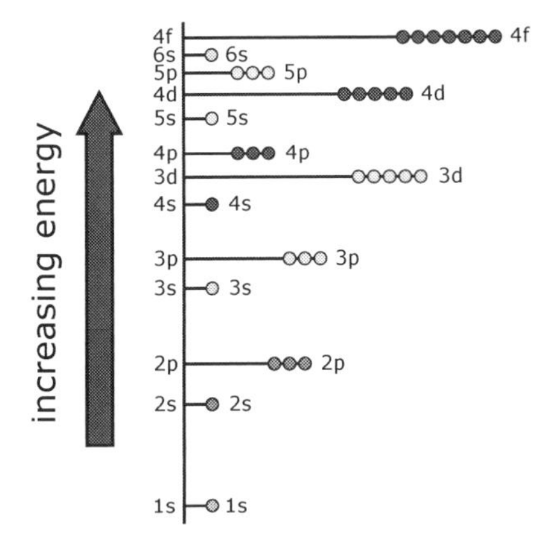

Figure 2.5.6 *Energy diagram for multi-electron atoms*

Quick Check

1. What does the fourth quantum number tell us about electrons?

____

2. Why can't two electrons in the same atom have the same four quantum numbers?

____

3. What is the maximum number of electrons that can exist in the energy levels $n = 1$ through $n = 4$?

____

Electron Configurations and Orbital Diagrams

We are now in a position to organize electrons into orbitals for the atoms of the elements. Understanding this organization will prove to be a powerful tool as we discuss the periodic table and bonding in the next chapter. In beginnning this process, we introduce the second rule associated with describing electrons in multi-electron atoms.

2. The **Aufbau principle**: When filling orbitals, the lowest energy orbitals available are always filled first. ("Aufbau" means a building or a construction in German.)

The order for filling orbitals is given above in Figure 2.5.6, showing sublevel energies. We start at the lowest energy orbitals and move up.

Let's begin with hydrogen. In its lowest energy or ground state, hydrogen's electron exists in the 1s orbital. We can represent this in two ways:

1. We can use a shorthand notation called an **electron configuration,** which is written in the format $n\ell^{\#\text{number of electrons}}$ showing the energy level, sublevel, and number of electrons respectively. Hydrogen's electron configuration is therefore written as: $1s^1$. Read as "one s one," this tells us that hydrogen's one electron resides in the 1s orbital in its ground state.
2. We can construct an **orbital diagram**, which depicts electrons and their spin using arrows facing up and down. The arrows are placed inside boxes or over lines representing individual orbitals in sublevels. Hydrogen's orbital diagram is shown as:

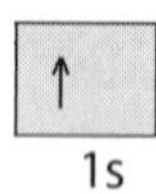

1s

The configuration for the next element, helium, is $1s^2$. This is read "one s two" rather than "one s squared." Following the Pauli exclusion principle, the orbital diagram shows the two electrons with opposite spins in the now full 1s orbital:

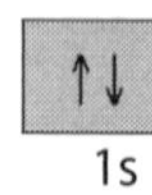

1s

To indicate increasing sublevel energy, the boxes can be written vertically or also left to right to save space on a page. Let's continue below by moving past helium to the elements in period 2 of the periodic table using horizontally written orbital diagrams.

Note that period 2 corresponds to the second energy level, $n = 2$. Following the Aufbau principle:

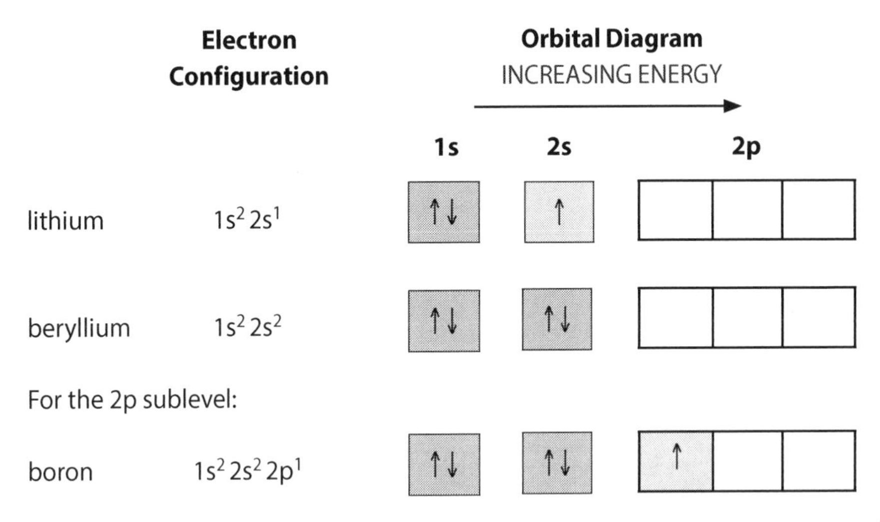

Note that the sum of the superscript numbers equals the total number of electrons present.

We must now use the third rule governing orbitals in multi-electron atoms:

> 3. **Hund's rule:** When orbitals of equal energy are being filled, the most stable configuration is the one with the maximum number of unpaired electrons with the same spin.

So carbon and nitrogen's orbital diagrams are:

		1s	2s	2p		
carbon	$1s^2 2s^2 2p^2$	↑↓	↑↓	↑	↑	
nitrogen	$1s^2 2s^2 2p^3$	↑↓	↑↓	↑	↑	↑

After nitrogen, we must again begin to pair electrons:

		1s	2s	2p		
oxygen	$1s^2 2s^2 2p^4$	↑↓	↑↓	↑↓	↑	↑
fluorine	$1s^2 2s^2 2p^5$	↑↓	↑↓	↑↓	↑↓	↑
neon	$1s^2 2s^2 2p^6$	↑↓	↑↓	↑↓	↑↓	↑↓

After a noble gas, a new period begins in the periodic table and so too, a new energy level. As we begin period 3, let's represent the elements up to scandium in Table 2.5.2 using electron configurations only. We can condense electron configurations using **core notation**, in which the configuration of the previous noble gas is represented by that noble gas symbol in square brackets as shown in the table. Outer electrons are indicated in **bold** type.

Table 2.5.2 *Electron Configurations of Period 3 Elements up to Scandium*

Element	Full Electron Configuration	Core Notation
sodium	$1s^2 2s^2 2p^6 \mathbf{3s^1}$	[Ne] $\mathbf{3s^1}$
magnesium	$1s^2 2s^2 2p^6 \mathbf{3s^2}$	[Ne] $\mathbf{3s^2}$
aluminum	$1s^2 2s^2 2p^6 \mathbf{3s^2 3p^1}$	[Ne] $\mathbf{3s^2 3p^1}$
silicon	$1s^2 2s^2 2p^6 \mathbf{3s^2 3p^2}$	[Ne] $\mathbf{3s^2 3p^2}$
phosphorus	$1s^2 2s^2 2p^6 \mathbf{3s^2 3p^3}$	[Ne] $\mathbf{3s^2 3p^3}$
sulfur	$1s^2 2s^2 2p^6 \mathbf{3s^2 3p^4}$	[Ne] $\mathbf{3s^2 3p^4}$
chlorine	$1s^2 2s^2 2p^6 \mathbf{3s^2 3p^5}$	[Ne] $\mathbf{3s^2 3p^5}$
argon	$1s^2 2s^2 2p^6 \mathbf{3s^2 3p^6}$	[Ne] $\mathbf{3s^2 3p^6}$
potassium	$1s^2 2s^2 2p^6 3s^2 3p^6 \mathbf{4s^1}$	[Ar] $\mathbf{4s^1}$
calcium	$1s^2 2s^2 2p^6 3s^2 3p^6 \mathbf{4s^2}$	[Ar] $\mathbf{4s^2}$
scandium	$1s^2 2s^2 2p^6 3s^2 3p^6 \mathbf{4s^2 3d^1}$	[Ar] $\mathbf{4s^2 3d^1}$

Notice in the table that, as we move from argon to potassium, the 4s sublevel starts to fill before the 3d sublevel. After the 4s sublevel, the 3d sublevel starts to fill, reaching the first transition metal, scandium. Although the 3d sublevel fills after the 4s sublevel, the 3d sublevel still contains electrons that spend most of their time nearer the nucleus and so is inside the 4s sublevel. Some periodic tables indicate the electron configurations in order of sublevel size and so will show scandium's configuration as [Ar] $3d^1 4s^2$.

Figure 2.5.7 is a simple way of remembering the order for filling sublevels. We begin at the top with the 1s and fill that sublevel. After reaching the end of each arrow, we then start at the top of the next arrow below it. When using this diagram, you must remember how many electrons each sublevel can hold.

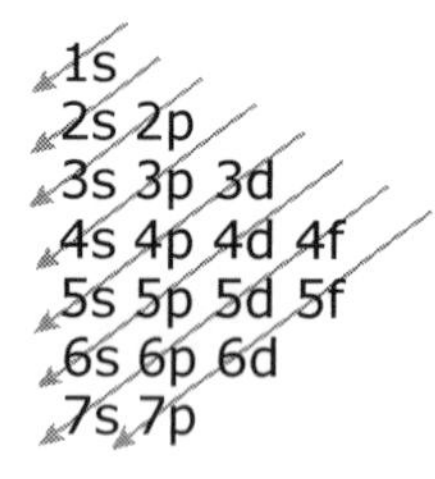

Figure 2.5.7 *This diagram indicates the order for filling sublevels.*

Sample Problem — Drawing an Orbital Diagram

Draw the orbital diagram and write the full electron configuration and the core notation for an atom of cobalt in its ground state.

What to Think about

1. Cobalt's atomic number is 27 and so the orbital diagram must account for 27 electrons. Cobalt is a transition metal in period 4 in the periodic table. We should expect the highest energy electrons to be in the 3d subshell.
2. Remember how many electrons are placed in each subshell as you fill the orbitals and employ Hund's rule as necessary.
3. Sketch the diagonal diagram to help you remember the order that subshells fill.
4. Represent each electron in an orbital using an arrow as in the notation described above.

How to Do It

Orbital diagram for cobalt:

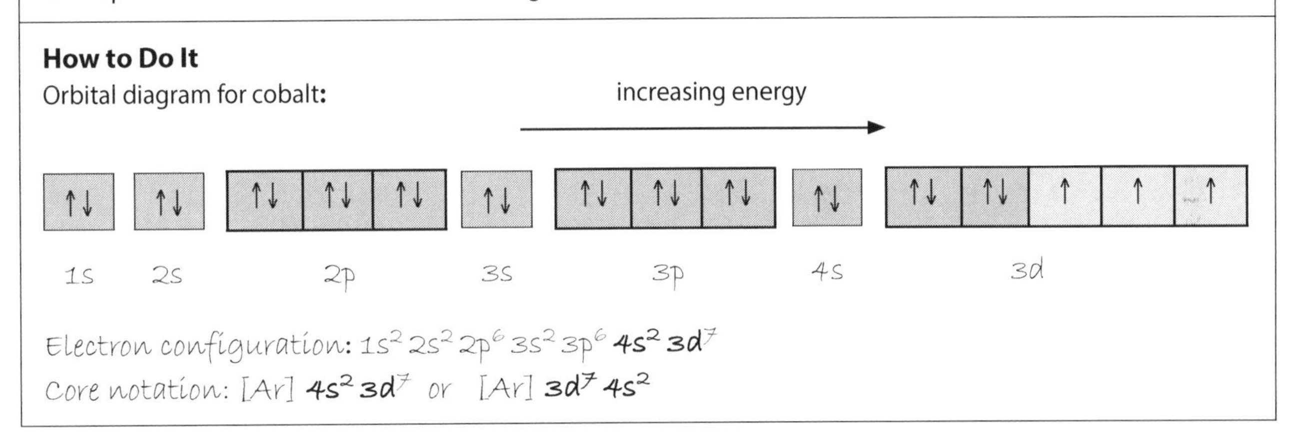

Electron configuration: $1s^2 2s^2 2p^6 3s^2 3p^6 4s^2 3d^7$

Core notation: [Ar] $4s^2 3d^7$ or [Ar] $3d^7 4s^2$

Practice Problem — Drawing an Orbital Diagram

1. Write the full electron configuration and draw the orbital diagram for an atom of titanium in its ground state.

Ions and Other Charged Topics

Recall that a cation has fewer electrons than the original neutral atom and an anion has more. This means that the electron configurations for ions will be different than those for neutral atoms.

The process is easily shown using examples. To write the electron configuration for the S^{2-} anion, we simply need to add two more electrons to the last unfilled sublevel. Thus the configuration: $1s^2\,2s^2\,2p^6\,3s^2\,3p^{\mathbf{4}}$ for the S atom becomes: $1s^2\,2s^2\,2p^6\,3s^2\,3p^{\mathbf{6}}$ for the S^{2-} anion. Notice that the sulfide anion now has the same electron configuration as the nearest noble gas argon. The sulfide ion is therefore considered to be **isoelectronic** with argon because the two species have the same number and configuration of electrons.

To write cation configurations, electrons are always removed *from the outermost orbitals with the highest energy first*. Therefore, it is sometimes worthwhile to first write the neutral atom's configuration in core notation with the final orbitals listed from smallest to largest, rather than in the order the orbitals fill. Then remove the appropriate electrons from the outer orbitals first.

For example, if asked to write the configuration for the Sn^{4+} ion, first write the configuration for a neutral Sn atom as [Kr] $4d^{10}$ $\mathbf{5s^2\,5p^2}$ rather than writing [Kr] $\mathbf{5s^2}$ $4d^{10}$ $\mathbf{5p^2}$.

Now remove the four *outermost* electrons to give the configuration for Sn^{4+}: [Kr] $4d^{10}$. This avoids the error of removing two 4d electrons to give [Kr] $\mathbf{5s^2}$ $4d^8$. Note that an Sn^{2+} ion would form by losing the two 5p electrons, as they are at higher energy than the 5s.

As a final note, there are several exceptions to the orbital filling order discussed here. The elements Cr, Cu, Mo, Ag, and Au are examples of such exceptions. Your teacher may choose to discuss these and others and the possible reasons.

We shouldn't be surprised that irregularities exist. We have already seen ample evidence that the quantum world is full of surprises!

2.5 Activity: A Post-it® Periodic Table

Question

Can we organize a series of Post-it® notes on a standard periodic table to represent the order that orbitals are filled according the Aufbau principle?

Materials

- a small pad of each of four different colors of Post-it® or other sticky notes
- transparent tape

Procedure

Refer to the diagonal diagram in Figure 2.5.7 showing the order for filling sublevels.

1.. Obtain a pad of small Post-it® or other sticky notes. Choose a separate color for each of the four shapes, s, p, d, and f, and write the symbol for each of the 19 sublevels (1s, 2s, 2p, etc....) on a separate note.

2. Place the notes from left to right on a flat surface in the correct order that each sublevel fills.

3. Obtain a copy of the periodic table from your teacher. Number each horizontal period of the table, beginning with 1 for the top period containing H and He, down to 7 for Fr.

4. Now "read" the periods left-to-right like words on a page, moving down at the end of each. Trim the bottom portion of each Post-it® note to fit, and stick the appropriate sublevel symbol onto each section of each period as you read it.

Results and Discussion

1. Once you're finished, confirm the correct location of each Post-it® note sublevel symbol with your teacher. Then place transparent tape over each to permanently attach it to the periodic table. Save this completed table for the discussion coming up in the next chapter.

2.5 Review Questions

1. If hydrogen's electron exists in a spherical orbital, why doesn't this mean that the electron moves around the nucleus in a circle?

2. What is the difference between a 1s orbital and a 2s orbital? What does that difference indicate about an electron possessing energy equal to $n = 2$ as compared to $n = 1$?

3. Describe the two differences between a $2p_x$ orbital and a $3p_y$ orbital.

4. The lobes of a p orbital disappear at the nucleus. What does this tell us about electrons in p orbitals?

5. You may have heard in previous science classes that the maximum numbers of electrons that can exist in the first four energy levels are 2, 8, 8, and 18 respectively. Do you agree with those numbers and if not, what should they be?

6. The electron configuration for phosphorus, written in core notation, is [Ne] $3s^2\,3p^3$.
What two things does Hund's rule tell us about the three electrons in the 3p sublevel?

7. Use the periodic table to complete the following table:

Atom or Ion	Full Electron Configuration	Core Notation
Ge		
Zn^{2+}		
Sr		
Br^-		
Sn		
In^{3+}		

8. (a) Use the periodic table to identify the neutral atoms having the following electron configurations:

Electron Configuration	Element Name
[Ne] $3\mathbf{s}^2$	
[Ar] $4s^2\,3\mathbf{d}^5$	
[Kr] $5s^2\,4d^{10}\,5\mathbf{p}^3$	
[Xe] $6s^2\,4\mathbf{f}^7$	

(b) Notice where each of these elements is located on the periodic table. Look at the highest energy sublevel being filled (**bold type**) in each of the atoms in the table, and identify the four different sections of the periodic table associated with each of these four sublevels.

9. Consider the following six stable ions: N^{3-}, O^{2-}, F^-, Na^+, Mg^{2+}, and Al^{3+}.
(a) How many electrons are present in each ion?

(b) Write a single electron configuration representing all of the ions.

(c) Which neutral atom possesses this electron configuration? What does this suggest about a possible reason for some ion formation?

10. (a) Complete the following table for some elements in two families of the periodic table.

Alkali Metals	Core Notation	# Outer Electrons	Halogens	Core Notation	# Outer Electrons
lithium			fluorine		
sodium			chlorine		
potassium			bromine		
rubidium			iodine		

(b) Consider the numbers of outer electrons present and suggest a reason why elements belonging to the same chemical family demonstrate similar chemical behaviour.

(c) What change occurs in the atoms as we move down each chemical family?

11. (a) On a separate sheet of paper, draw an orbital diagram for an atom of iron with sublevel energy increasing vertically. Arrange equal energy orbitals in each sublevel horizontally.

(b) Use a highlighter to label the electrons that would be lost when the Fe^{3+} cation forms.

2.6 Quantum Theory and the Bohr Model of the Atom

The Bohr Model

One of the scientists who paid particular attention to the work of Planck and Einstein was a young Danish physicist named Niels Bohr. As a young grad student, Bohr had met Ernest Rutherford at the Cavendish Laboratory in Cambridge and then worked with Rutherford at the University of Manchester. Bohr believed in the nuclear atomic model and started to see a way to "save" it using the quantum theory. If energy was indeed quantized and so could be seen to have only certain values and not others, perhaps the energies associated with electrons orbiting the nucleus had similar restrictions.

Bohr was working on this idea at Rutherford's laboratory in Manchester in 1912. In the middle of his experiments and calculations, he returned to Copenhagen to get married. He was so excited about his work that he managed to convince his new bride to cancel their honeymoon and return to England with him. Soon thereafter, Niels Bohr completed one of the most brilliant papers on atomic structure ever written. In doing so, he managed to rescue Rutherford's nuclear model of the atom.

Scientific theories are carefully constructed on a firm foundation of data gathered from a multitude of meticulously documented, rigorously controlled, and perpetually repeatable experiments. Bohr's theory was no exception. In Grade 11, we discussed the conduction of charges through gases in glass discharge tubes. Those experiments in the later years of the 1800s not only led to Thomson's discovery of the electron, but also provided Bohr with valuable data for his ideas about the nature of those electrons in atoms.

Quantum Theory Rescues the Nuclear Model

Bohr knew that when high voltage was applied across the electrodes of a sealed glass tube containing a gas such as hydrogen, the gas was heated and emitted light. As part of his investigations, Bohr looked at this light through a spectroscope. A spectroscope is a device similar to a prism, which separates the light into its component wavelengths. When Bohr viewed the light from the heated hydrogen through the spectroscope, he saw only a series of coloured lines against a black background, rather than a continuous rainbow of colour. For hydrogen, the same pattern of four coloured lines was always seen: a red, blue-green, blue, and violet line (Figure 2.6.1). For each gaseous element used, a bright-line pattern unique to that element called a **bright-line spectrum** always appeared (much like a bar code on a modern grocery item).

The phenomenon had mystified scientists. None could explain why only certain colours of light, each corresponding to specific wavelength, frequency, and energy, were emitted by the heated gases — until Bohr. Bohr realized that by applying quantum principles to the behaviour of hydrogen's lone electron, he could not only account for the existence of the bright-line spectrum, but also save Rutherford's nuclear model of the atom.

Figure 2.6.1 *Hydrogen's bright-line spectrum*

Bohr's Postulates

Bohr's postulates for hydrogen are summarized below:

1. The hydrogen atom had only certain **allowed energy levels** or **stationary states.** Each of these states corresponded to a circular electron orbit of a fixed size. The larger the allowed orbit, the greater the energy associated with it. No other orbits existed in the atom. Each allowed energy state was given an integer number "*n*" that Bohr called a **quantum number** with allowed values that ranged from 1 to ∞ (i.e., *n* could equal 1, 2, 3…etc). The lowest energy (smallest) orbit corresponded to the lowest allowed energy state called the **ground state** and was designated as $n = 1$. The larger orbits of greater energy were designated as $n = 2$, $n = 3$, $n = 4$, etc. and were said to be **excited states.**

2. As long as an electron moved in an allowed orbit or stationary state, the electron (and therefore the atom) did not radiate or absorb energy.

3. The electron could only move from one allowed orbit to another if it absorbed or emitted an amount of energy exactly equal to the energy difference between the two orbits, ΔE. This meant that the hydrogen atom could only change from one stationary energy state to another.

Bohr's Postulates — Another Look

Postulate 1 employed Planck's theory by quantizing the energies allowed for the hydrogen atom (and thus the electron). Because only certain-sized orbits were allowed, the atom was restricted to existing in only certain energy states and not others. Think of the electron as a ball on a staircase. Just as the ball can only rest on any particular stair and so have only certain amounts of potential energy and not others, so too is the electron restricted to only specific energies.

Postulate 2 meant that the nuclear model of the atom proposed by Rutherford would not collapse as predicted. Although the postulate violated the laws of classical physics, Bohr insisted that it must be true, even though he didn't know why.

Postulates 1 and 3 explained the origin and nature of hydrogen's bright-line spectrum. An atomic spectrum could not be continuous (i.e., a complete rainbow of colours) because an atom's energy states could only be certain values and not others. When a sample of hydrogen gas is heated in a discharge tube, the electrons in the hydrogen atoms absorb sufficient amounts of energy to "jump" to larger orbits. (In any one hydrogen atom, only one electron is involved, but in a sample of the gas, the electrons of many hydrogen atoms are undergoing many transitions). Once in a higher energy orbit, any electron could then return to a lower energy orbit by emitting a specific amount of energy corresponding exactly to the difference between the higher and lower energy orbits (Figure 2.6.2). If the frequency of that emitted energy corresponds to any part of the visible spectrum, then a bright line of that specific colour would be seen. Four of hydrogen's electron transitions emitted energy in the visible spectrum.

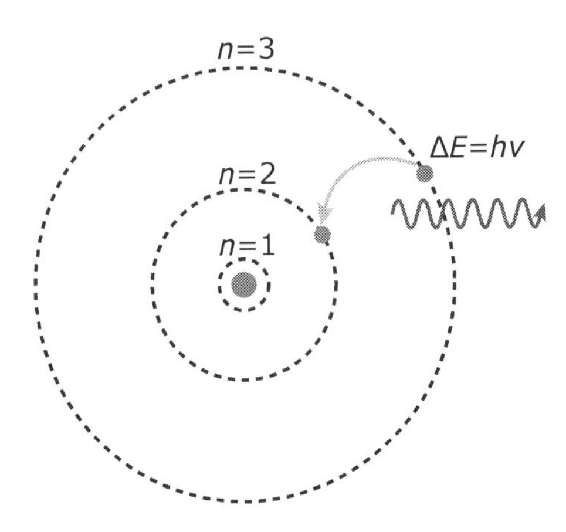

Figure 2.6.2 *When the electron moves to an inner energy level, it emits energy.*

If an excited electron emits energy and drops to $n = 2$ from a higher energy orbit, the wavelength of the emitted energy corresponds to a particular colour of visible light. If an electron drops from $n = 3$ to $n = 2$, the energy difference between the two orbits (and therefore the energy emitted) corresponds to that of red light. Hence the red line appears in the emission spectrum. The blue-green line results from an electron transition from $n = 4$ to $n = 2$, the blue line from an electron transition from $n = 5$ to $n = 2$, and the violet line from an electron transition from $n = 6$ to $n = 2$. This series of four bright lines in the visible spectrum is called the Balmer series, named after the Swiss schoolteacher who first derived a mathematical relationship between the lines in hydrogen's visible emission spectrum (Figure 2.6.3).

Bohr's model of the hydrogen atom was successful in explaining the mystery of bright line spectra. His calculations and predictions worked for hydrogen and he even calculated the radius of the orbit for hydrogen's electron in its ground state. In 1922, Niels Bohr was awarded the Nobel Prize in physics.

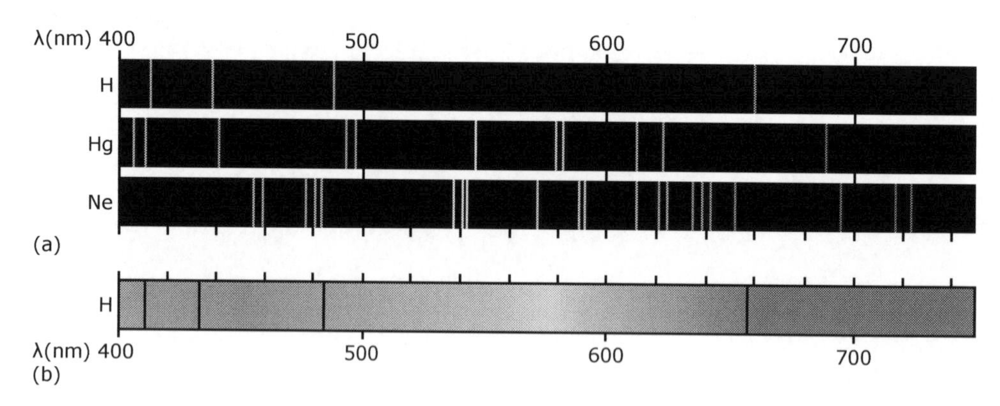

Figure 2.6.3 *(a) The emission spectra of hydrogen, mercury, and neon; (b) The absorption spectrum of hydrogen*

The Emission Spectrum of Hydrogen — Two Views

The diagram on the left in Figure 2.6.4 shows the circular orbits Bohr envisioned for the hydrogen electron and the transitions associated with the Lyman, Balmer, and Paschen emission spectra. The diagram on the right shows that the energy *differences* between various stationary states (n) decrease as the energies of those states increase. The arrows pointing down represent electrons falling to lower energy states and thus emitting energy. Electrons absorbing energy could be indicated by arrows pointing up and would represent absorption spectra.

Any electron transitions from an excited state down to $n = 1$ result in the emission of energy in the ultraviolet region of the electromagnetic spectrum (the Lyman series). Any transitions from excited states down to the third and fourth orbits result in energies in the infrared region being emitted (the Paschen and Brackett series respectively).

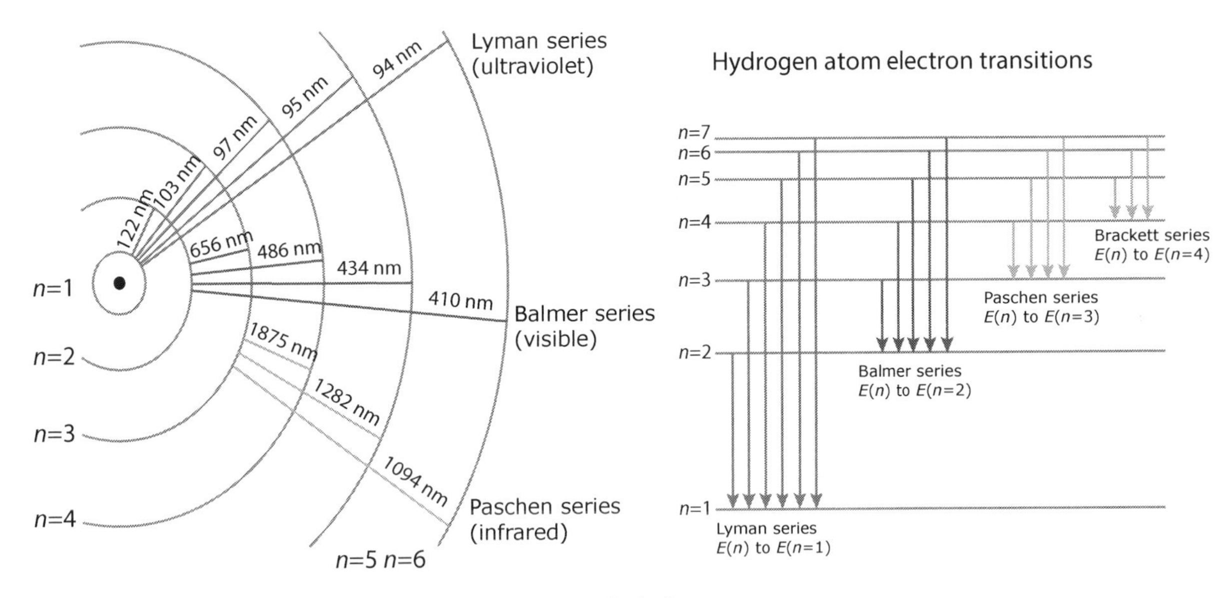

Figure 2.6.4 *The Lyman, Balmer, and Paschen emission series for hydrogen*

Quick Check

1. Describe the appearance of hydrogen's "bright-line" spectrum.

 ____

2. Briefly indicate how electrons generate each visible line in hydrogen's emission spectrum.

 ____

 ____

3. Which electron transitions in the emission spectrum generate lines in the UV region of the electromagnetic spectrum?

 ____

Equations for Calculating Energy, Wavelength and Frequency of Electrons in the Hydrogen Atom

In 1885, a Swiss schoolteacher named Johann Balmer found an equation that was able to determine the wavelengths of the lines in the visible portion of hydrogen's emission spectrum. Three years later, the Swedish physicist Johannes Rydberg derived an equation which used the Rydberg constant, $R_\infty = 1.097 \times 10^7 \text{ m}^{-1}$, that could be used to calculate the wavelengths of all of hydrogen's spectral lines.
This is worth mentioning because if a mathematical relationship exists for a natural phenomenon, it usually means there's a theoretical foundation waiting to be discovered. Both Balmer's and Rydberg's equations were based on data, rather than theory. Neither equation had any physical meaning in terms of atomic structure, but both worked.

The physical meaning was supplied by Niels Bohr. Bohr derived an equation for the energy associated with the electron in each allowed orbit. He correctly predicted the visible, ultraviolet, and infrared spectral lines in hydrogen's emission spectrum by calculating the energy differences between those stationary states.

Bohr proposed equation, to explain the stability of the hydrogen atom. The first equation *we will present* gives the change in energy ΔE (energy of photon released) when an electron initially in a higher energy orbit (with a higher quantum number n_h) drops to a lower energy orbit (and so with a lower quantum number n_l).

$$\Delta E = R\left(1/n_l^2 - 1/n_h^2\right)$$

The second equation arises from the fact that, according to Planck's equation, the energy of this photon, $\Delta E = hv$. Because $v = c/\lambda$, we can replace ΔE with hc/λ. Now dividing both sides of the equation by hc yields:

$$1/\lambda = R/\ hc\left(1/n_l^2 - 1/n_h^2\right)$$

This equation allows us to solve for the wavelength λ of the spectral line we would observe when the electron lost energy as it made the above transition.

The combination of the constants, R/hc, is itself a constant. Remembering that Planck's constant, $h = 6.626 \times 10^{-34}$ J·s and that the speed of light, $c = 3.00 \times 10^8$ m/s, we can combine these three constants to give $R/hc = 1.097\ 30 \times 10^7\ \text{m}^{-1}$. Let's use this to calculate the wavelength of the spectral line we would see when hydrogen's electron made the transition from $n = 4$ down to $n = 2$.

Sample Problem — Calculating the Wavelength of Emission Spectral Lines

Calculate the wavelength λ (in nm) of the spectral line seen in hydrogen's emission spectrum when hydrogen's electron falls from the fourth allowed orbit ($n = 4$) to the second allowed orbit ($n = 2$).

What to Think about	How to Do It
1. Consider the equation: $1/\lambda = (1.097\ 30 \times 10^7\ \text{m}^{-1})\left(1/n_l^2 - 1/n_h^2\right)$ The values of n_l and n_h are given in the question: $n = 4$ and $n = 2$.	$1/\lambda = (1.097\ 30 \times 10^7\ \text{m}^{-1})\left(1/n_l^2 - 1/n_h^2\right)$ $= (1.097\ 30 \times 10^7\ \text{m}^{-1})\left(1/2^2 - 1/4^2\right)$ $= (1.097\ 30 \times 10^7\ \text{m}^{-1})(0.1875)$ $= 2.0574 \times 10^6\ \text{m}^{-1}$
2. Convert this to nanometers. This value corresponds exactly to the green line seen in hydrogen's emission spectrum.	$\lambda = \dfrac{1}{2.0574 \times 10^6\ \text{m}^{-1}} = 4.8604 \times 10^{-7}\ \text{m}$ $4.860 \times 10^{-7}\ \text{m} \times \dfrac{1.0 \times 10^9\ \text{nm}}{\text{m}} = 486.04\ \text{nm}$

Practice Problem

1. Use equation $\Delta E = R\left(1/n_l^2 - 1/n_h^2\right)$ and the value for b given above to calculate the energy released when an excited hydrogen electron drops from the fourth allowed orbit ($n = 4$) to the second allowed orbit ($n = 2$).

Quick Check

1. (a) List three properties of waves such as water waves or visible light.

   ____

   (b) What would you expect to happen when two water waves moving in opposite directions met each other?

   ____

2. (a) List three properties of solid objects or particles such as the marbles in a bag.

   ____

   (b) What would you expect to happen when two marbles moving in opposite directions met each other?

   ____

3. Are any of your answers to question 1 identical to question 2? (Stay tuned…)

   ____

Waves Particle Duality

A serious challenge to Rutherford's atomic model arose almost immediately. A very secure prediction of the physics available at the end of the 1800s was that accelerating charges should radiate energy. Because orbiting electrons are accelerating charges, electrons in atoms should lose energy. That prediction was catastrophic for Rutherford's model. It meant that all atoms, and so also all matter, should collapse in a fraction of a second as their electrons lost energy and spiraled into the nucleus! Obviously, a significant piece of the atomic puzzle was missing and even Rutherford himself was ready to abandon his view of the atom. Yet, his conclusions and his nuclear model were correct. The real problem was that the physics of the day needed to be re-written to explain the behaviour of electrons in atoms.

To begin to understand how the solution came about, we must consider the work of German physicist Max Planck. In 1900, this conservative professor began nothing short of a revolution in physics. He proposed that energy, long considered to be strictly a wave phenomenon, could be shown to behave like particles in the form of very tiny, discreet energy packets or bundles he called quanta (plural for quantum). Planck called this the quantum theory and arrived at his conclusions (reluctantly) by studying the energy radiated from heated solids. Planck developed the following equation for the energy associated with each packet or quantum:

$$\boldsymbol{E = hv}$$

where $\boldsymbol{E}$ = energy, $\boldsymbol{v}$ = frequency, $\boldsymbol{h}$ = a very tiny proportionality constant ($h = 6.626 \times 10^{-34}$ J·s) called Planck's constant. According to Planck, energy could only be absorbed or emitted in whole numbers of quanta, that is, one quantum of energy ($E = hv$), two quanta ($E = 2hv$), three quanta ($E = 3hv$) and so on, but nowhere in between. Think of each energy quantum as a glass marble in a bag of identical marbles (Figure 2.6.5). In the same way that you could only ever add or remove a specific amount of glass from the bag in the form of a whole number of marbles, so too could amounts of energy only be absorbed or emitted in the form of whole numbers of quanta.

Figure 2.6.5 *Quanta of energy are like marbles in bag. The marbles can only be removed as whole units.*

At the end of the 1800s, the behaviour of waves and the behaviour of particles were seen as very different and mutually exclusive. Waves were disturbances that moved through space, could pass through and interfere with each other, and could have any value within a range. Particles were objects with definite boundaries that bounced off each other when they collided and could only exist in certain whole-number quantities. A firm experimental and mathematical foundation supported the idea that waves were fundamentally different from particles. To now suggest that waves could behave like particles was almost sacrilegious! Planck himself wrote about his work: "By nature, I am peacefully inclined and reject all doubtful adventures. …However, a theoretical interpretation had to be found at any cost….I was ready to sacrifice every one of my previous convictions about physical laws."

Planck's theory wasn't taken very seriously at first. But in 1905, a 26-year-old clerk in a Swiss patent office named Albert Einstein wrote five papers that changed the scientific world forever. One of those papers used the quantum theory to explain a phenomenon involving light called the "photoelectric effect" that had baffled physicists until then. According to Einstein, the only way to make sense of the photoelectric effect was to consider light as being composed of tiny discreet packets of energy. (These were later called "photons" by American chemist Gilbert Lewis.) Einstein's paper was the first practical application of the quantum theory and as a result, the theory soon began to gain widespread acceptance. In 1921, Einstein was awarded the Nobel Prize in physics for his explanation of the photoelectric effect.

Quick Check

1. Briefly state what it means for something to be a "quantized."

   ____

2. Give three common examples of things considered to be "quantized."

   ____

   ____

3. According to Planck, could an amount of energy equal to 2.5*hv* be absorbed or emitted by an object? Explain.

   ____

   ____

Practice Problems

I) The Lyman series in the emission spectrum of the hydrogen atom consists of transitions from higher levels to n = 1 level.

a) Calculate the maximum and minimum wavelengths lines, nm, of this series, noting the n values of the higher levels involved in each.

b) The series limit of the Balmer series, transitions to n = 2 occurs at about 365 nm, corresponding an energy of 5.49×10^{-19} J. Compare this energy to the lowest energy transition in the Lyman series and explain what this implies about the spacing between the energy levels in the H atom.

II) When light with a wavelength of 300 nm falls on sodium, electrons with a KE of 1.68×10^{5} J/mol are emitted. What is the minimum energy needed to remove an electron from sodium? What is the maximum wavelength of light that will cause an electron to be emitted?

III) The energy needed to dissociate a chlorine molecule into chlorine atoms is 243 kJ/mol. What is the maximum wavelength of light that will initiate the substitution reaction of chlorine with an alkane?

IV) a) Calculate the frequency of the radiation released by the transitions of an electron in a hydrogen atom from the n= 5 to the n= 3 level. Show all of your work.

b) Is this part of the Lyman, Balmer or Paschen series? In what range of electromagnetic radiation is the photon that is released?

2.6 Review Questions

1. Explain the serious problem initially associated with Rutherford's atomic model.

2. State Planck's quantum theory in your own words.

3. Why was this theory not accepted by most physicists at first?

4. What finally convinced the scientific community that Planck's theory was credible?

5. Explain how the work of Planck and Einstein contributed to Bohr's theory about electron behaviour.

6. State how Bohr's theory "saved" Rutherford's nuclear atomic model.

7. Briefly explain why hydrogen's visible emission spectrum does not resemble a continuous spectrum or rainbow

8. Describe what you would expect to see if hydrogen's visible emission and absorption spectra were superimposed upon each other.

9. Explain why, when hydrogen's electron transitions occur from excited states down to $n = 1$ or to $n = 3$, no visible spectral lines are observed.

10. Calculate the energy released when an excited hydrogen electron returns from $n = 5$ to $n = 2$.

11. Calculate the wavelength of the spectral line seen when the electron transition described in 10 above occurs, and use the wavelength to identify the colour of this line.

2.7 Spectroscopy: The Interaction of Matter and Electromagnetic Radiation

Warm Up

What is a photon?

What is the electromagnetic spectrum?

The Interaction of Light and Matter

Light is a form of electromagnetic radiation. The electromagnetic spectrum consists of a continuum of energies of different wavelengths. Visible light is a very small portion of this continuum. It includes wavelengths ranging from 380 to 750 nm. Light can be emitted in the form of a wave from a source or absorbed by various forms of matter. For example, plants appear green because all visible portions of white light except for the green wavelengths are absorbed by a magnesium complex in their chlorophyll.

At the atomic level, light energy is released or emitted when "excited" electrons fall to a lower potential energy state. Light that is emitted when an electron falls from a higher energy level to a lower energy level is called a *photon*. The energy of a photon is quantized, meaning that photons that exhibit a certain frequency of light have a fixed amount of energy. The energy associated with photons is always conserved.

$\Delta E = hv$ where v is frequency and h is Planck's constant, 6.626×10^{-34} Js

Electromagnetic waves oscillate in space and time, rising and falling as they move from point to point. Although wavelength and frequency vary across the electromagnetic spectrum, the speed of this radiation is fixed. The universal wave equation relates frequency and wavelength.

$c = \lambda v$ where λ is wavelength and c is the speed of light, 3.00×10^{8} m/s

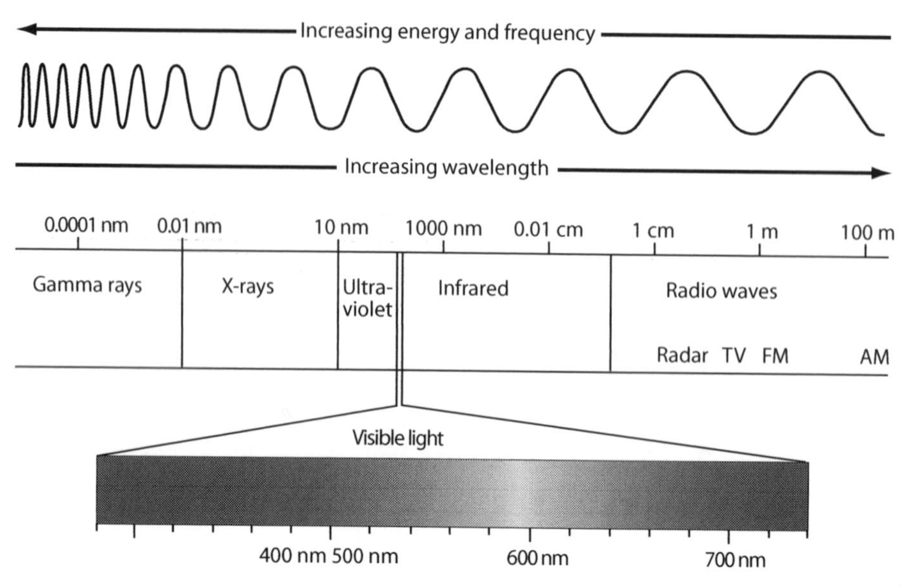

Figure 2.7.1 *The electromagnetic spectrum*

Quick Check

1. Microwaves are electromagnetic waves with a relatively long wavelength and low frequency. When a plate of spaghetti is warmed in a microwave, a photon with a wavelength of 12.2 cm is emitted.

   (a) At what frequency is this wave oscillating?

   (b) What is the transition energy of this wave?

   (c) What is the primary molecule being excited to higher rotational energies in the food being warmed in a microwave oven?

Spectroscopy

Various regions of the electromagnetic spectrum may be used to help us probe matter with the assistance of a variety of different instruments in a process called **spectroscopy** We will look at the following types of spectroscopy below:

- nuclear magnetic resonance
- infrared spectroscopy
- ultraviolet and visible-light spectroscopy
- X-rays: photoelectron spectroscopy

Nuclear Magnetic Resonance

The longest waves in the electromagnetic spectrum are called **radio waves**. The wavelengths of such waves vary from just below a metre to infinity. As can be seen by applying the equation above, wavelength (λ) and frequency (v) are reciprocally related. Since these waves have such long wavelengths, they oscillate at very low frequencies, from hundreds of megahertz down to tens of kilohertz. Superimposed on the pattern of these waves is a field of electromagnetic push-pull forces that is relatively low in energy. When radio frequency irradiation interacts with matter, there is no effect on electrons as their orbitals are separated by more energy than a radio wave can deliver. Radio waves cannot impact the position of the nucleus of an atom or the bonds in a molecule either. The matter continues to vibrate and rotate unchanged. Radio waves can, however, cause a change in **nuclear spin**. Nuclear spin is caused by the angular momentum of neutrons and protons and is analogous to electron spin as discussed in future sections. The combination of spin and charge of the nucleus creates a **magnetic moment.** This means that a "nuclear magnet" behaves like a quantum mechanical compass needle that may align either up or down with an applied magnetic field. By placing the nuclei of a sample in a magnetic field and supplying just enough radio frequency energy to reorient the spins, each time a spin flips we observe a **nuclear magnetic resonance (NMR)**. The internal magnetic fields within a molecule differ at each chemically distinct site.

> Each *signal (peak)* or *group of signals* in an *NMR spectrum* is due to the *nuclear spin change* of a *hydrogen atom* in a *distinct environment within a molecule.*

An NMR spectrum can help reveal the structure of a molecule, by showing the bonding pattern. This is commonly used in the identification of organic compounds. For example, in organic compounds, NMR indicates whether a molecule contains carbon atoms that have one, two, or three hydrogen atoms attached, whether the molecule contains double or triple bonds or exists as a *cis* or *trans* isomer. Nuclear magnetic resonance imaging can even produce visual images of the human brain.

Analytical work typically involves connecting an NMR spectrometer to a computerized bank of spectra of millions of different compounds. The unknown compound can thus be compared with the spectra of millions of known standards. The analytical chemist can then quickly and accurately identify a sample.

The recognition of functional groups and other compound characteristics following the observation of an NMR spectrum is far beyond what is required in a course such as AP Chemistry. However, spectroscopy is interesting and it is important to be aware that many different types of spectroscopy exist and may be used to help us understand more about the structure and function of various types of matter.

Quick Check

1. How do the two possible spin states of the proton in a hydrogen atom differ?

2. What causes different "signals" (distinct lines) to appear on an NMR spectrum?

3. Why would a methane molecule, CH_4, only have one distinct line on its NMR spectrum?

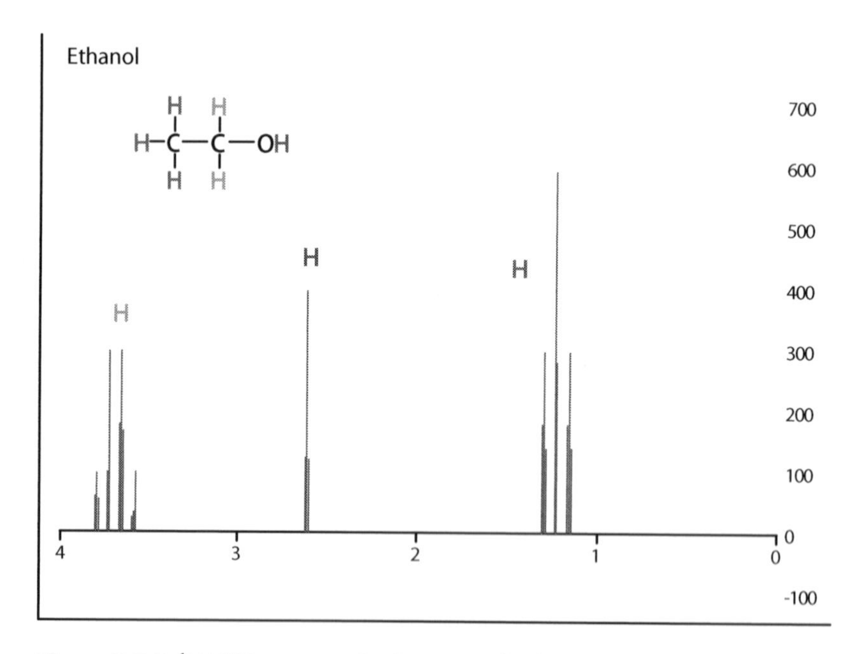

Figure 2.7.2 *^{1}H NMR spectrum (1-dimensional) of ethanol plotted as signal intensity vs. chemical shift. There are three different types of H atoms in ethanol regarding NMR. The hydrogen (H) on the –OH group is not coupling with the other H atoms and appears as a singlet, but the CH_3– and the –CH_2 hydrogens are coupling with each other, resulting in a triplet and quartet respectively.*

Infrared Spectroscopy

Infrared (IR radiation has a lower energy and a longer wavelength than visible light. $E = hv$ indicates the direct relationship between energy (E) and frequency (v). The relatively short wavelengths (between 1 μm and 1 mm) of infrared radiation mean more compressed and rapidly oscillating waves have a higher frequency (from $3 \times 10^{11}\ s^{-1}$ to $3 \times 10^{14}\ s^{-1}$ and a higher energy than radio waves. The electric force accompanying an infrared wave pushes and pulls the nuclei within a molecule.

The *absorbance of an infrared photon* causes increased forces of attraction between nuclei and electrons and increased forces of repulsion between nuclei. This leads to *bonds stretching, compressing, and bending (vibrating)* in the infrared range of frequencies. Bonds experiencing these forces are undergoing *resonance*.

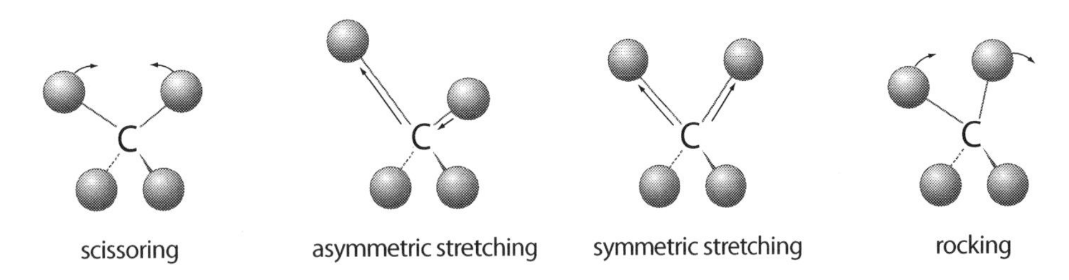

Figure 2.7.3 *All molecules routinely undergo the motions shown above. However, the absorbance of IR radiation excites a molecule from one quantum state to another, causing it to vibrate faster and more energetically than before.*

Nuclei attached to bonds may be likened to masses attached to springs. Strong bonds are like stiff springs and vibrate more rapidly. Heavy nuclei are like heavy masses and vibrate more slowly. The spring-bond analogy has limitations in that because they are quantized, molecular bonds can only vibrate with discrete energies levels. There are distinct vibrational levels just as there are distinct electronic energy levels and distinct spin levels.

In IR spectroscopy, the energy of infrared photons can equate to the difference between two allowed levels of vibration, exciting a molecule from one allowed state of vibration to another. In a molecule, each bond has its own unique difference in energy corresponding to the strength and elasticity of its vibration. This means that a bond between two particular atoms (e.g., C= O) will vibrate at nearly the same frequency in any molecule in which it is found. Consequently a vibrational spectrum is just a series of bands, each resulting from a different functional group or portion of the molecule. The spectrum as a whole is like a fingerprint for the molecule.

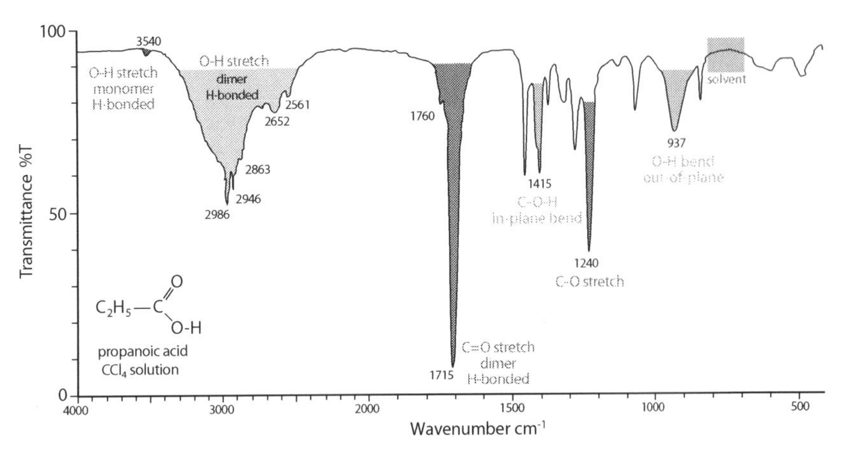

Figure 2.7.4 *Most IR spectra show the percentage of infrared radiation transmitted, rather than the percentage absorbed by different portions of the molecule. The "wavenumber" is simply a measure of the number of cycles per unit distance (in this case cm). It is analogous to a measure of frequency and hence, energy. As wavenumber decreases, so do frequency and energy, while wavelength increases.*

Even in different molecules, the *frequency of vibration of a particular functional group or structural feature* generally falls *within a narrow range* and hence can be used to *verify the presence of that group.*

Table 2.7.1 *Most Common IR Frequencies and Bond Stretches*

IR Frequency	Bond and Functional Group
3500–3200	O–H stretch in phenols
3400–3250	N–H stretch in amines, amides
3300–2500	O–H stretch in carboxylic acids
3330–3270	–C≡C–H (alkyne H)
3100–3000	=C–H stretch (alkene H)
3000–2850	-C– stretch (alkane H)
2830–2695	C–H stretch in aldehydes
2260–2210	C≡N stretch (nitrile)
2260–2100	-C≡C– stretch in alkynes
1760–1665	C=O stretch carbonyls (general)
1760–1690	C=O stretch in carboxylic acids
1750–1735	C=O stretch in esters
1740–1720	C=O stretch in aldehydes
1715	C=O stretch in ketones
1680–1640	-C=C– stretch in alkenes

Most functional groups absorb infrared light with a frequency above 1500 cm^{-1}. The region with frequencies below this primarily shows stretches between the *parent chain* atoms of the molecule and is of less use. Bizarrely this region is sometimes called the *finger print region*. It is largely ignored. As IR samples are dissolved in solvents that will themselves, absorb infrared radiation, a solvent spectrum is generally run for comparison.

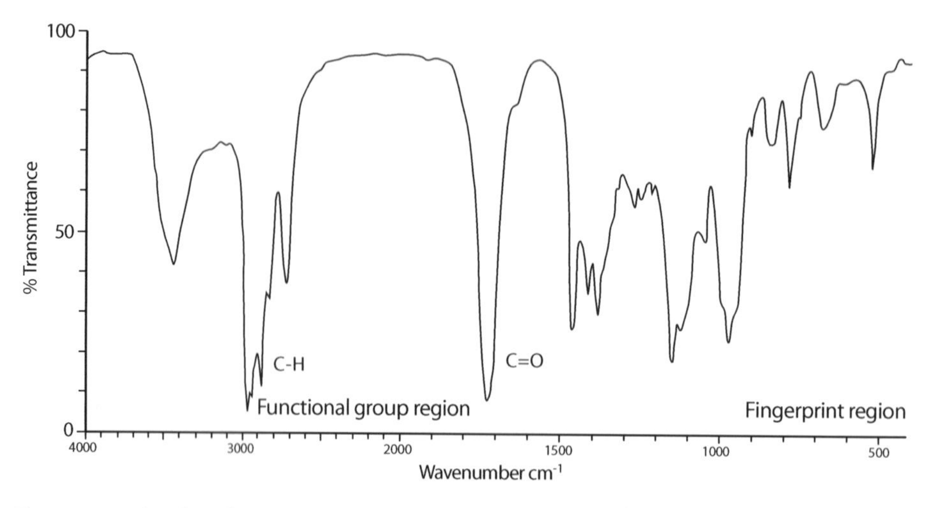

Figure 2.7.5 *A carbonyl group is extremely useful in elucidating the identity of an organic molecule. Though it generally absorbs in the region of 1660 to 1760 cm^{-1}, the exact position varies depending on whether it is part of a ketone, an ester, a carboxylic acid or an aldehyde group.*

Quick Check

1. What group might be indicated by the farthest left band in the IR spectrum in Figure 2.7.5?

2. Rank the following N to N bonds in order of increasing vibrational frequency:
N-N, N=N, N≡N.
Which will absorb infrared photons with the longest wavelength?

Ultraviolet and Visible-Light Spectroscopy

Visible and ultraviolet (UV) radiation are *above* infrared in terms of energy and below in terms of wavelength. Infrared radiation whose photon energies are *below* the red region of visible light gives way to visible red light at wavelengths between 800 and 700 nm. This is the region of the electromagnetic spectrum within which human beings perceive colour. The visible light portion of the spectrum extends from above 700 to just below 400 nm. The sum of all of these wavelengths makes up so-called **white light**. Wavelengths below 400 extending down to around 10 nm are associated with EMR (electromagnetic radiation) having energy above that of the violet portion of the visible range. For that reason, this portion of the spectrum is called **ultraviolet.** It is also the region within which photons may affect the most weakly held electrons, the so-called *valence electrons*. They may be excited out of their energy levels, and chemical bonding may be affected. The behaviour of these valence electrons is to a large extent governed by **Coulomb's law**.

$$F = \frac{kQ_1Q_2}{r^2}$$

This relationship between the force (F on two charged objects, the charges (Q_1 and Q_2 and the distance between them (r was determined in 1785 by French physicist Charles-Augustin de Coulomb. The law is sometimes referred to as the *inverse square law* for obvious reasons, and it resembles Newton's law of universal gravitation. The law shows that as the charge on one or both objects, such as a nucleus and an electron, increases, so does the force of attraction. It also shows that as the distance between an electron and the nucleus increases, the force of attraction decreases. This law can, and *should* (particularly in an AP course) be used to explain most of the atomic and ionic trends in the periodic table.

The valence electrons have the greatest *r* value and are screened most effectively from the charge on the nucleus. The reduced charge experienced by the valence electrons is sometimes referred to as Z_{eff} or the **effective nuclear charge**. *Z* represents the atomic number, which is, effectively, the number of protons.

$$Z_{eff} = Z - \textit{number of screening electrons}$$

The screening electrons are all those found in energy levels below that of the valence shell. This equation indicates that the effective nuclear charge is essentially constant moving up or down a family in the periodic table. However, it definitely increases moving across a period. The reduction in the nuclear charge *felt* by a valence electron is often referred to as the **shielding effect**. While any explanation of nuclear and ionic trends such as ionization energy and radius should certainly be centred on Coulomb's law, an explanation of Z_{eff} and the shielding effect are definitely appropriate.

UV/Vis spectroscopy involves absorption of light by the valence electrons. Valence electrons occupy orbitals far from the nucleus and high in energy. Consideration of Coulomb's law and the shielding effect tells us that these electrons are attracted by an attenuated and distant nuclear charge. Consequently they are the easiest electrons to disturb. They may be ionized and, under milder excitation, may be promoted to higher levels of energy (moved from their **ground state** to an **excited state**. Transition metal ions may experience movement of electrons between *d* orbitals of different energy levels. Such movement may be accompanied by the absorbance or release of visible light of specific wavelengths (*d* orbital splitting, or *non-degenerate d* orbitals, is a topic beyond the level of an AP Chemistry course; however, your teacher may encourage you to investigate this topic further. As a consequence, compounds containing transition metal ions with partially filled *d* orbitals will exhibit colour and hence are most suitable for study with visible spectroscopy. In organic molecules, valence electrons may be excited from a *bonding* orbital to an *antibonding* orbital (see Section B.1 on molecular orbital theory). Such excitations are not associated with colour, but rather with ultraviolet (UV) light. Finally in a lanthanide series or rare-earth containing compound, valence electrons may transition between non-degenerate *f* orbitals. Splitting of *f* orbitals leads to electron transitions associated with coloured light much like those that occur in solutions containing transition metal ions.

Ultraviolet–Visible Light Summary

- Solutions of transition metal ions produce colour due to *d* orbital electron excitation and return to ground state. (The colour of such solutions is due to the region of the spectrum they absorb in. This is in turn affected by the presence of other species such an anions or bonded ligands.)
- Organic compounds (and frequently the solvents they are dissolved in) absorb UV and visible light as they promote electrons from bonding to antibonding molecular orbitals.
- Compounds containing rare earth elements (elements from the lanthanide series – 4f) absorb UV and visible light due to f orbital excitation. (The region of the spectrum in which absorption occurs is impacted in a similar way to that of the transition metal ions.)

There is no sharp cut off between species affected by visible and invisible EMR, or colourless and coloured. The important point is that energy in this region of the electromagnetic spectrum can promote valence electrons. Moving a valence electron from an occupied to an unoccupied orbital may impact a molecule's size, shape, bond strength, polarity, paramagnetism, or colour, at least until the electron returns to its ground state. UV/Vis spectroscopy is most commonly used in *quantitative* rather than qualitative analysis of solutions, although solids and gases may also be studied.

Sometimes, a valence electron may be completely removed resulting in the creation of an ion. This process is called **photoionization** — ionization caused by a photon. Such an ionization caused by light is also called the **photoelectric effect**. Most molecules require UV radiation with wavelengths below 200 nm to produce such an effect.

Quick Check

Examine the UV/Vis spectrum shown here. (a) and (b) represent two different samples of the *same* compound in aqueous solution.

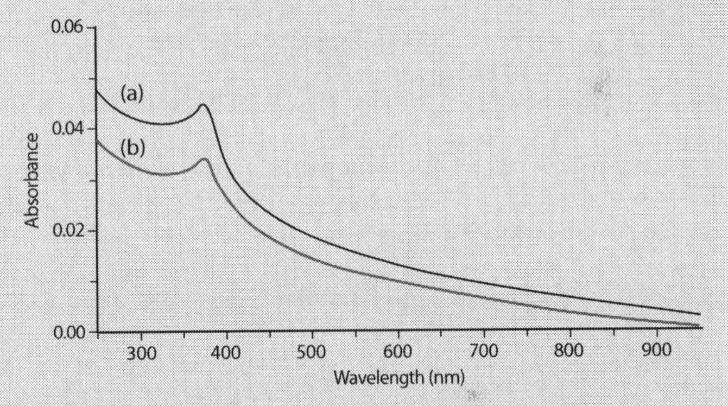

Figure 2.7.6

1. Which sample absorbed more light?

2. Which sample transmitted more light?

3. How does sample (a) differ from sample (b)?

4. At what wavelength is maximum absorbance occurring?

X-Rays: Photoelectron Spectroscopy

Core electrons (those below the valence shell) are considerably more difficult to remove from their atom. Consideration of Z_{eff} and Coulomb's law indicates that core electrons are attracted to a poorly shielded, more positively charged nucleus, and because they exist in an orbital that is lower in energy, their average distance from the nucleus is considerably less than that of the valence electrons. Each of these factors tells us that core electrons are much more difficult to remove. The removal of core electrons requires the significant energy of an X-ray photon with wavelengths below 10 nm all the way down to less than 0.01 nm.

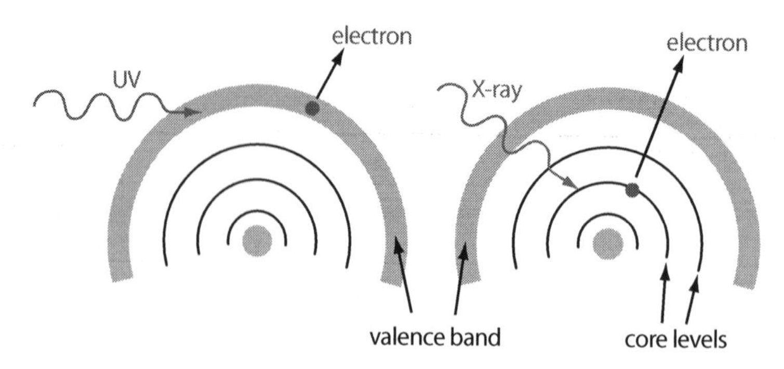

Figure 2.7.7 *UV and visible radiation have sufficient energy to remove valence electrons only, while X-rays may remove core electrons as well.*

Photoelectron spectroscopy (PES) was formerly known as *X-ray electron spectroscopy* or *XES*. It involves the use of a device that focuses a monochromatic beam of X-rays at a solid sample. Random atoms in the sample may then release electrons from any energy level in the atom. Emitted electrons are collected by a lens and passed through an electron energy analyzer to a detector. A computer then visualizes the electrons in the form of a photoelectron spectrum.

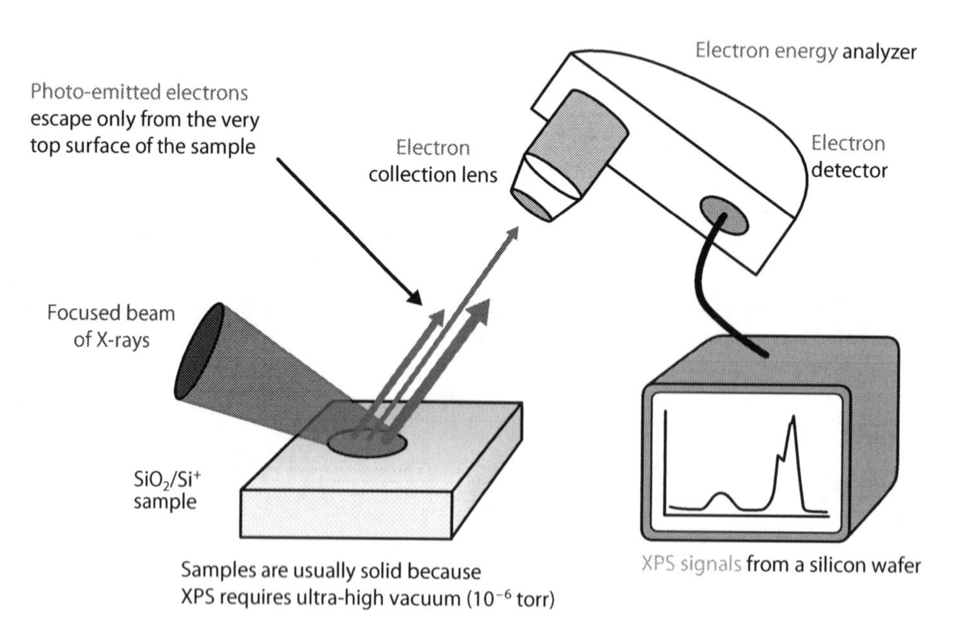

Figure 2.7.8 *Schematic diagram of the PES process*

The kinetic energy (KE of the emitted electrons is measured by the electron energy analyzer. The energy of the X-Ray photon is simply calculated as hv. This means the energy required to remove an electron from an inner energy level of an atom is simply the difference between these two values.

$$E = hv - KE$$

This process is virtually identical to the one used to determine the first ionization energy of an atom except that very high energy UV or X-ray photons are required to emit core electrons. (It should be noted that occasionally the vacant orbital produced by an ejected electron may be filled by an electron *falling* from a higher energy orbital. The energy from such a fall may cause the emission of another X-ray photon or could be absorbed to cause the emission of a second electron. These are called Auger transitions and require a more complex calculation.)

A computer visualizes the data from a PES instrument as a series of peaks in a spectrum plotting the intensity of the signal on the *y*-axis against the energy needed to eject an electron, *E*, on the *x*-axis. Some PES spectra show energy increasing on the *x*-axis; however, the most common convention (and the one that is being used in sample AP assessments) is to show energy *decreasing* from left to right. Inspection of the sample NMR and IR spectra shown earlier in this section indicates that they follow the same convention. The height of each peak in a PES spectrum is directly proportional to the number of electrons of equivalent energy. The energy units found in PES spectra are MJ/mol and less commonly eV/mol. Because actual PES spectra contain extraneous peaks referred to as "noise" that are not useful to us, we will study *simulated* PES spectra.

The following simulated photoelectron spectra of elements one through five in the periodic table have been adjusted to allow direct comparison of the peak heights. This would be the case if all the spectra were produced using equivalent sample sizes.

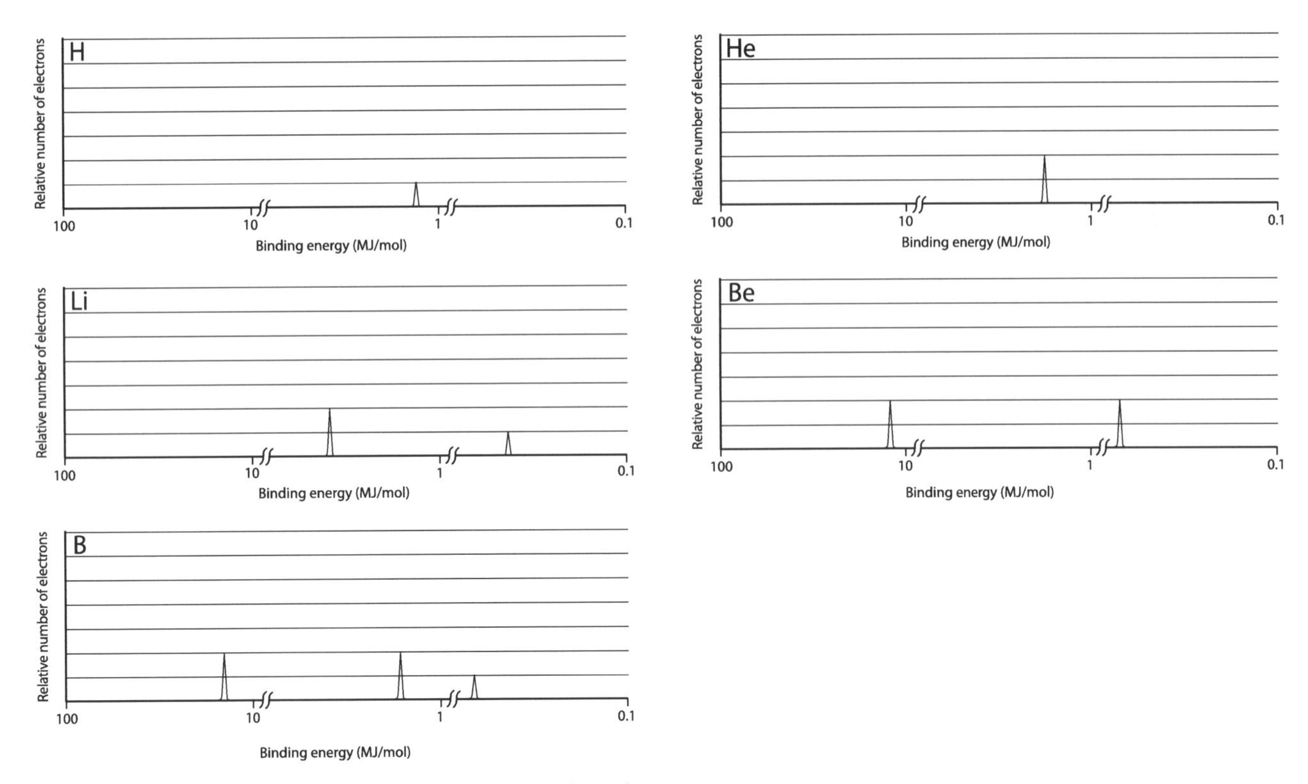

Figure 2.7.9 *Simulated photoelectron spectra of elements 1 through 5*

The number of peaks in a PES spectrum may be used to determine the number of orbitals existing in an element. The smallest peaks represent s orbitals. Full p orbitals are three times the height of a full s orbital. A full d orbital is five times the height of a full s. The highest energy peaks appear farther left and represent electrons in orbitals that are closer to the nucleus.

Quick Check

Refer to the simulated PES spectra in Figure 2.7.9.

1. Draw an orbital diagram for elements 1 through 5 in the periodic table.

2. Give three points of comparison between the orbital diagram and the PES for boron.

3. Compare and explain the position of the first peak for each of the elements 1 to 5.

4. Compare and explain the heights of the final peak (farthest right) for each of the elements 1 to 5.

Sample Problem — The PES Spectrum

What element is represented by the following PES spectrum? Note that the *x*-axis is not shown to scale.

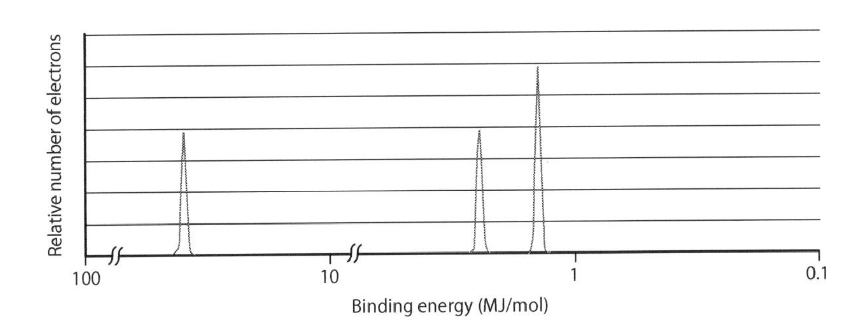

What to Think About	How to Do It
1. Count the peaks, keeping in mind that each peak represents an orbital.	There are three peaks in total.
2. Assume the highest energy peak (farthest to the left) represents the orbital closest to the nucleus.	The innermost peak must represent the 1s orbital. It follows that the other two represent the 2s and the 2p orbitals.
3. Use the relative heights of the peaks to determine the number of electrons in each orbital.	The 1s and 2s orbitals are full. However, the 2p is only 1.5 times as high as the s orbitals, and hence must contain only three electrons.
4. Use this information to discern the electron configuration and hence the identity of the element.	$1s^2 2s^2 2p^3$ represents atomic number 7 or nitrogen.

Practice Problems—The PES Spectrum

1. Identify the element represented by each PES spectrum below.

(a)

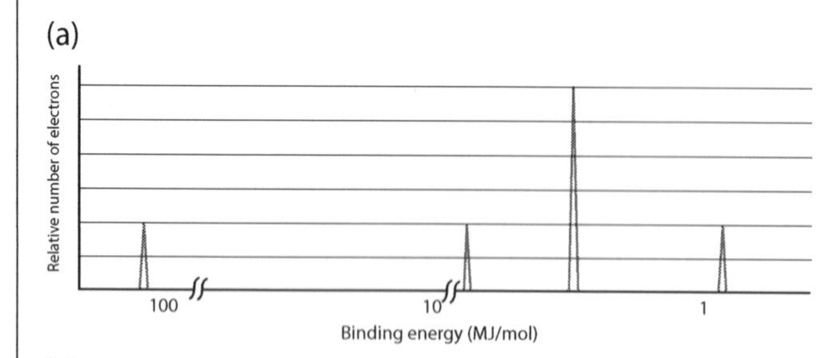

(b)

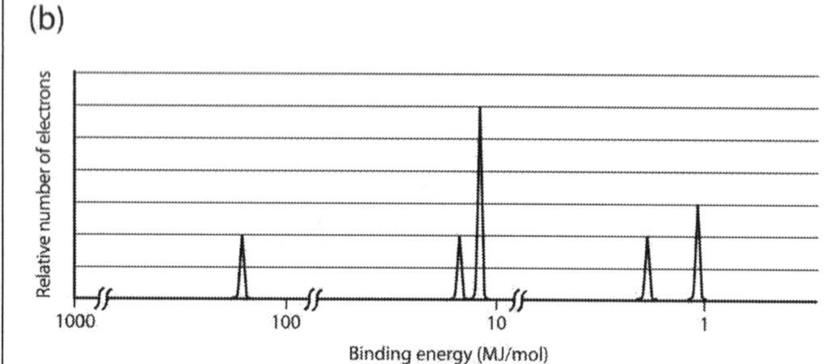

(c)

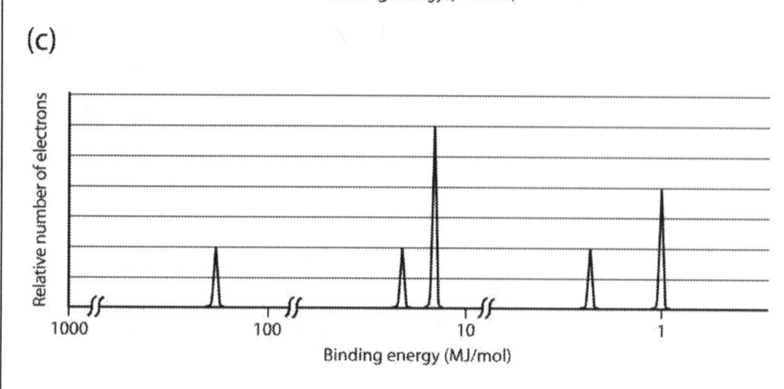

2. Use the following axes to sketch the PES spectrum you would expect for the element potassium. Pay attention to the relative heights and positions of each of the peaks. Exact values for binding energies are not required.

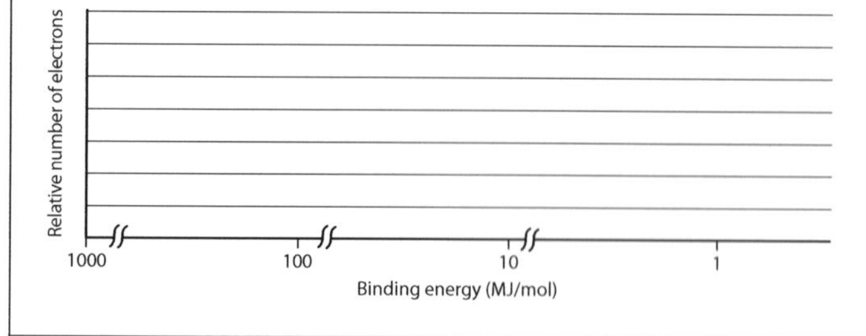

Examination of each of the spectra provided thus far indicates that the energy required to remove the innermost electrons varies significantly from element to element. The trend shows that as the atomic number increases, so does the binding energy. The following spectra moving from element number 6 to 8 to 10 across period 2 illustrates this trend for all three peaks in each element.

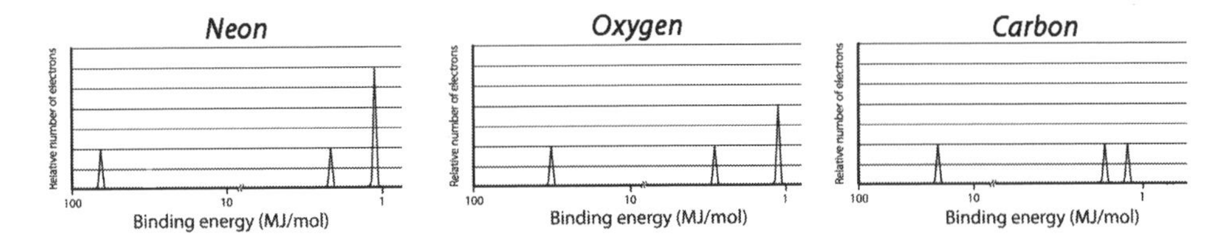

Figure 2.7.10 *PES spectra for neon, oxygen and carbon.*

The principal explanation for the increased energy required to remove the innermost electrons is the increased effective nuclear charge, Z_{eff}, as we move to the right across a period. Note this is not only true for the *1s* orbital electrons, but also holds true for the *2s* and the *2p* orbitals.

Quick Check

1. Practice Problems 1(a), (b), and (c) on page 186 represent Mg, P, and S respectively. Reexamine your answer to Practice Problem 2. Make any changes you now think necessary for your spectrum.

2. Examine Figure 2.7.10. Use the *Q* values in Coulomb's law to explain why the energy associated with the first peak is larger in neon and smaller in oxygen. Do the same for the third peak referring to both the *Q* and *r* values.

3. Examine Figure 2.7.10 again. Why are the first and second peaks the same height for all three elements while the third peak heights vary?

PES Summary

- The number of peaks = the number of orbitals (s, p, d, or f)
- The magnitude (height) of a peak is directly related to the number of electrons in the orbital the peak represents. The ratio of heights of peaks representing full *s:p:d:f* orbitals is 1:3:5:7. A full orbital is twice the height of a half full.
- The highest energy peaks appear farther *left* on the *x*-axis and represent electrons that are *closer* to the nucleus of an atom.

2.7 Review Questions

1. Complete the following table:

Region of EM Spectrum	Spectroscopic Technique	Photons Used To
Radio Waves	NMR (nuclear magnetic resonance)	Measure energy changes causing nuclear spin to study molecular structure.
Infrared		
UV/Visible		
X-rays		

2. The first ionization energies for selected elements from the second period of the periodic table are as follows:

Atom	Li-3	Be-4	C-6	N-7	F-9	Ne-10
1st IE (kJ/mol)	520	899	1086	1302	1681	2081

Use Coulomb's law to explain the trend in ionization energies in terms of the relative location of the electrons and the charge of the nucleus.

3. (a) Calculate the photon frequencies in 1/s for each of the following regions of the electromagnetic spectrum.
   (b) What range of the spectrum does each energy correspond to?
   (c) What type of spectroscopy might it be useful for?

Wavelength Range	(a) Frequency (1/s)	(b) Range	(c) Spectroscopy
700 nm to 400 nm			
400 nm to 10 nm			
10 to 0.01 nm			

4. Note the IE's for the 1*s* electron of the following second row elements:

Element	Li	Be	B	C	N	O	F
kJ/mol	4820	10 600	18 300	27 000	38 600	51 100	66 600

A substance is bombarded with X-rays having a wavelength of 1 nm. A photoelectron is ejected from the substance. Its energy is 69,500 kJ/mol. Which of the elements listed above must be in the sample?

5. What element does each PES spectrum below represent?

(a)

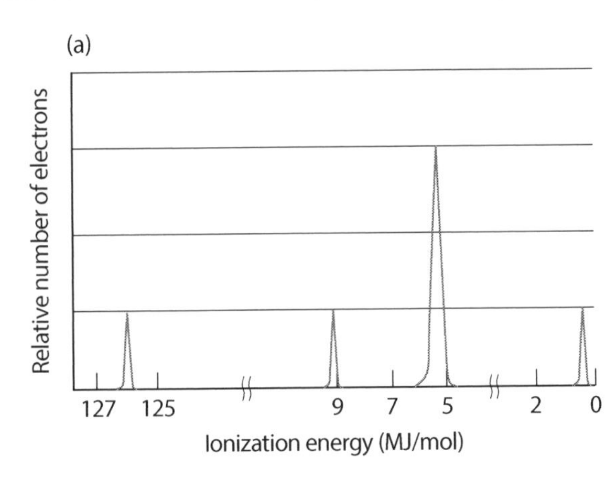

(b)

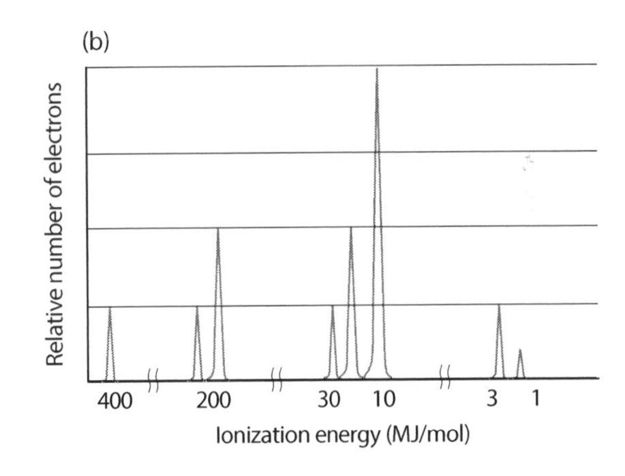

(c)

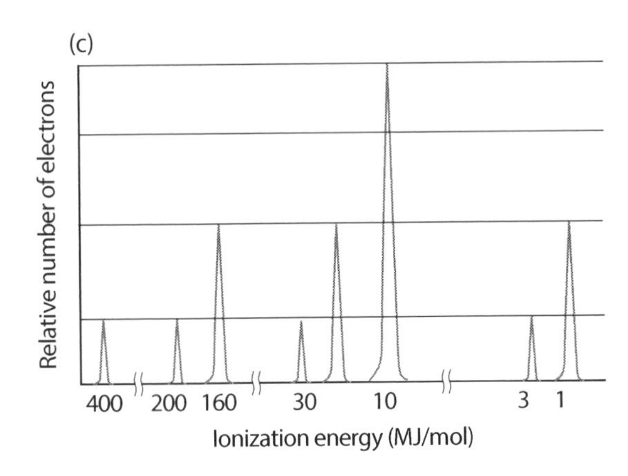

(d)

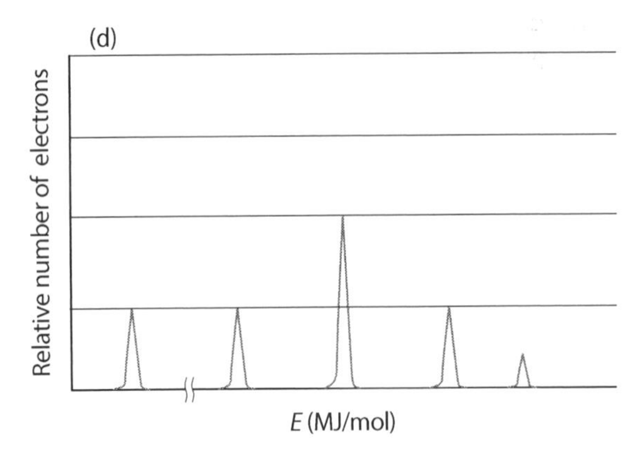

6. (a) Identify the element whose PES spectrum is shown.

(b) Draw the Bohr diagram for this element.

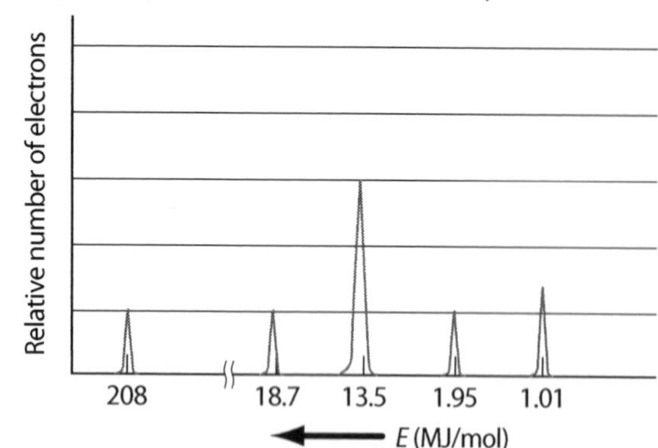

(c) Sketch the PES spectrum for the atom having 8 fewer protons than this atom. Label the axes clearly and show the approximate energies.

(d) If photons of wavelength 1.25×10^{-8} m bombarded the original element, which, if any, of the electrons could be emitted?

7. Study the following simulated photoelectron spectrum.

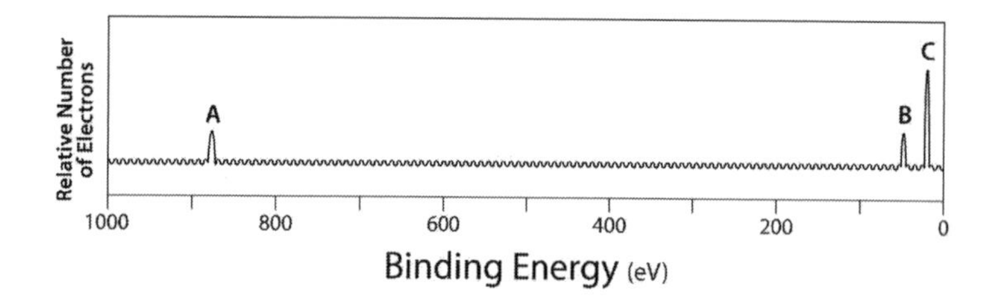

(a) What element is represented by the simulated spectrum?

(b)What orbitals' binding energies are represented by peaks A, B and C?

(c) Why is peak A so far to the left of peaks B and C?

(d) Why is peak C three times higher than peak B?

Answer Key

Chapter 1

Chapter 2

Made in the USA
Columbia, SC
06 September 2019